COMMUNITY
COLLEGE EDUCATION
FOR NURSING

COMMUNITY COLLEGE EDUCATION FOR NURSING

AN EXPERIMENT IN TECHNICAL EDUCATION FOR NURSING
Report of the Cooperative Research
Project in Junior - Community College
Education for Nursing

MILDRED L. MONTAG, Ed.D.
Professor of Nursing Education
Teachers College, Columbia University
and Director of Project

With Part II by

LASSAR G. GOTKIN, Ed.D.
Research Assistant

WY
18
C726

4558

Blakiston Division
McGRAW-HILL BOOK COMPANY, INC.
New York   Toronto   London   1959

Community College Education For Nursing

Library of Congress Catalog Card Number 59-7316

FOREWORD

No innovation in the system of education for nursing since the introduction of organized instruction to augment apprenticeship training has had the far-reaching influence that the project described in this report is likely to exert.

The Division of Nursing Education of Teachers College, Columbia University, is dedicated to the improvement of nursing service and education and carries out its mission both through preparing nurses to give leadership in education for the health field and also through experimental research in nursing and education for nursing. The Division is proud to have initiated and sponsored the Cooperative Research Project in Junior and Community College Education for Nursing under the direction of Dr. Mildred Montag as the first major research undertaking of the Institute of Research and Service in Nursing Education of Teachers College. The earlier availability of funds for the project meant that it was launched in 1952 and had been under way for a year before the Institute, to which the project staff was ultimately appointed, began to function.

Research literature in the field of nursing education is still meager compared with that in many other professional fields. In recent years, however, the increase has been notable. The number of studies and experiments already reported indicates that the educational system in nursing is no longer static. Change is evolving, not by accident, but with purposeful design

v

and direction. The variety of studies that have been undertaken reflect an earnest attempt to improve nursing by finding more dynamic and more economical ways of preparing more young women and men for effective service to humanity as nurses.

This publication, which is the final report on the co-operative project, should prove a useful addition to the literature. Seldom has there been a more fortuitous juxtaposition of (1) "an idea whose time has come," a well-thought-out philosophy, plan and proposal for research and experimentation; (2) the availability of a competent researcher, eager to undertake the project; (3) the offer of financial support from an anonymous donor who was eager to help assure better nursing services for America through improving education for nurses, and (4) a milieu in which the policies of the College permitted its resources and the experiences of its faculty to be brought to bear upon the fullest accomplishment of the purposes of the research.

This publication described the process, progress, and results of the study and of a systematic appraisal of effectiveness, on the job, of graduates from the pilot programs associated with the project. One other publication and two manuscripts as yet unpublished were prepared by research staff assigned to aspects of the study who utilized the research data in their own doctoral projects.*

---

*J. F. Marvin Buechel, Ed.D., Principles of Administration in Junior and Community College Education for Nurses, G.P.Putnam and Sons, New York, 1956.
Walter E. Sindlinger, Ed.D., Experiment in Education for Nursing at Orange County Community College, Unpublished Doctoral Project, Teachers College, Columbia University, New York, 1956.

The project's study and experimentation extended through five years and involved the cooperation of seven junior and community colleges and one hospital school throughout the United States.

As in many another attempt to experiment with an educational plan that deviates markedly from the familiar pattern, considerable skepticism was expressed at the outset by many nurses, nurse educators, and others about both the practibility and the wisdom of the new type of program envisioned. At the time the program was launched there was even less acceptance than there is today of the idea that education for nursing should be geared into the nation's system of higher education as recommended by Esther Lucile Brown in 1948.* Few nurse educators sensed in 1952 that the junior and community college movement, rapidly being extended across the country, would attract an increasing proportion of youth, including many needed in nursing who would be lost to this field unless nursing programs became an integral part of the junior college curricula. Both nurses and educators questioned the possibility of shaping the technical education characteristic of these colleges into an accelerated new type of program to prepare young people for licensure as registered nurses and for what has been named the associate degree in nursing. Answers to the questions raised are to be found in the programs developed by the pilot schools

_____

*Esther Lucile Brown, Ph.D., Nursing for the Future, Russell Sage Foundation, New York, 1948.

vii

in coopération with the Teachers College project staff, in the success that graduates of these programs met in their licensing examinations, and in the quality of their subsequent work as registered nurses. All are described in this report.

Even graver fears were voiced about the consequences to other types of schools and to the profession as a whole if the experiment should prove successful.

If a nursing program without service obligations, supported as are other programs in junior and community colleges, could prepare for registered nurse licensure in two calendar or even two academic years, would not the knell toll for the traditional three-year basic school? These fears still exist, but they seem to be subsiding. An increasing number of communities are turning to their junior and community colleges to plan education for nursing specifically because hospitals are finding the costs of educating health personnel of various kinds increasingly onerous. Hospital directors are coming to understand that the junior college offers release from the burden of supporting the nursing school, and at the same time a means to increasing the supply of nursing service for the community. The fact that one of the pilot schools was a hospital school has provided an explicit step-by-step adaptation of technical education to a new type curriculum for the two-year program that is not based on the student's service obligations.

Even the concern about the impact of the experiment upon the nursing profession -- the inevitable questions as to the relative professional status of R.N.'s with different types of preparation -- is being eased by a relentless march of events. The National League for Nursing has recognized that 67 per cent of the positions for registered nurses in this country are in situations -- the hospital, the doctor's office -- where supervision or direction is available and is expected.* These by definition are technical positions. Perhaps more than any one other factor, this recognition has paved the way for the acceptance of the new two-year technical program that has been shown to qualify nurses for technical positions.

Acceptance was further fostered when the National League for Nursing established the position of educational consultant in junior college education for nursing and appointed Dr. J. F. Marvin Buechel, a former research assistant in the cooperative project, to that position. Advice was thus made available through the profession itself to many colleges wishing to explore the potentials of the new nursing education program.

Graduates of the experimental programs have been successful in the licensing examinations. They have performed satisfactorily in service situations after orientation to the particular institution or agency employing them. Employers' fears about the product of the new programs have therefore been allayed.

---

*Nurses for a Growing Nation, National League for Nursing, 2 Park Avenue, New York 16, New York.

Other nurses have found the two-year graduates competent as co-workers and cooperative as members of their professional organizations.

During the past five years the differences in purpose and nature of professional and technical education have been greatly clarified. In consequence, avowedly basing a new program upon principles of sound technical education to prepare graduates to become registered nurses no longer seems a threat to the profession as a whole.

Rather, the development has challenged the senior colleges and universities anew to examine their programs in terms of the principles of professional education and their graduates as registered nurses whose competence and functions should be above and beyond those of nurses prepared through diploma and associate degree programs. Indeed, it has become increasingly clear that the vital professional functions of the nurse leader today must be clarified and adequate education for the leadership group provided by the universities if the nation is to have satisfactory health services.

If the functions of the technical engineer, prepared for in many two-year programs in junior colleges and other technical schools, and the functions of the professional engineer had not long ago been clarified, first within the engineering occupation and its educational system and then for society in general, there would probably be less recognition than there is today that both groups are needed, and less effective use of the two types of services.

It is assumed that technical engineers and nurses should both enjoy opportunities to benefit from senior college study in the humanities and other general fields and earn a liberal arts degree. However, to justify using the adjective "professional" in connection with a baccalaureate program and its graduates, the program must include professionalized content, utilize methods characteristic of professional education, and prepare for a distinctively professional role as compared with the technical role of the technical program graduate.

To what extent do baccalaureate programs in nursing professionalize the nursing content? To what extent do they use professional education methods and prepare for the functions that are professional rather than merely technical? What is the professional role in nursing coming to be? Is the distinctively professional role a therapeutic role? Should the professional baccalaureate program prepare a "nurse therapist" who will be an independent practitioner while the junior colleges and hospital schools prepare for staff nurse positions exclusively? Will not the difference in the breadth of preparation in the fundamental sciences required for the technical program and that necessitated as a base for professional functions present in nursing the same barrier to progression from technical to professional roles without considerable re-training that it has in engineering?

As frequently happens, in finding answers to certain questions this research has raised others. Innovations indicated by this report involve marked changes in the institution in which the nursing program is offered, in the setting in which instruction is carried on, and in the selection and organization of learning experiences and curriculum design. This study has demonstrated that the junior and community college can attract into nursing a desirable group who would not be able, because of age, family responsibility, or other factors, to enter other types of nursing programs, thus augmenting the numbers entering the profession as well as preparing them for service more quickly. The study opens an avenue to rapid development of other research that can clarify the differentiated roles of the technically and professionally prepared nurses and how nursing care can be improved through the more effective use of the skills of both. It has raised significant questions which others now must consider. It is hoped that research now on the drawing board that promises answers can soon be undertaken.

Few investments of money, time, and cooperative endeavor have yielded greater dividends to donor and participants in the research, to the educational institutions and the profession involved than has the Cooperative Research Project in Junior and Community College Education for Nursing. May it ultimately reward as richly the public in need of nursing services.

R. Louise McManus
Director, Division of Nursing Education
Teachers College, Columbia University

PREFACE

Community College Education for Nursing is the final
report of the Cooperative Research Project in Junior and
Community College Education for Nursing. This report has
three purposes. First, it is a description of how a new type
nursing program was developed. Second, it is a report of a
systematic evaluation of the graduates of this new program;
and third, it attempts to draw implications for the profession
of nursing, nursing services and nursing education.

Many people have contributed to this Project throughout
its five years. The faculties and student groups of the
several colleges have given freely of their time as data were
collected in the various phases of the Project. The American
Association of Junior Colleges gave encouragement and support
through official resolutions of the Association and through
opportunities to hold discussion groups and conferences in
connection with the annual conventions. The Advisory Committee
to the Project gave valuable counsel to the staff as it worked
through the many problems which arose as the new nursing programs were developed. The staff of the Project were enthusiastic and eager workers whose influence and contributions may be
seen in the total results of the study as well as in their
individual studies carried on concurrently.

It has been a gratifying experience to see an idea grow into a reality. It is not often that an author has an opportunity to see proposals made as a result of a study implemented so promptly. It may be said that the grant became available because there was an idea, translated into a design for research and planned in sufficient detail to interest a person who was vitally concerned with finding an answer to the problem of providing adequate nursing service to those who need it. We are grateful for the opportunity to try out these proposals.

We wish to acknowledge assistance with the preparation of the manuscript. Mrs. Eleanor Singer gave editorial assistance and Mrs. Jean Meeker typed the manuscript. Mrs. Bernice Zelditch prepared the index.

Mildred L. Montag

TABLE OF CONTENTS

LIST OF TABLES

Table   Page

COMMUNITY
COLLEGE EDUCATION
FOR NURSING

CHAPTER I

INTRODUCTION

The growing demand for the services nurses render has created what is often called, though perhaps erroneously, a shortage of nurses. As a result many proposals have been made as to how the requisite number of nurses might be recruited, how inactive nurses might be brought back to active service, how various types of auxiliary personnel might be used to relieve nurses of non-nursing duties, and how nursing education might be revised to prepare more nurses more quickly. Little serious attention has been given, however, to a critical evaluation of the system of educating nurses and of the time required to prepare for nursing. This volume is the report of a five-year project concerned with the establishment of a new type of nursing program in a new setting.

The research project stemmed, at least in part, from the proposals made in <u>The Education of Nursing Technicians</u>.[1] The design for the study was actually on paper before funds had been made available for the project itself. This design was easily developed into the Cooperative Research Project when a

---

[1]Mildred Montag, <u>The Education of Nursing Technicians</u> (New York: G. P. Putnam's Sons, 1951).

1

grant of $110,000 from an anonymous donor was received in 1952. The project was established within the Division of Nursing Education, Teachers College, Columbia University, in January 1952. Continued until 1956, it enlisted the cooperation of seven carefully selected junior-community colleges and one hospital school in developing and setting up an entirely new, two-year nursing program.

When the Institute of Research and Service in Nursing Education was established in March 1953, this research project came under its general administration. The pattern of the program had been set, however, and it was carried on substantially as had been planned at the time of the grant.

Purpose

The Cooperative Research Project in Junior and Community College Education for Nursing had as its purpose the development and testing of a new type of program preparing young men and women for those functions commonly associated with the registered nurse. The term bedside nurse has also been used to describe the kind of nurse that would be prepared by this new program. This term is intended to imply certain limitations of activity that differentiate the role of this nurse from that of the nurse with broader professional preparation. It was felt that there is a function to be performed by many registered nurses (not practical nurses or aides) in giving direct care to patients, where these nurses have access to the supervision of other nurses more broadly prepared. This should not be taken to imply, however, that nurses with broad professional preparation will not give direct care to patients.

There is growing interest and effort within the nursing profession to realign education for nursing in harmony with changing functions in nursing. The need for the nurse who is able to perform the professional functions of nursing is clear. Equally clear is the need for those to carry on the technical, or semi-professional, functions, and it is in this area that great numbers of nurses are needed. Therefore, the move toward the development of both the four-year, professional type of program and the shorter, semi-professional type is consistent with the need for nurses to carry on the whole range of nursing functions. It is with the latter type of program that this project has been concerned.

Assumptions

Certain assumptions were basic to the development of the proposal for the project. Others were identified by the project advisory committee in its first meeting. The assumptions which underlie the whole project are:

> The functions of nursing can and should be
> differentiated into three basic categories:
> the professional, the semi-professional or
> technical, the assisting.

The great bulk of nursing functions lie in
the intermediate category, the semi-professional or technical. Therefore, the greatest number of persons should be prepared to
fulfill these functions.

Education for nursing belongs within the organized educational framework.

The junior-community college, the post-high
school educational institution specifically
suited to semi-professional or technical education, is the logical institution for the
preparation of the large group of nurses.

When preparation for nursing is education-
rather than service-centered, the time
required may be reduced.

The aims of the project, as accepted by the advisory
committee in conference with the staff, were concerned primarily
with the graduates of the new type of program. It was hoped
that the graduates would:

Qualify for the registered nurse's license.

Meet the junior-community college requirements for the associate degree.

Perform technical (or semi-professional)
functions at the registered-nurse level.

Be prepared for beginning practitioner
positions (with supervision and, if possible, in situations where in-service
training would be available).

On graduation, be prepared to become competent nurses rather than be fully competent.

A last anticipated outcome had to do with the program
itself:

This new type of program would be terminal,
but qualified individual graduates would be

eligible for professional education in
nursing at the upper-division level.

Advisory Committee

An advisory committee of sixteen members was appointed
early in 1952. The committee was composed of individuals from
the fields of nursing, junior-community college education and
higher education, allied hospital and medical groups, and those
representing the consumers of nursing (Appendix B). The member-
ship of the group remained constant for the period of the
project, except for the replacement of one member, who died
during the first year.

Besides representing various professional groups, committee members were selected from the several regional areas of
the United States. For example, the Board of Directors of the
Junior College Association was requested to suggest several
junior college administrators from each of the regions which
comprise the Junior College Association. One person was
selected from each region. In the same way, the representatives
of nursing education were selected not only from different kinds
of nursing programs but also from different sections of the
country. Three hospital administrators who were also physicians
were members of the committee. It has been said that these
administrators did not really represent the profession, since
most hospital administrators now are not physicians. This may
constitute a justifiable criticism of the selection of this group.

The committee's chief function was advisory. It was extremely helpful in the initial development of the criteria used to select cooperating institutions and in identifying the questions that might be answered in the course of the research. Later, as the project developed, the committee evaluated the progress being made and suggested changes that might facilitate progress and additional undertakings that might make the project results more meaningful. The inclusion of a hospital school in the study, for example, was strongly recommended by the committee, and it approved the particular hospital school the staff selected. Again, in the evaluation of the graduates, the advisory committee recommended an intensive evaluation by a staff member who was not a nurse.

The committee met annually for two days, holding six meetings in all. At each meeting a different aspect of the project was emphasized, with a general report of activities and progress included. For example, at one meeting a visit of one day was made to the Orange County Community College in Middletown, New York, so that committee members might see the setting of one of the programs and talk with both faculty and students. At another meeting the presidents of the cooperating colleges and the chairmen of the nursing departments met with the committee to give progress reports of each program and discuss generally the issues and problems these programs encountered. In addition to these reports, the director of the project prepared a semiannual report of the activities being carried on within the project. In these ways, the committee members were kept informed about the project activities and the nursing programs themselves.

Another function of the advisory committee was in the area of public relations. Members were often called upon by individuals and professional groups to interpret the project and its activities. Since they were representative of large groups as well as different areas of the country, it was help-ful to have them as interpreters.

Staff

The staff of the project was small, with the director the only continuing member (Appendix C). In all but one year there was a member of the staff with special training and in-terest in the community college. It was felt desirable to have the staff include a nursing educator and a junior-community college educator in order both to understand and to interpret nursing programs and the junior-community college. In addi-tion to general assistance in project activities, such as con-sultation to the programs and conduct of workshops, each of the research assistants on the staff carried on an individual research project which also provided data for the development of doctoral projects. One of these was in the area of administration,[2] another in the area of curriculum,[3] and a third on evaluation of student performance in nursing.[4] The fourth,evaluating the graduates of the several nursing programs, is included as Part II of this volume.

In a very real way, the faculties of the nursing programs in the cooperating institutions constituted a part of the project staff. They were the ones who actually developed the curriculum and carried on the teaching.

Methodology

Since this project was essentially a curriculum study, it was agreed that its objectives could be achieved most effectively if nursing programs were developed in several institutions. The project was organized as a type of action research, in which those actually participating in the several nursing programs developed the curriculum and tested new methods of teaching. The project staff assisted in this process by means of consultation with individual faculties and through workshops attended by the faculties of all cooperating institutions.

---

[2]J. F. Marvin Buechel, Principles of Administration in Junior and Community College Education for Nursing (New York: G. P. Putnam's Sons, 1956).

[3]Walter E. Sindlinger, "Experimentation in Education for Nursing at Orange County Community College," Unpublished Doctoral Project, Teachers College, Columbia University, New York, 1956.

[4]Alice R. Rines, "A Concept of Evaluation of Student Progress in Learning the Practice of Nursing," Unpublished Doctoral Project, Teachers College, Columbia University, New York, 1958.

The over-all administration and evaluation of the project rested with the project director and staff.

Data concerning students were obtained through questionnaires at the time of entrance to the program and just prior to graduation. Reports of withdrawal and progress during the two years were also collected. The results of licensing examinations and the performance of graduates as employed nurses were systematically studied.

Questions for Which Answers
Were Sought

Many questions were identified at the inception of the project. Some were more significant than others, and some could not be answered completely within the five years allowed for the project. Some of the questions of concern were the following:

> What are the objectives of this type of nursing program?
>
> What learning experiences are best, and how may they be organized most effectively?
>
> What kind of facilities does this program require?
>
> How does general education and a part in college life affect the product?
>
> Is the product of this program usable?
>
> Will the program tap new resources of personnel for nursing?
>
> What kind of students select this kind of program, and why?

What are the reasons for withdrawal?

How do graduates perform on the job?

Can this program become an integral part
of the college in which it is established?

The problem of studying the costs of this type of program was discussed at some length. It was decided not to make specific cost studies but rather compare the cost of the nursing program in each institution with the cost of other programs within that institution and with the costs the institution set as acceptable per-student costs.

Summary

The Cooperative Research Project in Junior and Community College Education for Nursing was made possible by a grant of $110,000 in 1952. Its purpose was the development and testing of a new type of program preparing young men and women for those functions commonly associated with the registered nurse. An advisory committee composed of representatives from the fields of nursing, junior-community college education and higher education, allied hospital and medical groups and consumers of nursing was helpful in the initial development of the criteria used to select cooperating colleges, in evaluating progress as the project developed and in suggesting additions and changes. A small staff carried on the basic work of the project with the faculties of the nursing programs actually developing the curriculum and doing the teaching.

The methodology used in the project was that of action research. Certain data were collected by the project staff but the essential work of curriculum development and teaching was done by those actually in the nursing program. Many questions were identified at the beginning of the project but only selected ones could be answered in part.

CHAPTER II

SOCIAL AND EDUCATIONAL PERSPECTIVES

FOR EXPERIMENTATION

The constantly increasing discrepancy between the need
for nursing services and the supply of nurses makes it necessary
to look at where and how, and how quickly, nurses are being prepared. The growth of the community college concept, with its
implications for the extension of free public education, makes
a look at the institutions providing the thirteenth and four-
teenth years of education essential. It is against this social
and educational background that the Cooperative Research Project
should be viewed.

Social Need for Nurses

The demand for nursing service continues to rise. This
increase in demand is due both to the increase in population
and to the social changes that have resulted in a greater demand for the services nurses render. The population of the
United States doubled between 1900 and 1950. In 1900 there
was one nurse per 100,000 population, in 1940 it was 216 per
100,000, and in 1956 the ratio was estimated to be 258 per
100,000. It is assumed that the demand for nursing service will

12

continue to increase:

> In the years ahead the population will
> increase by an unprecedented measure.
> More people will live to an older age,
> heirs to the degenerative diseases of
> longevity. Medical practice will broaden
> in scope, with progressively more precise
> methods of diagnosis and treatment.
> Public health and community service will
> expand. Society will demand more of the
> benefits of a growing knowledge of health
> and medical science as people become
> increasingly aware of these benefits.[1]

How many nurses will be needed in the future can only
be estimated. There are now approximately 430,000 registered
nurses actively practicing -- the largest number in the history
of American nursing. Most would agree that the present ratio
must at least be maintained, and there is some evidence to support the belief that the ratio should be significantly increased. The two regions of the United States which have
larger ratios than the national average -- the North Atlantic,
which has 336 nurses per 100,000 population, and the West, with
277 per 100,000 -- report nurse shortages as well as those regions which fall below the national figure.[2] We do know that
the actual number of nurses must be increased proportionately
as the population increases if the present ratio is to be maintained. Estimates made in 1948 that 600,000 nurses would be

---

[1]National League for Nursing, Nurses for a Growing
Nation (New York: The League, 1957), p. 5.

[2]Ibid., p. 9.

needed by 1960 are supported by the estimates of the Committee
of the Future of the National League for Nursing. This committee states:

> The personnel needed by 1970 to reach the
> goals thus set for professional nursing
> indicates a rise to more than 600,000 pro-
> fessional nurses to attain the 300 goal;
> to 700,000 to arrive at the higher goal of
> 350 nurses for 100,000 population. The
> lower goal projects an increase of 40 per
> cent in nurse supply over the present level
> by 1970; the higher, an increase of 60 per
> cent.[3]

It should be noted here that the term _professional_ is used by
the committee to distinguish this group of nurses from the
group known as _practical_ nurses.

There can be little doubt that the need for nursing
service will continue to increase. The responsibility of the
nursing profession resolves itself into providing the quantity
and quality of nursing care society demands. This is no small
responsibility. The Cooperative Research Project on Junior
and Community College Education for Nursing, in developing a
new program to prepare nurses, was seeking another and quicker
way to help meet the ever-increasing need.

---

[3]_Ibid_., p. 12.

Problems in Nursing Education

The administrative and teaching personnel in nursing
programs are vitally concerned with any discussion of both
present and future demand for nurses because it is they who
must produce the nurses needed. The present system of educating nurses has failed to produce the requisite quantity and
quality of nurses to meet the demand. Enrollment in nursing
schools rose slightly each year from 1951 to 1955, but in 1956
the number admitted fell below the number admitted in 1955, and
in 1957 the number was less than in 1956. More than 85 per cent
of all schools of nursing are owned and controlled by hospitals,
and they offer programs of a predominantly apprenticeship type,
directed primarily toward the immediate care of the hospital's
patients. Only 13.7 per cent of schools of nursing offer a
baccalaureate degree, and these schools account for about 15
per cent of all students. The ability of schools of nursing to
attract students is of utmost importance when the problem of
supplying the demand for nursing service is considered.

There has been a marked increase in the number of young
people of college age who are enrolled in college. In 1940
only 15 per cent of college-age youth were in college. By 1952
the number had risen to 31 per cent, and it is estimated that
the figure will be 50 per cent in 1970.[4] This would mean a

---

[4]Lucile Petry Leone, "People, Nurses, Students,"
American Journal of Nursing, 55 (August 1955), 933.

total of 6,600,000 students in college, compared with 3,000,000
in 1956. The number of eighteen-year-olds is rising rapidly.
In 1959 there will be 300,000 more than in 1955, and in 1965
there will be 1,500,000 more. If those eighteen to twenty-one
years are included as potential first enrollees in college,
then the number of potential enrollees will be more than nine
million in 1960 and thirteen and one-half million in 1970.[5]
Colleges have been and are planning ways of meeting this tidal
wave of students. The question is whether this surge toward
college will be felt in schools of nursing. Leone states:

> To answer our question -- whether
> the increase in American youth will
> provide the needed increase in nursing
> school enrollment -- we must consider
> these factors: the nature of the supply
> of potential candidates, the conditions
> of the schools, and the public attitude
> toward nursing.
>
> . . . .
>
> It is difficult to predict whether the
> onrush of youth seeking education beyond
> the high school will bring a correspond-
> ing increase in candidates to Schools of
> Nursing. Comparison of figures for col-
> lege admissions and nursing school
> admissions over the last few years seems
> to indicate a negative answer.[6]

---

[5]Malcolm S. MacLean and Dan W. Dodson, "Educational
Needs Emerging from the Changing Needs of Society," The
Fifty-fifth Yearbook of the National Society for the Study of
Education (Chicago, 1956), p. 15.

[6]Lucile Petry Leone, "How Many Will Choose Nursing,"
American Journal of Nursing, 55 (October 1955), 1195.

She gives this partial explanation of her conclusion:

> Nursing is one of the largest occupations for which preparation is not generally thought of as "going to college."
>
> Less than 1 per cent of young women in college are enrolled in degree programs in nursing.[7]

To meet the need for a ratio of 300 nurses per 100,000 population as the need has been estimated would mean an average annual admission of 57,000 students. In only one year have schools of nursing admitted 57,000 students -- in 1944, when 67,051 were admitted. It must be remembered that in that year we were in the midst of World War II and that, moreover, there was substantial financial aid to all students. It seems quite obvious that the present system of nursing education is not meeting and is not likely to meet the needs.

The Junior-Community College Movement

The development of junior-community colleges in the United States has been outstanding. In 1900 there were eight junior colleges enrolling one hundred students. In 1955-56 there were 635 junior colleges enrolling 765,551 students, and this figure represents an increase of 10 per cent over the previous year.[8] The number of students enrolled is certain to

---

[7]Ibid.

[8]Jessie P. Bogue, "Analysis of Junior College Growth," Junior College Journal, 28:357, 1958.

rise. Some estimates have put the enrollment at two million by 1970-75. The community college has been developing because communities have realized the desirability of extending educational opportunities for their citizens. That the number of junior-community colleges will increase seems certain. Mention of a few instances will serve to illustrate the trend. Governor Leader of Pennsylvania made the following recommendation in relation to the development of junior colleges in Pennsylvania:

> To provide for free educational opportunity, regardless of economic status and place of residence, college education must be brought to those students who can combine their college studies with continued residence at home. This program therefore provides for a system of junior colleges which can be built and operated within daily commuting distance of Pennsylvania college-age men or women, where adequate college facilities and curriculum are not available.[9]

In New York James E. Allen, State Commissioner of Education, stated that the state may eventually provide for two years of college as part of the free public school system of the state. He stated further that the Board of Regents had found the community college the answer to providing "the best in higher education for the most students at the earliest possible moment at the lowest possible cost."[10] There is

---

[9]Governor George M. Leader, Message to the General Assembly of Pennsylvania, Harrisburg, Pa., April 23, 1957.

[10]Newsday, Garden City, New York, June 10, 1957.

discussion in California about an increase in the number of junior colleges there. These are only a few indications that the junior-community college can lay claim to being the "fastest-growing collegiate enterprise in America today."[11]

The junior-community colleges differ widely in their pattern. The President's Commission on Higher Education states:

> Whatever form the community college takes, its purpose is educational service to the entire community, and this purpose requires of it a variety of functions and programs. It will provide college education for the youth of the community certainly, so as to remove geographic barriers to educational opportunity and discover and develop individual talents at low cost and easy access. But in addition, the community college will serve as an active center of adult education. It will attempt to meet the total post-high school needs of its community.[12]

The functions of the junior-community college are also varied, but Basler groups them into four categories:

1. The provision of the duplication of the first two years of a standard, liberal arts program.

2. The provision of "Terminal Education," consisting of both general education and vocational education of a semi-professional or sub-technical nature, including supervised work experience -- all related to occupational opportunities in the community area served by the college.

---

[11]Ibid.

[12]President's Commission on Higher Education, Higher Education for Democracy (New York: Harper and Bros., 1937), pp. 69-70.

3. The provision for "Adult Education" for persons who may or may not have completed the 12th grade, including general education in either full time or part-time programs running for either long or short periods of time and offered on a flexible day, evening, weekly or annual schedule for persons employed either full or part time.

4. The provision of a variety of services to the community through media other than courses and regular classes -- forums, lectures, musical events, community surveys, services of staff to local businesses, industrial enterprises, service agencies and the like.[13]

Within this framework, each junior-community college determines its own objectives and its own contribution to the community it serves. The junior-community college usually is a two-year institution with curricula and offerings determined by community needs. There may be four-year community colleges, but it can be seen that the two-year institution, or junior college, is well suited to the concept of the community college.

It is in this type of institution that programs preparing nurses were developed within the Cooperative Research Project. The inclusion of a nursing program within the community college was a natural development, since one of the basic functions of the community college is to meet the needs of its community for essential services. Nursing is an essential service in every community. Furthermore, the community

---

[13]Roosevelt Basler, "Consistent and Increasing Adaptability of the Junior College," Junior College Journal, 25:427-29, April 195

college is free to develop such new programs without being hampered by tradition. The flexibility of the institution is one of its hallmarks. The second function which Basler has identified -- the provision of terminal education -- makes the junior-community college a logical institution for a new nursing program. Dressel reports that "education of junior-college level is terminal for the great majority of enrollees."[14] The increase in the number choosing terminal-education programs may be explained by the fact that more occupations need semi-professional workers and more students are finding that these programs meet their needs.

Junior-Community College Participation in Nursing Programs

Junior colleges have been participating in nursing programs in a variety of ways for many years. This participation has ranged from the "selling" of a course or series of courses to the hospital school to the providing of an instructor for a course at the hospital. Many junior colleges offer what they term pre-nursing curricula, but these are usually the typical transfer program and not specifically developed for nursing. A survey by the National League for Nursing in 1955 showed that more than half of the junior colleges were involved

---

[14] Paul L. Dressel, "Educational Demands Arising from Individual Needs and Purposes," The Public Junior College, The Fifty-fifth Yearbook of the National Society for the Study of Education (Chicago: University of Chicago Press, 1956), p. 55.

in some way in nursing education. The increasing involvement
of junior colleges in nursing education has resulted in a National League for Nursing - American Association of Junior Colleges joint committee to deal with the problems which develop.
This group has been active since 1950. In 1955 a set of guiding principles was adopted by the National League for Nursing
and the American Association of Junior Colleges to help those
colleges wishing to share in providing education for nursing.[15]

One series of principles is designed for the college
which wishes to organize and control a nursing program, and the
other deals with the relationships arising when the hospital
controls the program but uses some of the college offerings.
The first group of principles draws heavily on the philosophy
and principles underlying the programs developed by the Cooperative Research Project.

Two major conferences on junior-community college education for nursing were held in 1956 and 1957 under the sponsor-
ship of the joint committee and the Cooperative Research
Project. Both conferences were attended by junior college representatives, nursing education representatives, and state
boards of nursing. These conferences were significant in part
because for the first time both college administrators and

---

[15]National League for Nursing and the American Association of Junior Colleges, Guiding Principles for Junior Colleges Participating in Nursing Education (New York: The League,
1955).

nursing educators met together in a national meeting to consider the development of nursing programs in collegiate institutions. They were significant for other reasons as well.
In the Foreword of the report of the first conference
Littlefield wrote:

> This conference, more than any other single
> event, establishes the possible patterns
> for the nature of nursing education in
> junior-community colleges.
>
> . . . .
>
> Fundamentally the conference gives full
> historical perspective and future pros-
> pects for nursing education in junior-
> community colleges.[16]

Although junior-community colleges have participated
in some phases of nursing education for many years, the kind
and amount carried on in the pilot programs is new. The
actual control of the entire program in nursing by the
junior-community college is new. The curriculum in nursing
as developed in the pilot programs is new. There is in
reality no similarity between the new nursing programs and the
experiences of junior colleges in nursing programs in years
past.

---

[16]National League for Nursing and the American Association of Junior Colleges, Nursing Education in Junior and
Community Colleges (New York: The League, 1956), p. iii.

Summary

The need for nurses has increased steadily through the years and the discrepancy between the supply of nurses and the need for nursing services has become increasingly apparent. To maintain the present ratio of nurses to population in future years will require an increase in the number of nurses proportionate to the increase in population. The present enrollment in schools of nursing gives little evidence that the need can be met without changes either in the way nurses are prepared or in the institutions involved in preparing nurses.

The community college is said to be the "fastest-growing collegiate enterprise in American today." Its major purpose is to meet the community's needs for essential services. It is with this institution that the Cooperative Research Project worked to develop new nursing programs. The new programs represent a change in the way nurses are prepared and a new responsibility on the part of junior-community colleges for the education of nurses.

CHAPTER III

THE COOPERATING INSTITUTIONS

The decision to use in the Cooperative Research Project already established junior colleges interested in developing nursing programs was made for two principal reasons. First, this cooperative undertaking would permit funds to be used for educational research rather than the operation of an experimental school. Second, the development of nursing programs in a variety of types of community colleges in all sections of the country would allow for much wider experimentation and tend to assure continuation of the programs once the experimental phase had been completed. Moreover, several junior and community colleges had already approached the Division of Nursing Education of Teachers College for advice and continuing consultation in curriculum development, thus indicating an interest in nursing programs. The considerable experience of Teachers College in cooperative educational projects in other fields also influenced the decision. The selection of several junior-community colleges was then necessary.

25

Selection of the Cooperating Colleges

Following the announcement of the research project in
the press, a considerable number of colleges requested participation. These were in addition to those institutions that had
already requested advice and consultation from the Division of
Nursing Education. There were also many inquiries and expres-
sions of interest from colleges not desiring to participate but
wanting to be kept informed of the progress made.

A questionnaire was developed to gain information about
the colleges requesting active participation in the project
(Appendix D). This questionnaire was sent to forty-two colleges,
and returns were received from twenty-four. The twenty-four
colleges were located in twenty states. Of these about half
were publicly controlled institutions and half privately controlled. All but three were coeducational. The tuition charged
ranged from about $500.00 per year to a nominal college fee.
Seventeen institutions indicated that they would continue to be
interested in developing nursing programs even though not
selected as participants in the project. Nineteen institutions
requested consultation service to help them in setting up new
nursing programs. This initial expression of interest was not
transitory. There has been consistent, though not rapid, development of associate-degree nursing programs outside the
aegis of the project, until, in 1957, there were as many functioning outside the project as those with whom cooperative

arrangements had been made -- perhaps more.

Following a review of the questionnaires and applications, certain institutions were selected for visits by the project staff. Extended conferences were held with college personnel, state boards of nursing, and representatives of community agencies likely to be used in the program. Visits were made to the agencies, and the educational and physical facilities of the colleges were reviewed. When the staff was assured that the college met the criteria agreed upon, the opinion of the advisory committee was sought. Thus seven colleges were selected, which remained in the project until its conclusion.

Criteria for Selecting Cooperating Institutions

The need to limit the number of cooperating institutions was obvious from the beginning. Since the purpose of the project was research and experimentation that would contribute to the preparation of nurses, it was agreed that the institutions selected should represent a variety of geographic areas, types of financial support, size, and type of students. The possibility of licensure of the graduates was another important consideration.

The advisory committee at its first meeting discussed and recommended criteria that might be used in selecting institutions for participation in the project. These criteria were found to be very effective. They might well be used by other institutions contemplating the establishment of nursing programs, for unless these criteria are met, the possibility of developing a sound nursing program diminishes.

The criteria were:

1. There should be an interest in a new type of nursing program and the desire to develop a program that departs widely from traditional nursing programs, both in colleges and in hospitals.

   This criterion includes an acceptance of the assumptions described in Chapter I as consistent with the philosophy of the educational institution.

2. The initiative for the development of the program should come from the educational institution rather than a hospital.

   Traditionally, nursing programs have been initiated and maintained by hospitals in order to obtain service. The new type of nursing program will not give this kind of service. It must be seen as an educational program; hence, it is the responsibility of the educational institution to introduce it.

3. There must be readiness in the community for this type of program.

   Complete understanding must exist on the part of all community agencies likely to be involved concerning the nature of the program and their probable role in it. It is important also that nurses already in the field, allied professional groups, and potential students understand the program and are kept informed about it.

4. The institution must be willing to assume complete control of the program.

    The importance of this criterion is obvious when the past, and even present, practices of colleges in this respect are reviewed. It has been common practice for colleges and universities to control only the academic part of the program, leaving the nursing part to the hospital. In these new programs the college must look upon nursing as it does on all other programs it offers, taking responsibility for all parts of it.

5. The institution must be willing and able to provide and pay for the new program in nursing.

    This criterion is actually implied in the former one but required further emphasis. Sometimes control of a program is claimed when in fact it is only partial control because the hospital assumes the expense and, therefore, the control of the faculty for the nursing part of the curriculum.

6. There must be acceptance of the nursing program by the college faculty and provision for the students in the nursing program to become, in fact, full students of

the college, eligible to participate in all activities
of the college.

It is not enough to have the college administration
and governing body of the institution convinced that a
nursing program is possible and desirable. The entire
faculty must understand what is proposed and how the
proposal will be implemented. The inclusion of nursing
in the college curriculum has not always been understood
nor accepted by college faculties. Some have not found
it difficult to accept the requirement of certain academic courses in a nursing program, while others see no
need for even this. Still fewer have fully accepted the
belief that courses in nursing itself are legitimate college offerings and should be treated as other college
courses are treated. Until the college faculty accepts
the nursing program as an integral part of the college,
neither the nursing program nor its faculty and students
become true units of an educational enterprise.

7. The learning experiences necessary for a nursing program
must be available.

This criterion means that hospital facilities must
be available and, in addition, other facilities, such as
community health agencies, convalescent homes, homes
for the aged, nursery schools, and the like. The nature
of the program requires that the student move freely

between the college classroom and the hospital or other
health agency. No attempt was made to specify the size
of these institutions, for it was believed that simple
quantitative criteria were not sufficient to determine
adequacy. It was believed that a variety of appropriate
facilities was more important than the mere number of
beds in a hospital.

8. The hospital and other community agencies must be willing to have the college use their facilities in providing
learning experiences for students.

The understanding that the agency can expect no service in return for the use of its facilities must be
assured. The use of hospitals and health agencies by
the new type of program will be different from the use
customarily made of these facilities by nursing programs.
They must see themselves as cooperating in an educational
enterprise, not as recipients of service from students.
The mere presence of facilities does not assure their
availability.

9. The educational institution must have community relationships that will permit coordination of the various
facilities.

The need for the educational institution to have
such public relations with other community resources as
to make a cooperative venture possible is apparent.

Since community colleges exist to serve the community and in turn are supported by the community, this criterion is undoubtedly among the easiest to meet.

10. The division or department of nursing must be of adequate size.

The size of any department must of necessity be proportionate to the size of the entire institution. The success of the program will be measured not in terms of quality alone but also in terms of the cost for each person prepared. The decision to offer a nursing program will depend, in part, on the ability of the college to pay its cost. A program may be educationally possible, yet priced at a figure it would be hard to defend. Consciousness of the need to keep the costs of a nursing program proportionate to other programs does not necessarily jeopardize the quality of the program.

11. Licensure of the graduates must be possible.

Licensure laws and regulations in the various states may present obstacles to experimental programs. Since licensure of graduates must be assured, early discussion with the appropriate licensing body is imperative. Application of this criterion to the selection of cooperating colleges meant that it was necessary to begin in those states where laws did not prohibit a nursing program of less than three years. It was obviously not

possible at this time to assure graduates of anything
but licensure within the state in which the college was
located.

12. There must be reasonable assurance that the graduates
of the new type of program will be employed.

Although employment of graduates cannot be guaran-
teed before the program itself is even begun, there
should be some indication of willingness on the part of
potential employers to hire the graduates. It was also
considered the responsibility of the college to explain
in detail the nature of the experimental program to those
seeking admission. Potential students should understand
the problems involved and the difficulties that might be
encountered as graduates of an experimental program.

13. The community's need for a nursing program should be considered.

This criterion does not necessarily mean that because there are several hospital programs in the community, there is no need for a new type of community college nursing program. Experience has shown that the
students attracted to a college nursing program are not
necessarily those who would be interested in a hospital
program. (See Chapter VI.) Neither does this mean that
every community or every community college should have
a nursing program. The other criteria should be

considered carefully along with this one, for some of
the others may be more pertinent in a given community or
area.

14. Colleges selected as participants in the project should
be prepared to carry through the experimentation to a
logical conclusion.

Each one of the participating institutions established the nursing program as one of the continuing
offerings of the college, not as a temporary measure.
Their only reservation was that the programs must produce
graduates capable of successful employment or changes
would be made sufficient to accomplish this. All eight
cooperating institutions, therefore, continued the nursing programs when the period of the project ended.

Colleges Selected

The seven colleges selected joined the project at different times, depending on their readiness to begin a nursing
program. They are located in six states: New York, New Jersey,
Michigan, Utah, California, and Virginia, representing various
sections of the United States. They are located in communities
of different sizes,ranging from Pasadena, a large city, to
Middletown, New York, a relatively small city. Information concerning the location of the colleges is shown in Table 1.

TABLE 1

COLLEGES PARTICIPATING IN COOPERATIVE RESEARCH PROJECT

Location and Date of Establishment

College	City	State	Established
Fairleigh Dickinson University	Rutherford (17,411)[a]	New Jersey	1941[b]
Henry Ford Community College[c]	Dearborn (94,994)	Michigan	1938
Orange County Community College	Middletown (22,586)	New York	1950
Pasadena City College	Pasadena (104,707)	California	1924
Virginia Intermont College	Bristol[d] (15,964) Bristol (16,771)	Virginia Tennessee	1912
Virginia State College Norfolk Division	Norfolk[e] (213,513)	Virginia	1935
Weber College	Ogden (57,112)	Utah	1916

[a]Population figures from 1950 census.

[b]Date is of establishment as two-year community college.

[c]Established as Dearborn Junior College. Name changed in 1952.

[d]Bristol population divided between Virginia and Tennessee.

[e]Virginia State College (parent institution) located in Petersburg, Virginia.

The cooperating colleges are under different types of control. Two colleges are privately controlled while five are under public control. One of those privately controlled is under church auspices. The public institutions represent local, county, and state control. The colleges also show a considerable range in age. Virginia Intermont College was established in 1912; Orange County Community College in 1950. All but one of the colleges is coeducational. Table 2 shows the control, type, and accreditation status of the colleges cooperating in the project.

The number of students enrolled in the several colleges varies greatly. The smallest institution in the group has only slightly more than 300, while the largest has almost 30,000 students. The faculties vary in size correspondingly. Since both public and private institutions are included, there is wide variation in student cost. One institution (Pasadena City College) has no tuition or miscellaneous fee, while another institution (Fairleigh Dickinson University) has an annual tuition charge of $525. Table 3 gives information concerning the size of the several institutions and the yearly cost to students.

All the colleges are junior or community colleges except Fairleigh Dickinson University. This institution began as a two-year community college in 1941, became a four-year institution in 1948 and a university in 1956. It has maintained a number of two-year terminal programs even though it has moved

TABLE 2

COLLEGES PARTICIPATING IN COOPERATIVE RESEARCH PROJECT

Control, Type, Accreditation, and Date of Project Entry

College	Control	Type	Accreditation[a]	Project Entry
Fairleigh Dickinson University	Non-Profit	Coed. Four-Year and Graduate	M.S.	1952
Henry Ford Community College	Local Public School District	Coed. Two-Year	N.C.	1952
Orange County Community College	County	Coed. Two-Year	State	1952
Pasadena City College	Local Public School District	Coed. Two-Year	W.A.	1953
Virginia Intermont College	Baptist Non-Profit	Coed. Four-Year[b]	S.A.	1954
Virginia State College -- Norfolk Division	State	Coed. Four-Year Two-Year	S.A.	1955
Weber College	State	Coed. Two-Year	N.W.	1953

Source: Junior College Directory, 1956.

[a]M.S.: Middle States Association of Colleges and Secondary Schools
N.C.: North Central Association of Colleges and Secondary Schools
W.A.: Western College Association
S.A.: Southern Association of Colleges and Secondary Schools
N.W.: Northwest Association of Secondary and Higher Schools
State: The University of the State of New York

[b]College also offers the third and fourth years of high school.

38

TABLE 3

COLLEGES PARTICIPATING IN COOPERATIVE RESEARCH PROJECT

Enrollment, Faculty Size, Student Costs

| College | Enrollment[a] | | | Faculty[b] | Student Cost (Annual) | |
	Total	Fresh.	Soph.		Tuition	Misc.
Fairleigh Dickinson University	6,000+	c	c	500[d]	$525	$50
Henry Ford Community College	8,421	691	296	103	130 Res. 234 Non.	15
Orange County Community College	2,042	427	199	54	200 Res. 400 Non.	
Pasadena City College	32,736	9,049	5,343	364	None	Optional
Virginia Intermont College	345	194	101	31	300 Day 1,050 Boarding	
Virginia State College Norfolk Division	3,482	491	226	89	255 Res. 395 Non.	
Weber College	5,156	861	572	106	75	37

Source: Junior College Directory 1957. College Catalogues 1956-1957.

[a]Total enrollment includes special and adult students. Fresh. and Soph. indicate full-time day students.

[b]Equivalent full time.

[c]Figures not comparable since this is a four-year institution and those enrolled in two-year programs are not tabulated separately, therefore, not included in table.

[d]This figure includes both full and part time but not equated as full time.

toward four-year programs and graduate work. The nursing program is only one of the two-year programs offered.

The colleges were selected according to the criteria suggested by the advisory committee. They were selected also to provide as broad a cross section of junior and community colleges as possible. It was believed that this would help to eliminate differences caused by size, control, location, and cost, and thus give a more accurate picture of nursing programs in junior and community colleges.

Selection of the Hospital Nursing Program

The inclusion of a hospital nursing program in the project was provided for in the initial request for the grant making the project possible. It was pointed out in this initial statement that in some states it might be possible for a hospital to qualify for a charter from the proper state authorities for the establishment of an educational institution, in fact a junior college of nursing. Such an institution would require a specified amount of capital, an annual budget, and adherence to certain curricular patterns in order to be empowered to grant an associate degree. Actually no hospital evidenced interest in this proposal. It should also be noted that many junior college educators express disagreement with the development of new single-purpose institutions. They call attention to the disappearance of those institutions initially set up with a single purpose, which have either closed or become multi-purpose institutions.

At the first meeting of the advisory committee the need for including a hospital school in the project was emphasized by the committee. At the same time it was made clear that a hospital school, to be a part of the experiment, would need to reorganize its program along the same lines as the experimental programs. An adjustment merely to shorten the existing nursing school program would not be enough.

Hospital schools inquired about participating in the project practically from the beginning, but progress in the actual establishment of one was slow. The point at which the hospitals seemed to lose interest was when the strictly educational purpose of the school was made clear. When it was realized that no nursing-service advantage could be obtained from the presence of the school, the cost of the program loomed large. Some hospital administrators frankly admitted that they could not operate their hospitals without the service of students. Others tended to minimize the service they got from students, pointing out that they continued their schools at great cost. In neither case interest in becoming part of the project sustained.

The advisory committee, at its 1954 meeting, questioned whether sufficient publicity had been given to the possibility of including a hospital school. A recommendation was made that a letter describing the project and the conditions under which

a hospital program might qualify be sent to the secretaries
of the several state hospital associations and to the secretaries of the American Hospital Association and the American
Medical Association. A letter was sent to these associations in February 1954. The number of letters sent to
hospital associations was 49. By June 1, 1954, 18 replies
had been received. Of this number, 8 expressed approval of the
idea and 3 objected to the criteria to be used in determining
the eligibility of a hospital school. The remaining replies
simply acknowledged receipt of the letter, stated that the
information was referred to local hospitals, or indicated that
state laws or financial considerations prevented their participation at this time. As a result of this same letter, there
were 22 communications directly from hospitals.

Following the request from these 22 hospitals a questionnaire was developed similar to the one used in gaining information from the colleges (Appendix E). By June 1, 1954,
5 questionnaires of the 19 requested had been returned. Again
following the pattern used in selecting the colleges, field
visits were made to 3 hospitals. Conferences were held with
hospital administrators, boards of directors, and nursing service personnel. Each of the three hospitals visited was located
close to a junior-community college, and some had either used
certain of the courses the college offered or had obtained the
services of certain members of the faculty in the teaching of
some courses. This fact led to the identification of two kinds

of hospital schools it might be desirable to include. These
were: (1) a hospital school that purchases courses in general
education from a community college through a cooperative
arrangement and (2) a hospital school that is a self-contained
school and conducts all courses as part of the hospital educational program. In the first type the hospital students attend
some classes in the community college but are under the control
of the hospital school. In the second type the hospital employs
personnel to instruct the students in various general education
courses as well as nursing courses.

The school finally found interested and eligible is of
the first type, and it is the only hospital school included in
the program.

Criteria for Selecting Hospital Program

Although it had been agreed that the educational program
in a hospital school should be essentially the same as the
junior-community college nursing program, specific criteria
for determining eligibility of the hospital school were set
up at the 1954 annual meeting of the project advisory committee.

The criteria were:

1. The school is owned and operated by the hospital.

The hospital must recognize that it alone is responsible for the nursing program. This also means that the
diploma or certificate upon completion of the course
will be issued by the hospital.

2. The school must develop a two-year program which prepares the graduate to take the licensing examination
   in the state.

   Like the college programs, this program must prepare the graduate for licensure. This meant early
   approval of the program by the licensing body.

3. The educational administration should be directly responsible to the board of directors of the hospital, which
   also performs the function of the board of directors of
   the school.

   To meet this requirement, the school of nursing and
   the nursing service must be completely separate. This
   separation must extend from the chief administrators
   of the school and service through the faculty of the
   school and junior administrative officers of the nursing
   services (supervisors and head nurses). This means, in
   effect, that the hospital which chooses to operate a
   school is actually conducting two entirely different
   enterprises. One, the school, has the sole purpose of
   education, while the second has as its purpose nursing
   service to the patients in the hospital. These two
   purposes, being so different, cannot be met by the same
   means.

4. The school must have as its purpose the education of
   the students.

This criterion is closely related to the one immediately preceding. It needed specific emphasis, however, since confusion about what a school is and does often stands in the way of sound educational programs in nursing. With education as its purpose, the school has no obligation to provide nursing service to the hospital.

5. The school must have faculty, facilities, and funds for its operation.

This statement appears to be obvious, but it was considered necessary for various reasons. In 1950, <u>Nursing Schools at the Mid-Century</u> reported that 73 per cent of hospital schools of nursing had no separate budgets. When the nursing program receives its funds through the nursing service budget, there are inevitable conflicts. Similarly, when nursing service personnel are assigned two roles -- whether prepared or not, interested in teaching or not -- conflicts and confusions arise. Any other kind of school would not attempt to exist without these three -- faculty, facilities, funds -- and it becomes increasingly clear that a school of nursing cannot exist without them either. It is in this area, of course, that the question of cost of a nursing program in a hospital becomes paramount.

6. The curriculum and program plan must be in line with the proposals for the new nursing programs in junior and community colleges.

There must be as sharp and clear a change in the curriculum as in the administration of the school. The inclusion of general education courses and a complete reorganization of the nursing courses were considered necessary.

With these criteria now quite specific, a hospital program for inclusion in the project was sought.

Hospital Selected

The hospital school selected was Monmouth Memorial Hospital in Long Branch, New Jersey. The hospital administrator was notified by the Executive Secretary of the New Jersey Hospital Association that the Cooperative Research Project was interested in including a hospital school. This was the letter sent to each state hospital association in February 1954. Immediate interest was expressed by the hospital administrator and the administrator of the school of nursing.

There were a number of reasons for this interest. The Board of Governors of the hospital and the administrator were becoming increasingly concerned about the rising costs of maintaining the three-year nursing school. The community was growing rapidly, with a corresponding need for more nursing personnel. The shorter program would make prepared nurses available faster. The director of the school and faculty recognized this as an opportunity to improve the educational program. They had worked within the rigid framework required by the State Board of Nursing and now welcomed a chance to build a curriculum which they felt would prepare a nurse qualified to function in a staff nursing position in nursing service. The inclusion of general education courses was seen as another asset. The Dean of Monmouth Junior College (later Monmouth College) indicated his interest and the willingness of the college to continue its twelve-year association with the school of nursing.

Approval of the development of a two-year program was sought from the State Board of Nursing. A proposed curriculum plan was presented to the Board, and, after several conferences, was accepted. On August 27, 1954, official approval was received from the Board of Nursing. Concurrently with the conferences held with the Board of Nursing, the advisory committee of the School of Nursing (known as the Board of Managers) studied the proposed program and its implications for the school. The Board of Managers recommended the change to the hospital Board of Governors. On September 18, 1954, the Board of Governors approved the change. In June 1954 the Cooperative Research Project notified the Director of the School of Nursing that if the criteria as specified were met, the Monmouth Memorial Hospital School of Nursing would be admitted to the project.

With action along these different lines going on concurrently, it was possible to have final decisions made about eight
months after the initial contact. The decision was made to continue the three-year students until completion of their courses,
but to offer only the two-year program beginning in 1955.

The first students were admitted into the new program
in September 1955, thus giving the school time to make the
necessary division of nursing service and school personnel.
The faculty had approximately one year to plan the new curriculum
in detail. These changes necessitated revision of the educational policies previously followed. This new two-year program
was the first major change in the nursing school curriculum
since the establishment of the school in 1896.

During the year of planning, there were monthly meetings
of the nursing school faculty with those instructors at the
junior college who taught subjects in which nursing students
were enrolled. More frequent meetings of the nursing school
faculty were held. The fact that a school of nursing had been
operating in this hospital meant that a faculty was almost immediately available. It was necessary, however, to make a division
of those functioning in dual positions. Each individual was
given the opportunity to express a preference for the function
she wished to pursue. Some were more interested in nursing service, and so made that their choice, while others preferred
teaching. As a result, four full-time faculty members were
designated, and they were available for planning the new program.

The students were selected according to the same criteria that had been used previously for the three-year students. They were given the choice of living in the residence at a specified rate for their rooms, with meals available in the hospital cafeteria, or of living at home. During the first semester about half of the students "lived in," but by the second semester all were living at home. The tuition was set at $500 per year. This amount was based on the tuition for full-time study at Monmouth Junior College, since the hospital had no basis for setting this fee from its own experience. In addition, housing, uniforms, books, and transportation costs were the responsibility of the student.

The question of the cost of a nursing program to a hospital is a somewhat controversial one. To the best of our knowledge this is the first attempt on the part of a hospital to set up a truly educational program with no service provided to the hospital by the students. Therefore there is no basis for comparing costs. No specific cost study has been done at Monmouth Memorial Hospital, since the program has been in existence less than two years. The first year the number of students was small (it more than doubled during the second year), and not all of the full-time faculty members were needed to teach the courses offered in the first year. Moreover, the three-year students were in their second year, and some of the faculty spent most of their time with this group of students. There is no denying that the cost of such a program is a very important consideration. It was felt that the cost of the Monmouth Hospital program for the first two years was not typical of the cost as the program developed and the number of students reached a maximum.

Whether or not it is socially efficient for a hospital to finance an educational program is another question which will not be discussed here. It is well known that tuition fees charged students do not pay for the cost of an educational program. This means that in the hospital situation the difference between cost and tuition fees would have to be made up by hospital funds. The desirability of this procedure must be considered.

The curriculum of the nursing program at Monmouth Memorial Hospital is similar to those developed by the colleges. Therefore, the discussion of the curriculum and teaching methods applies to all eight programs equally (Chapter V). It must be made clear, however, that the hospital school's original curriculum was completely reorganized and educational policies changed. The new nursing program represents not only a shortened period but a new curriculum. The belief that a hospital can have this new type of nursing program simply by eliminating the third year, leaving the first two virtually intact, is erroneous.

The nursing program at Monmouth Memorial Hospital had not yet graduated its first class when the project came to an end, so no data are available with respect to licensing examinations or employment. The program has developed in the pattern of the college programs, so that the only real differences are in the control of the program and the awarding of a diploma instead of an associate degree.

Agreement with Cooperating Institutions

The setting up of a continuing organizational unit at Teachers College to develop and give direction to an organized program of research and experimentation in cooperation with selected junior and community colleges required some form of agreement between the institutions concerned. It will be remembered that each cooperating institution was independent and was alone responsible for the programs it offered. Therefore, its participation in this endeavor was purely voluntary.

The philosophy which is fundamental to the new associate-degree nursing program was considered most important from the beginning. It was felt that the understanding and acceptance of this philosophy was more significant in the development of the program than were specific regulations or specifications. Unless the right philosophy were present, the program would not be satisfactorily initiated or maintained even if the most detailed and specific bill of particulars were drawn up and agreed to. Therefore a good deal of attention was given to a statement of philosophy to which all could agree.

A preliminary statement was drafted by the project staff. The presidents of the first six colleges selected as

cooperating institutions and the chairmen of the nursing programs of five colleges (the sixth program had not been finally
approved and had not yet appointed a chairman) met with the
project staff in January 1954. The statement of the agreement
was reviewed, discussed, and revised. Later, the final statement was prepared and submitted to each college (Appendix F).
A simple acknowledgment of its receipt constituted the only
acceptance of this agreement. It has, however, constituted the
basis of our working agreement since that time. Each institution
subsequently added to the project also accepted this agreement.

This statement of agreement differs considerably from
the contracts usually considered necessary by both hospital and
college schools of nursing. What each party agreed to do was
simply stated without specific detail. The emphasis was on the
basic philosophy. In making agreements between the cooperating
institutions and their respective community agencies, the same
principle was followed. In other words, all agreements have
been simple and brief. The feasibility of this simple agreement, based on a clear understanding of the philosophy upon
which the programs rest, has been attested to by the very
pleasant and productive years of cooperative endeavor.

Ways of Working Together

Each institution participating in the Cooperative Research Project was independent and has been associated with
the project staff in a cooperative effort based on a general

agreement. There has been no specific or written agreement between the several institutions in the project, but rather an implied willingness on the part of each to work together with all others chosen by the project. This rather loosely arranged association has been the means by which the objective of the project -- a new type of nursing program -- has been achieved.

The advantages of a cooperative arrangement with a number of independent institutions are evident. It was possible to obtain a variety of types of institutions, of varying sizes, located in different sections of the country. Each institution operates under unique policies and procedures. Thus the nursing program has had to be developed locally within these differing frameworks. It can be shown, then, that the program is not dependent on a set pattern but can be adapted to the various community college settings.

Each institution has financed its nursing program as it has all other programs, and none has had special grants or funds for this purpose. Each has financed the program in its entirety. In the light of past experience with the financing of nursing programs -- in colleges and universities -- this fact was seen to merit special attention. Had a single program, as a sort of sample program, been developed under the auspices of the Cooperative Research Project, this valuable experience would have been lost.

The willingness on the part of administrators and faculties to follow closely the principles agreed upon in the

development of the nursing programs was outstanding. Equally
significant was the willingness to share with the faculties of
the other colleges. Problems and solutions of problems, proposals for action and suggestions for study, were freely shared
during the annual workshops and more frequently by correspondence
between workshops. The consultation visits made by staff members to each program, at least yearly, facilitated both the
sharing just described and the implementation of the program.
The project office also served as a clearinghouse for information to and from individual programs.

One point that might have been considered a disadvantage
was the lack of control by the Cooperative Research Project
over the individual programs. This meant that no action was
taken unless the individual institution wished to and would do
so. Fortunately, the cooperative spirit never was in jeopardy.
In fact, there was eagerness on the part of faculty groups and
on the part of individuals to receive suggestions and to give
help to others. Thus what might be considered a disadvantage
was really an advantage in working toward curriculum development.
Working with a group of colleges sharing a common purpose but
utilizing many ways of achieving this purpose has been a rewarding experience for all concerned.

Summary

The decision to use established junior-community colleges interested in developing nursing programs was made to

insure the funds being used for educational research, to allow
for wider experimentation and to assure continuation of the
programs once the experimental phase was finished. The selection of the cooperating colleges was made according to the
criteria developed with the advice of the advisory committee
and from those institutions seeking to participate in the project
Questionnaires were sent to forty-two colleges with returns from
twenty-four. Certain of these colleges were visited and extended conferences were held with college personnel, state
boards of nursing and representatives of community agencies.
Seven colleges were selected. These colleges are located in
six states and include both publicly and privately supported
colleges, both large and small institutions and coeducational
and women's colleges.

A hospital school was selected to participate in the
project on the advice of the advisory committee. The program
offered was the same as that in the college but the control was
that of the hospital.

Some form of agreement between the continuing organizational unit at Teachers College and the cooperating colleges was
necessary. Each cooperating institution was independent and
its participation in this endeavor was purely voluntary. A
statement of agreement was drafted cooperatively and it served
as the basis of our working agreement. This statement was
general in nature with an emphasis on the basic philosophy.

CHAPTER IV

THE FACULTY

This chapter deals with the faculty -- its preparation,
its size, its stability, and its availability.

Preparation of the Faculty

Since the program in nursing is an integral part of
the college, the requirements for appointment as a member of the
faculty in the nursing program are the same as those for similar
programs, or for the college as a whole. It was felt that no
concessions should be made for the nursing program. In some
states a teaching credential is required before a regular faculty
appointment can be made. In at least one of the states concerned
in the pilot programs, a master's degree is required as well as
specific preparation in the area in which the teaching is to be
done. Therefore, in this particular state, all nurse faculty
members in the program have a master's degree.

Of the 59 persons who have held or now hold faculty
appointments in the pilot programs, 55, or 95 per cent, have
a bachelor's or a master's degree. Thirty one, or 52 per cent,
hold a master's degree. Only 3 persons, or 5 per cent, do not
hold a degree. One of these lacks only 3 credit hours for the

bachelor's degree.

A survey conducted in 1957 by the ANA Research and Statistics unit showed that 77 per cent of faculty members included in the survey held a bachelor's or a higher degree. Twenty-six per cent held a master's or higher degree. The report also indicated that in collegiate schools of nursing, 59 per cent of the faculty members held a master's degree or higher, and only 2.5 per cent had no degree.[1] These figures are almost the same as those for the pilot programs within the project (Table 4).

According to Koos,[2] three-fourths of the academic teachers in junior colleges hold a master's degree, while about one-half of the special teachers hold this degree. The chairman of the department or division in each pilot program (100 per cent) holds the master's degree. In collegiate schools generally, this degree or higher is held by 92 per cent of those in comparable positions.

It seems obvious that the college programs do, and should, attract the better-prepared nurse instructors. Colleges rarely appoint an instructor who does not have at least a bachelor's degree. Although junior and community colleges have not usually required preparation beyond the master's degree,

---

[1] American Nurses Association, 1957 Facts about Nursing (New York: The Association, 1957), p. 95.

[2] Leonard V. Koos, "Preparation for Community-College Teaching," Journal of Higher Education, 21:309-17, 1950.

TABLE 4

PREPARATION OF FACULTY

| Position | Pilot Programs | | Schools of Nursing[a] | | | |
| | Baccalaureate or Higher % | Master's or Higher % | Collegiate | | Hospital | |
			Bacc. or Higher %	Master's or Higher %	Bacc. or Higher %	Master's or Higher %
Dean-Director	100	100	98.5	92	93	48
Faculty	95	53	97.5	59	75	17

[a]American Nurses Association, 1957 Facts about Nursing (New York: The Association, 1957), pp. 95-99.

those who teach in these institutions are increasingly seeking
the doctorate. Jarvie states there is general agreement with
Koos's statement that the doctor's degree should become the
prevailing standard ultimately, but he also believes this to be

> ... unrealistic for the foreseeable
> future.... There is widespread belief that
> a master's degree is presently inadequate
> for the academic preparation of junior
> college teachers.[3]

Several educators have recommended at least two years of graduate study, which would include specific preparation in the
junior college.

The faculty members of the pilot programs represent
widely varied backgrounds of experience, both in education and
in nursing. Twenty-five had had less than one year's experience in teaching prior to this appointment, while 19 had had
more than five years of teaching experience, most of it in hospital schools of nursing. The teaching experience included
teaching of physical and biological science; social science;
nursing arts; medical, surgical, maternity, pediatric, and
psychiatric nursing; pharmacology; public health nursing; history of nursing; and professional adjustments. Several had had

---

[3] J. L. Jarvie, "Making Teaching More Effective,"
The Public Junior College, The Fifty-fifth Yearbook of the
National Society for the Study of Education (Chicago: The
Society, 1956), p. 223.

teaching experience in the public schools, in practical nursing programs, and in the programs of the Red Cross.

The nursing experience of faculty members varied even more widely than their teaching experience, with practically every type of nursing represented. Nine of the 59 had had less than one year of nursing experience, while 28 had had more than five years. Twelve had had experience as public health nurses, and all of these had had more than six months' experience. Administrative positions ranging from head nurse to director of nursing service had been held by 23 faculty members.

Size of Faculty

The size of the nursing faculty will necessarily depend on the number of students as well as the type of program being offered and the location of the facilities being used. At the beginning of any new type of program there is no certain or specific way to ascertain just how many faculty members will be required. It was necessary, however, for each institution contemplating a nursing program to have some idea of how many new staff members would be needed. This number was important from the standpoint of both availability of personnel and cost. An attempt was made to indicate the minimum number of instructors required at the beginning of the program. No attempt was made to identify the ultimate number of instructors who might be needed.

Since the broad-fields approach (see Chapter V) had
been accepted as a basis for developing the curriculum, the
number of instructors was projected accordingly. At least four
persons would be needed to carry on the nursing aspects of the
program. These were the chairman of the department or division,
an instructor in fundamentals of nursing, one in maternal and
child care, and one in the area commonly known as medical-
surgical. Chairmen of departments in colleges customarily teach
in addition to their administrative duties, and so the chairman
might have her preparation also in one of these teaching areas
or a division of it. The nature of the nursing program, with
its use of multiple facilities outside the college, means that
the teaching load of the chairman may be less than that of the
chairman whose teaching is confined to college-located classrooms and laboratories.

In 1957 collegiate schools of nursing which offered the
baccalaureate degree reported an average of nine full-time
nurse faculty members, while all other types of nursing schools
reported an average of seven full-time nurse instructors.[4]
In the eight pilot programs, the average number of faculty members (including the chairman of the department) was five.
The number varied from three to nine full-time instructors,
with at least four of the eight programs using one or two
part-time instructors. The number of students as well as

[4] 1957 Facts about Nursing, p. 95.

instructors varied among the programs, but the average ratio of nurse instructors to students was one to ten. No studies of ratio have been carried out, and therefore there is no specific information about the optimal ratio of students to faculty. There is considerable evidence, though, that the ratio of one instructor to six students, commonly accepted and widely quoted, is not essential.

The question of ratio of instructors to students is a difficult one. For one thing there are different ways to look at the question and, therefore, different answers which are not comparable. There is first of all the question of over-all ratio, that is, total number of students to over-all number of instructors. In this instance the college instructors who teach the general education subjects must also be included. Then there is the ratio of students to faculty in the classroom and in the laboratory. In the classroom one instructor can satisfactorily teach more students than in the laboratory. For certain experiences and at certain times the instructor and student are in a face-to-face relationship and hence in a one to one ratio. At the same time the same instructor may be responsible for other students, perhaps in the same room or at least on the same hospital floor. They may be responsible also for students who are caring for patients on another hospital floor. Therefore, the teacher is at one and the same time in three different relationships to students located in different locations within the institution. No matter how

small or large the number of students, the instructor can never
be with all students simultaneously and she always finds herself in the situation described above. Sometimes when the problem of ratio is discussed it appears that it might be desirable
for the ratio of students and instructors to be equal in all of
the situations described above. This is unrealistic, of course,
but perhaps even more important it is scarcely desirable.
There is considerable evidence in other fields that skills can
be taught more effectively to groups than to individuals.
Surely some of these technics can be used in nursing. The instructors in the pilot programs report that most laboratory
sections have at least ten students. There is no real evidence
that the number may not be increased.

Still another point should be emphasized in this discussion of the size of the faculty. Those who visit nursing programs of the traditional type for official or voluntary accredit-
ing groups are accustomed to seeing faculties with few full time
and many part time members. They usually look at those whose
responsibilities include nursing service as if they were full
time instructors. In these situations the numbers are confusing
and the ratios commonly cited, erroneous. In the pilot programs
the only responsibility the instructor has is in the educational program. Therefore, when she is with students she has
no obligation other than teaching the students. There is no
accurate way of comparing the time a head nurse or supervisor
spends teaching the few students on a given unit with that

which the full time college instructor spends with two or three
times as many students in her laboratory section. The instructors report the satisfaction of having but one obligation,
that is, teaching.

There is still another difference between traditional
programs and the pilot programs that has a distinct bearing on
faculty ratio and that is the amount of time spent in nursing
functions. The student in the traditional school spends a work
day in the hospital, and usually a forty-hour week (which includes varying numbers of hours of class). The student in the
pilot programs has laboratory hours assigned to nursing functions as for laboratory work in other courses. This means that
one instructor may have more than one laboratory section each
week and so can teach many students in the laboratory during
the course of the week. This constitutes a far different
picture than when all students are in the hospital simultaneously
throughout the week.

The size of the faculty is extremely important both from
the standpoint of education and of economics. Neither can be
considered without the other. It will do the nursing profession no service if we continue to use unsubstantiated arguments for faculty requirements. Colleges will find it difficult to accept nursing programs which indicate faculty needs
so far out of proportion with those of other quite similar programs. Instructors need to find new methods of teaching which
are more effective for larger groups. If the number of

students increases as experts predict it will if future nursing needs are to be met, instructors must learn how to teach larger groups of students. While the number of students probably has some influence on the effectiveness of teaching, it is probably equally true that a good teacher will be good even when the number of students is large and a poor teacher poor even when the number is small.

Conditions of Employment

The colleges participating in the Cooperative Research Project have appointed faculty members in the nursing program according to the same policies and procedures applied to faculty members of the college generally. The prevailing salary schedule has also been applied. The policies concerning rank, tenure, retirement, and promotion are alike for all.

Thus the conditions of employment vary from one institution to another. There is no salary that can be listed as typical for those who are employed either as chairman of the department or as faculty members.

Stability of Faculty

The stability of a faculty is of great importance in any educational program, and in the development of a new program this factor takes on additional significance. The two oldest programs within the project have completed five years, and the

two newest programs two years. Therefore, no faculty member
has been employed in this new type of program very long. In
three of the eight programs there have been no changes in
faculty except for the addition of new members as the program
expanded. Eighteen of the 37 currently employed full-time
faculty members have been in the program since its inception.
Five were added later, so that 23 of the 37, or 62 per cent,
represent those with initial appointments to faculty positions.
In two of the programs there has been considerable turnover in
the faculty since 1952, but in one of these there has been no
change for two years except for additional appointments.

It would appear, therefore, that these programs tend to
keep their faculty members. No recent studies of faculty turnover in traditional programs are available; consequently no
pertinent comparisons can be made.

Availability of Faculty

The procurement of faculty members has been, and continues to be, a very difficult problem. The over-all shortage
of prepared nurse faculty is part of the difficulty. The
higher academic requirements of the college, compared with those
of the traditional hospital school, make the number available
for junior-community colleges even smaller. Moreover, the newness of the program as well as its distinctive characteristics
have made some potential faculty members wary of undertaking

the task. The attitude of some nurses and nurse educators
toward those teaching in the new program has deterred a few
otherwise interested. This same attitude has made working in
the new program difficult in certain areas.

The need for instructors has increased and will continue
to increase, as is evident from the number of colleges wishing
to develop the new type of nursing program. Until more nurses
prepare to teach in these programs, the shortage of available
instructors will remain a problem.

Summary

The faculty of the nursing programs was appointed to the
college according to the policies and procedures of the college
for the appointment of all faculty members. The preparation
of the faculty in the pilot programs compares favorably with
that of the faculty of schools of nursing generally. The background of those teaching in the pilot programs varied widely
and included both teaching of a variety of subjects and working
in various nursing service activities.

The size of the faculty varied with the number of students.
No attempt was made to identify the ultimate number of instructors who might be needed but an attempt was made to indicate the minimum number of instructors required at the beginning
of the program. In the eight pilot programs the average number
of faculty members was five. The programs tended to keep their

faculty members.

The need for instructors has increased and will undoubtedly continue to increase. Unless more nurses prepare to
teach in these programs the problem of securing personnel will
continue.

CHAPTER V

CURRICULUM AND INSTRUCTION IN JUNIOR COMMUNITY
COLLEGE NURSING PROGRAMS

Introduction

The development of a new and different curriculum and
appropriate teaching methods for the preparation of nurses
were identified as the central factors in the Cooperative Research Project. The years since the first school of nursing
was begun by Florence Nightingale have seen relatively few
changes in the pattern of preparing nurses. Even these few
changes were not major ones when compared with the changes
that have occurred in education. These facts made the development of a new curricular pattern more interesting and more
challenging.

To accomplish a change in curriculum that is more than
a superficial one requires considerable time and effort. It
requires many changes, with perhaps the most fundamental taking
place within the individuals who must carry out the change --
that is, within the teachers themselves. Sharp describes this
process when he states:

> ... The reorientation of a traditional teacher
> requires a process of re-education which will

> help him to work through his older conception
> of the curriculum and his older mode of teach-
> ing to a new conception and a new mode of
> teaching.[1]

Tourtillott has described what our faculty tried to do

as follows:

> We have tried to rework the traditional
> course content into a sequence of student-
> oriented problems. We have developed
> student-teacher planning and carrying out
> the procedures as planned followed by an
> evaluation of the learning experiences.[2]

The full potential of this new type of curriculum has by no

means been developed, nor will it ever be. Changes must occur

frequently and regularly if it is not to become the traditional

curriculum of tomorrow.

This chapter describes the curriculum and methods of

teaching as both have developed during the term of the Coopera-

tive Research Project.

General Characteristics

Each of the programs in the participating institutions

differs from the others. Since one of the basic principles

followed was that the nursing program should become an integral

---

[1]George Sharp, Curriculum Development as Re-education of
the Teacher (New York: Bureau of Publications, Teachers College,
Columbia University, 1951), p. 5.

[2]Eleanor Tourtillott, The Rationale of the Two-Year
Nursing Program at Henry Ford Community College, Unpublished
manuscript, 1957.

part of the institution, the nursing programs differ from one
another just as each college differs in its policies and procedures and in its curriculum from the others. There are, however, certain characteristics common to all of the nursing programs, for two reasons. One is that certain general characteristics were formulated at the start of the project as those
that would be accepted by the cooperating institutions; the
second is that the faculties worked cooperatively in developing
the curriculum through workshops and with the project staff.

The first characteristic of the new nursing curriculum
is that it includes both general and specialized education.
The educational concern of the junior-community college is
threefold. It aims at development of the individual as a
person, as a citizen, and as a worker. Therefore, general education accounts for from one-third to one-half of the curriculum,
with specialized education, or nursing, accounting for the remaining two-thirds or one-half. Each of the colleges has specific requirements for all students who are candidates for the
associate degree. The requirements in general education vary
widely, some colleges having developed integrated or core
courses while others have course or credit-hour requirements in
the several areas. All have a requirement in communication
skills, in the social sciences, and in the physical and biological sciences. Some have a requirement in the humanities. All
make some provision for electives.

Tables 5, 6, and 7 show the general education requirements in three of the pilot programs. The nursing students
take the same general education and elective courses as other
students in the college. No course in general education has
been developed exclusively for or is limited to them. The
scheduling of these courses has taken into account the schedule
of nursing courses so that no required course is made up only
of nursing students. This has meant close cooperation between
the chairman of the nursing department and the registrar or
other college official whose duties include the scheduling of
classes.

The second characteristic of the curriculum is that the
specialized or nursing courses have been reorganized and placed
in a different sequence. Instead of the numerous small courses
found in the traditional nursing curriculum, the content and
learning experiences have been grouped around a central theme
into fewer courses. The fractionalization of subject matter in
traditional programs was thought to be repetitive, time-consuming,
and not conducive to effective learning. Therefore the number
of nursing courses in the new type of curriculum generally
varies from four to six. Tables 5, 6, and 7 show the nursing
courses offered and the sequence followed in three representative
colleges. Within these courses, learning experiences have been
organized with care but also with flexibility to provide meaningful learning without unnecessary repetition.

TABLE 5

CURRICULUM PLAN FOR 1957-58

Orange County Community College

Credits Given in Semester Hours

First Year

Winter Semester		Spring Semester	
Course	Credits	Course	Credits
English Communic.[a]	3	English Communications[a]	3
Human Relations[a]	3	Human Relations[a]	3
Science for Living I (Biol. Backgrounds)	4	Science for Living II (Human Biology)	3
Nursing (fundamentals)	6	Science for Living III (Chemical and Physical Backgrounds)	3
Electives	2-3	Nursing (mothers and children)	6
	18-19		18

Second Year

Winter Semester		Spring Semester	
Course	Credits	Course	Credits
Social Science[a] (Community Problems)	3	Social Science[a] (Community Problems)	3
Nursing (Clinical Nurs. Sc.)	12	Nursing (Clinical Nurs. Sc.)	12
Electives	2-3	Electives	2-3
	17-18		17-18

[a]Courses required of all students.

TABLE 6

CURRICULUM PLAN FOR 1957-58

Weber College

Credits Given in Quarter Hours

First Year

Fall Quarter			Winter Quarter	
Course	Credits		Course	Credits
Basic Communications 1[a]	3		Basic Communications 2 [a]	3
Orientation[a]	2		Physical Science 1	5
Speech	2		Bacteriology 1	5
Physiology 1[b]	5		Home Economics 35	3
Home Economics	3		(Child Development)	
(Nutrition)			Nursing 21	3
Nursing 20	2		(Fundamentals)	
(Fundamentals)				19
Physical Education[a]	1			
	18			

Spring Quarter			Summer Quarter	
Course	Credits		Course	Credits
Basic Communications 3[a]	3		Psychology	5
Physical Science 2	4		Nursing 26	12
Social Science	3-4		(Maternal and Child Care)	
Home Economics 36	3		Physical Education	1
(Nursery Observation)				18
Nursing 25	5			
(Maternal and Child Care)				
	18-19			

Second Year

Fall Quarter		Winter Quarter		Spring Quarter	
Course	Credits	Course	Credits	Course	Credits
Humanities 1	3	Humanities 2	3	Humanities 3	3
Social Science	3-5	Nursing 29	12	Nursing 30	12
Nursing 28	12	(Clin.Nurs.Sc.)		(Clin.Nurs.Sc.)	
(Clin.Nurs.Sc.)		Electives	3	Electives	3
	18-20		18		18

Special Conference Report Weber College Two-Year Nursing
Program, March 1957.

[a]Required of all students in the college.

[b]Four quarter-hours of laboratory science required of all students.

TABLE 7

CURRICULUM PLAN FOR 1957-58

Monmouth Memorial Hospital School of Nursing

Credits Given in Semester Hours

First Year

Winter Semester		Spring Semester	
Course	Credits	Course	Credits
Anatomy and Physiol.[a]	3	Anatomy and Physiology[a]	3
Chemistry[a]	3	Microbiology[a]	3
College English[a]	3	College English[a]	3
Social Psychology[a]	2	Social Psychology[a]	2
Fundamentals of Nursing	6	Medical Surgical Nursing	6
	17		17

Summer Session

Course	Credits
Medical-Surgical Nursing	3
Psychiatric Nursing	3

Second Year

Winter Semester		Spring Semester	
Course	Credits	Course	Credits
Rise of Western Civiliz.[a]	3	Rise of Western Civiliz.[a]	3
Electives[a]	3	Electives[a]	3
Medical Surgical Nursing	12	Maternal and Child Health Nursing	12
	18		18

Summer Session

Course	Credits
Maternal and Child Health Nursing	4
Group Nursing Experience	4

---

[a]Courses taken at Monmouth College.

The allocation of credit to the nursing courses follows the pattern of the specific institution. Common practice, however, is one credit for each class hour and one credit for either two or three laboratory hours. What is commonly called clinical experience is considered laboratory experience and is so conducted, and the credit allotment therefore follows that of the laboratory. Table 8 shows the distribution of credits among nursing courses in the pilot programs and, in addition, the breakdown into class and laboratory hours. It should be noted that there is considerable variation among these programs. These variations are the logical outcome of allowing each curriculum to be developed by the faculty. There has been no desire or attempt to standardize the length, content, or sequence of the courses.

A third general characteristic of the curriculum is its use of the many facilities for rendering health services which each community provides. The number and variety of these, and the way in which they were used, are considered more fully in a subsequent section of this chapter. Table 9 shows the agencies which have participated with each of the colleges in offering the nursing program.

A fourth characteristic of the new type of program is its duration over a two-year period, though the term two-year has been variously interpreted. The length of the program is dealt with more fully later in the chapter. Table 10 shows the length of each program in the project. Students qualify for the

TABLE 8

DISTRIBUTION OF CREDITS IN NURSING COURSES

(Includes only those courses common to all programs)

Institution	Fundamental Nursing			Maternal and Child Health			Clinical Nursing Science[a]			Psychiatric Nursing		
	Semester hrs. (total)	Class hours weekly	Laboratory hours weekly	Semester hrs.	Class hours weekly	Laboratory hours weekly	Semester hours	Class hours weekly	Laboratory hours weekly	Semester hours	Class hours weekly	Laboratory hours weekly
Orange County Community College	6	5	7	6	5	7	24	8	12	c	–	–
Fairleigh Dickinson University	4	2	6	4	2	6	16	3	15	c	–	–
Henry Ford Community College	6	6	7	8	6	12	26	6	21	–	–	–
Weber College	5[b]	1	3[d]/6[d]	15[b]	1[d]/5[d]	12[d]/15[d]	33[b]	5	18	c	–	–
Pasadena City College	3	1	6	12	6	18	21	3-8	12-17	7	8	18
Virginia Intermont College	6	3	6	4	7	21	23	5	12	3	7	2
Virginia State College	6	4	6	12	6	12-16	8	11	4	–	–	
Monmouth Memorial Hospital	6	3	9	16	6	12-24	21	4-8	6-12	3	4	2

[a]Includes what is traditionally called medical-surgical nursing and specialties.

[b]Quarter-hours -- equivalent to 3/4 semester-hours.

[c]Included in medical-surgical or equivalent.

[d]Refers to two quarters since laboratory hours differ.

TABLE 9

HOSPITALS AND OTHER AGENCIES COOPERATING
WITH PILOT PROGRAMS

Participating Institution	Hospitals	Type	Other Agencies
Orange County Community College	Horton Hospital St. Luke's Hospital Middletown State Homeopathic Hosp. Orange Farm Infirmary	General General Special (Psych.) Geriatric	Public Schools Physicians Offices Cerebral Palsy Clinic
Fairleigh Dickinson University	St. Barnabas Hosp. Passaic General Hosp. Essex County Overbrook Hosp.	General General Special (Psych.)	Central Bergen Visiting Nurse Serv. Hickory Dock Nursery School Rutherford Playground Physicians Offices
Henry Ford Community College	Oakwood Hospital Wayne County General Hosp. Herman Keefer Hosp. Harper Hospital Pediatric Div. Detroit Receiving Hosp. Prenatal Clinics	General Special (Communicable) General	
Weber College	Thomas D. Dee Hosp. Utah State Tuberculosis Hospital Shriners Hospital	General Special Special (Orthopedic)	Cerebral Palsy School Elementary School Nursery School
Pasadena	Huntington Memorial Hospital St. Luke's Hospital City of Hope Medical Center Metropolitan State Hospital	General General Special (Tbc, cardiac, etc.) Special (Psych.)	Pasadena Dispensary Pasadena Visiting Nurse Association Pasadena Public Health Nursing Assoc. Pasadena City Nursery Schools Child Guidance Clinic Pasadena Well Baby Clinic School for Cerebral Palsied Children Sister Kenny Institute

TABLE 9 (continued)

HOSPITALS AND OTHER AGENCIES COOPERATING
WITH PILOT PROGRAMS

Participating Institution	Hospitals	Type	Other Agencies
Virginia Intermont College	Bristol Memorial Hospital	General	Washington Sinyth County Health Dept.
	Eastern State Hosp.	Special (Psych.)	Nursery Schools Cerebral Palsy Center Public School -- Class for Retarded Children
Virginia State College	Norfolk Community Hospital	General	First Baptist Church Home for the Aged
	Norfolk General Hospital	General	Liberty Park Nursery School
	Kings Daughters Pediatric Unit		
Monmouth Memorial Hospital School	Monmouth Memorial Hosp.	General	Monmouth County Organization for Public Health
	Allenwood Sanitarium	Special(Tbc)	Long Branch Health Dept.
	Essex County Isolation Hospital	Special (Communicable)	Monmouth County Welfare Home Vocational Rehabilitation Center St. Vincent's Foundling Hosp. (Orphanage) Community Day Nurse Elementary Schools Obstetricians' Offi

79

TABLE 10

LENGTH OF COURSE AND DISTRIBUTION OF CREDITS

Institutions	Total Credits[a]	General Educ. Credits	Nursing Credits	Total Semesters	Summer Session (Weeks)
Orange County Community College	70-73	18	36	4	None
Fairleigh Dickinson University	72	34	33	4	6 for 2 summers
Henry Ford Community College	65	20	39	4	None
Weber College	$94\frac{1}{2}$[b]	24[b]	$43\frac{1}{2}$[b]	4	10 for 1 summer
Pasadena City College	81	23	42	4[c]	9 for 2 summers
Virginia Intermont College	74	12	46	4	7 for 2 summers
Virginia State College	74	20	36	4	$6\frac{1}{2}$ for 2 summers
Monmouth Memorial Hospital	84	32	50	4	8 for 2 summers

[a]Total credits includes general education courses required of all students, nursing courses and electives. Therefore, total in general education and nursing courses differs from grand total.

[b]Quarter credits. All other figures refer to semester credits.

[c]Plus a practicum of one year.

associate degree and, on graduation, are eligible for the licensing examination of the state in which the college is located. One obvious exception to the granting of the associate degree is in the case of the hospital program. The principle that the institution which controls the program grants the degree or diploma, whichever is appropriate, has been adhered to. The graduates of this program receive the diploma of the school.

Another characteristic of the programs is that all faculty members are selected, appointed, and paid by the college. They are responsible for the development of the curriculum, for the teaching of the student wherever that teaching is done, and for evaluation of the students and program. Chapter IV discussed the faculty, its composition and its function.

Still another characteristic of the program is that the students in the nursing program enjoy the same status as all other students in the college. They are eligible for the same cultural, social, and academic opportunities and are held to the same standards and obligations as are other students. Their individual programs are very similar to those of other students in pattern and in the number of credits taken.

The final characteristic of the curriculum, which in fact makes this kind of curriculum possible, is that it is college-controlled and financed. The financing of nursing educa tion as it is customarily found has had a tremendous effect on the curriculum. The service demands of the hospital have caused the curriculum to be what it is in the great majority of hospital schools.   Montag has stated:

> ... The need to have students ready early
> for service on the hospital wards is respon-
> sible for the length of the preclinical
> period and also for the order in which the
> subjects are taught and, indeed, the content
> of the courses.[3]

The opportunity to build the curriculum considered
necessary was provided by college control of the program.   As
has been noted, however, the program at Monmouth Memorial Hospital differs from that of the colleges only in that no degree
is offered.

Development of the Curriculum

The development of the curriculum was considered to be
both a responsibility of and an opportunity for the faculty.
Hence, each college took the responsibility for developing its
own curriculum.   The dean or other appropriate officer of the
college assumed the leadership in this enterprise, along with
the chairman of the nursing department.

It was deemed desirable to have the nursing department
chairman appointed at least a year prior to the beginning of
courses, but the shortage of available personnel did not make
this uniformly possible.   Experience showed that a year's time

---

[3]Mildred Montag, The Education of Nursing Technicians
(New York: G. P. Putnam's Sons, 1951), p. 44.

was desirable, and, where it was possible, the program began and proceeded more smoothly.

In the absence of the chairman of the nursing department, the dean and other faculty members took the initiative in the early planning. The entire college faculty was subsequently involved, either through its regularly constituted curriculum committee or through a special committee appointed for the purpose of assisting with the development of the nursing curriculum. As the nursing faculty grew, it assumed major responsibility for the nursing courses within the curriculum.

The procedure followed by the college in introducing new curricula and in changing existing ones was adhered to and is still followed in each of the cooperating colleges. Making the nursing program an integral part of the college was the principle which governed the way the curriculum developed and changed.

The first step in developing the nursing curriculum was to review the college requirements for all seeking the associate degree and to look critically at those courses which would become part of the new curriculum. Some adjustments in courses were necessary, particularly in the biological and physical sciences, but in no case were these of such a nature as to reduce their usefulness for other students. Changes in these courses have continued through the years covered by the project, and there is agreement that these changes have improved the courses for all students. In no instance was the pattern of general education

courses changed for nursing students. As will be seen from
Tables 5, 6, and 7, the general education courses generally
account for a somewhat larger proportion of credits in the first
year than in the second year.

Nursing Courses

The development of the nursing courses constituted the
biggest job to be done. The state board of nurse examiners had
in each instance given permission to the college faculty to
evolve nursing courses as it saw fit. The functions the professional nurse was to perform were the controlling factors. In
other words, the objectives of the nursing courses were based
upon what the graduate should be able to do. At the first
meeting of the advisory committee, the following statement concerning the nursing curriculum was proposed by the project
staff and discussed and approved by the committee:

> Nursing curriculum will be developed around
> knowledge of man, his development and be-
> havior, contemporary society and its prob-
> lems, including major health problems, and
> the specialized services which nursing
> should render in relation to human and
> social needs.[4]

At the first workshop for faculty members of the pilot
programs, three major technical or nursing curricular areas
were identified. These areas were fundamentals of nursing,
maternity and child care, and medical-surgical nursing. The

---

[4]Report of the First Meeting of the Advisory Committee
on the Cooperative Research Project in Junior and Community
College Education for Nursing, March 12-13, 1952.

latter area was called medical-surgical for want of a more
descriptive term. This area included the nursing of all
patients exclusive of those comprising the maternity area and
that of the well child. The notion of nursing specialties
within the medical-surgical area was discarded. Emphasis was
placed on the broad grouping of subject matter.

At the same time, the principle of having learning experiences move from normal to abnormal conditions, from simple
to complex tasks, was accepted. The sequence of courses was determined by this principle. "Fundamentals of nursing" was described as including the needs of ill persons based on the fundamental needs of the well person and the health guidance and
nursing care appropriate to these needs. It is not, however,
simply an introductory course in the nursing curriculum. The
fundamentals are introduced in the basic course but are developed
throughout each of the courses subsequently given. They represent
the total skills, concepts, and understandings necessary for good
nursing care. An understanding of the normal health needs and
the variations in these needs resulting from illness and the
body's reaction to disease are basic to the care of any patient,
regardless of diagnosis, degree of illness, therapy, age, sex,
and confinement at home or in the hospital. In all of the pilot
programs this course has been given in the first semester (or
quarter) of the first year.

The second course in practically all of the programs was
maternal and child care. There was general agreement that the

emphasis in this area should be on the normal maternity cycle and the normal child.

The third area was approached in several ways by faculty members in the workshop sessions. It was agreed that the content would include that commonly called medical-surgical and the specialties in the traditional curriculum, but with major emphasis on nursing problems encountered instead of on disease entities or diagnoses. It included a continuation of those fundamental concepts, understandings, and skills begun in the previous courses, with adaptations to the care of patients with specific nursing problems. It should be noted that the nursing of the mentally ill as well as those physically ill was included in this area.

Subsequent workshops were concerned with the curriculum, but the agreements reached at the first one were not changed. Refinement of the objectives, further exploration of desirable learning experiences, discussions of teaching method and planning for evaluation were considered, so that each year new aspects of the curriculum were developed. In the intervals between workshops, each faculty group worked on the curricular problems of the particular program with which it was concerned, always conscious of the need to try out new ideas. Each faculty member was concerned with further development of the course for which she was responsible. Each year the project staff, in visits to the programs, consulted with the faculty on curricular problems.

Major changes in curriculum have not been numerous, but whenever they occurred, the procedure of the college for curricular change was followed. The way one faculty brought about changes in the curriculum will serve as an illustration. First, the nursing faculty was dissatisfied with the fundamentals of nursing and maternal and child health courses as they were being planned and conducted. The faculty worked together during one school year to reconstruct Nursing I and Nursing II, as these courses were called. The changes proposed were implemented the following September. Since they were within the framework of the nursing courses approved by the faculty curriculum committee, these changes could be put into effect as desired and at such time as the nursing faculty wished.

The nursing faculty also consulted with the science instructor concerning the progress of the integrated science course and its relationship to the nursing course taught concurrently. The science instructor was dissatisfied with the time allowed and the methods being used in this course. Together, the two groups reviewed and then reconstructed the science course so that it would extend over the two-year period instead of being completed in one year.

The chairman of the nursing department and the chairman of the psychology department had worked together in planning the mental hygiene course. Because of certain core course requirements, it had been necessary to have this mental hygiene course given to the students in their second year. When the science course was changed the two department chairmen proposed that the mental hygiene course be given during the first year instead.

The chairmen of the three departments concerned met with the college curriculum committee at the time these changes were proposed. Discussion of the proposals was carried on, with all present actively participating. After this discussion, which considered both the advantages and disadvantages of the proposed changes, the committee approved the proposals, which were implemented in the three departments in the following school year. Thus a rather important change was brought about, not without considerable time and effort, but nevertheless with relative speed to avoid prolonging practices no longer considered desirable.

The curriculum in each of the pilot programs has continued to develop. Each faculty is actively engaged in continuous curriculum study. It has been found that setting a regular and specific time, usually once a week, for departmental discussion and planning of the curriculum is desirable, and this practice has been continued.

Length of Program

The length of the new program has received so much emphasis that it has taken on an unusual significance. The length of the program is important because one of the basic assumptions was that the time of the traditional program could be shortened. The purpose of the project, however, was not simply to shorten the time but rather to devise a new program.

The Cooperative Research Project includes programs of different lengths (see Table 10). Each college determined the length of the program it would offer. This decision was based in part on college policy, in part on what the faculty felt was necessary, and in part on what concessions as to time the board of nursing examiners would make. In all but one state, California, the law governing the licensure of the graduates specified less than three years, if time was specified at all. Therefore, with the exception of California, the boards of nursing examiners were able to grant exceptions to the regulations as to time. Two of the programs are 2 academic years, or 4 semesters; one program is 7 quarters, or 2 academic years plus 1 summer quarter between the two years; four programs are 2 academic years plus 2 summer sessions; and one program is 2 academic years plus 2 summer sessions plus one year which has been called a practicum.

The practicum in the Pasadena City College program, which was required to meet the requirements of the law, was in essence a year of work experience. The educational program was completed within the two-year period. During the practicum the student was treated essentially as an employee of the nursing service, but the college assigned a member of the faculty to the planning of this period and to working with both students and nursing service. It was her function to give general supervision to the students and to serve as liaison between the college and the hospital. The student worked as a member of the nursing-service staff in any department and on any shift for thirty-seven hours a week. Three additional hours were spent in instruction that was very similar to what any normal in-service education program might include, thus making a forty-hour week. The three hours of instruction were divided between orientation to the hospital and its general functions and instruction in nursing in the area to which the students were assigned. For this year the student was paid a salary midway between that of the licensed vocational nurse (practical nurse) and the registered nurse. Within a few weeks of the beginning of the practicum, the students were carrying a full staff nurse load and considered the same as graduate nurses. In the evaluation of graduates, the students in the practicum were considered as graduates.

The practicum was included because of the time specification in the law. In June 1957 the Nurse Practice Act in California was amended to permit nursing programs of less than three years. The amendment states that:

> ... the board may accredit a school of nursing which has been approved by the board and which gives a course of instruction prescribed by the board, covering not less than two years. Any course of instruction prescribed by the board pursuant to this section shall provide a quality of education not less than the current standards established and adopted for a basic two years'

course of professional nursing education by
both the National League of Nursing and
the American Association of Junior Colleges.[5]

The faculty of the Pasadena City College, in anticipation
of this change in the law, directed their planning during the
1956-57 year toward elimination of the practicum. Major changes
in the curriculum were planned to take effect in September 1957.
The program at Pasadena City College, as of September 1957, has
been two academic years plus two summer sessions.

At no time during the five years covered by the Cooperative Research Project was an internship or practicum advocated
or recommended. As the programs have developed and the faculties
have become more secure, there has been less and less insistence
on the internship, and even the summer sessions have appeared
less than essential. At least two faculties are now working on
a plan for the elimination of the summer sessions. It is their
belief that they are able to include sufficient instruction
within the regular academic years. There is some feeling among
the instructors that the summer sessions were included to comply
with a time requirement instead of being determined by student
needs. Emphasis on time spent, rather than on content and experience, seems to have prompted the board of examiners to in-
sist on the inclusion of summer sessions.

---

[5]Section 2786.5 of Business and Professions Code relating to schools of Nursing, State of California.

It must be emphasized that the length of the program
is less significant than the philosophy underlying it and the
methods employed in implementing it. The program is not a
three-year program condensed to fit into two years, nor is it
a three-year program with the third year eliminated. It is
unfortunate that the pilot programs have been referred to so
frequently as two-year programs rather than junior-community
college nursing programs or associate-degree programs. This has
put the emphasis on their length rather than their character.
At the same time, it should be remembered that these programs
are in fact shorter than traditional nursing programs leading
to licensure.

Selection of Learning Experiences

Control of the educational program by the college made
possible the selection of learning experiences regardless of
where they were provided. The fact that there is no obligation
for students to render service at stated times and for stated
periods freed the instructors to select whatever experiences
would be helpful to the student. The problem was to determine
what learning experiences were desired in order to meet the
objectives, and then to seek the agency or situation in which
they could be found. It was the responsibility of the chairman
of the department to initiate arrangements with these agencies,
although in some cases more formal agreements were made later

by the chief administrative officers of the college and the
agency. For observations or single field visits, no formal
agreements were needed.

The wide variety of agencies used can be seen by the
pilot programs from Table 9. The determination of how long
the student would be in the agency, and for what purpose, was
made by the instructor. Representatives of the agencies
shared in this decision by identifying what the agency could or
could not provide, and at what times the specified experiences
would be available. It is obvious that hospitals, either
general or special, would be used more than any other agency,
since a great deal of the nurse's work is carried on in hospitals. It is equally important to note that it was in the
hospital situation that the greatest departures from traditional
assignments were made. The hospital setting will be used as
an example of how the learning experiences were provided for
the students.

The instructor was responsible for developing the objectives of the course she taught. These objectives were necessarily the concern of the whole nursing faculty, for no one
course or set of experiences could be developed in isolation.
What was included in one course inevitably affected and was
affected by the content and experiences in another course.
The term course is used here to include all experiences related
to the area, regardless of the type of experience or where the
teaching was done. There was a concerted effort to bring what

is commonly called theory and practice into a unified whole.
Whether the student was in class or in the laboratory was not
considered important, but rather what objective was being met,
and by what experiences. Once the objectives had been stated,
the desired content and learning experiences were selected.
When the learning experiences were identified as being those
provided by a hospital, then plans to have a laboratory experience in the hospital were made.

Planning learning experiences far enough in advance
made the arrangement of the desired sequence possible. For
example, the instructor decided what learning experiences were
desired in a given laboratory period. She discussed with the
head nurse or supervisor in the area concerned what these
needed learning experiences were. The head nurse then identified the patients whose nursing care would best provide these
experiences. This conference between head nurse and instructor
took place either the afternoon before or early in the morning
of the scheduled laboratory period and permitted the instructor
to familiarize herself with the patients' nursing problems.
The head nurse, on the other hand, was able to adjust the assignment of other workers in order to make the student's experience
possible. The assignment of the student to the desired learning
experience was made by the instructor, and the instructor was
responsible for the teaching which accompanied and guided this
experience and for the care given the patient thereby. The
close cooperation necessary between instructors and hospital

personnel is clear. It is equally clear that although the head nurse or supervisor shared in this process, it was the instructor who was responsible for the student's learning experience. It is necessary to recognize that this relationship does not come about spontaneously. It must be developed.

Similar examples might be given from any of the other agencies used. The principle remains the same. How long any specific learning experience would be used was determined by the instructor and the student. There was no attempt to keep a student on a specific hospital unit for a specific time. Nor was there any attempt to move the student from unit to unit at stated intervals. The important consideration has been what does the student need to learn, not, to what unit should she be assigned. It is quite conceivable that one widely varied hospital unit might provide experiences needed by the student for a whole semester. In other situations a student might have experiences on several units in a week. It is not the management or administration of the unit, nor its variation from others, which the student needs to learn, but rather her role in the nursing care of patients.

The learning experiences which require practice in the actual situation were thus organized as laboratory periods. At no time was the student simply put on the hospital unit or assigned to the agency as a worker for a full part of a work day. Instead, laboratory periods with well-defined learning experiences were set up. Table 8 shows the time spent in the nursing laboratory as well as in more formal class experiences. The amount of time spent in the laboratory varied from course to course and from program to program. Part of this variation was due to differences in objectives, and part to differences in the way the objectives were met. This variation was felt to be desirable, since there was no exact way of determining what the right amount or the right way was. The faculty had the freedom and the courage to experiment and to assume responsibility for evaluating the results and for instituting changes as they were needed. It is to be expected that, as courses develop and the skills of teachers improve, different ways of using time will result.

This type of laboratory experience is not hampered by needless repetition, nor is it diluted by extraneous activities desirable for doing the work of the hospital but not conducive to learning by the student. Tourtillot has described the concern of our faculty group with providing sufficient, but not excessive, repetition:

> Retention of learned materials is increased if practice continues beyond the point of the first errorless reproduction. Overlearning works to reduce forgetting and accounts for the retention of skills in some degree after long periods of disuse. Our program is designed to eliminate unnecessary repetition, in both theory and practice; however, great care and careful planning are necessary to assure sufficient practice to provide overlearning of the basic skills.[6]

---

[6]Eleanor Tourtillott, The Rationale of the Two-Year Nursing Program at Henry Ford Community College, Unpublished manuscript, 1957.

It is important, however, while providing sufficient overlearning to assure retention, to help the student to continue to learn through each experience. Psychologists have pointed to the dangers inherent in repetitive practice beyond the point where new meaning is gained, a point which is indeed hard to find in a work-centered program. When behavior or responses become routine and automatic, learning is arrested and even further learning is thwarted.

The selection of learning experiences according to objectives, and their planning in specifically designed laboratory periods, make demands upon the instructor that the traditional methods in nursing schools do not. It is easier to depend on time-spent units according to a master rotation plan. The reliance on time-spent units gives a false sense of security, however, for to place a student on a certain unit gives no assurance of specific learning experiences or of learning even if the experiences are there. Difficult though this new plan may be, it is more rewarding for both teacher and student.

The quality of the learning experiences in the pilot programs was safeguarded because the instructor retained control of their selection and conduct. The aim has been to give the student all the experiences needed to prepare for nursing, and to make these experiences adequate learning experiences.

Facilities Used to Provide Experiences

One of the advantages of a college-controlled nursing program is its ability to select the desired learning experiences and then to find the facilities for them. One of the principles fundamental to the pilot programs was the use of a variety of facilities in the community, and the ability of the college to provide varied experiences was one of the criteria used in selecting the cooperating institutions (see Chapter III).

No attempt has been made to identify the facilities that should be used in a nursing program. It was agreed that several different kinds of agencies might provide the same learning experiences. There was no feeling that every student must go to each agency, but rather that the use of multiple agencies would facilitate the provision of the desired experiences.

The agencies used by the pilot programs vary considerably in number, in kind, and in size (see Table 9). All of them are located near enough to the college so that they can be easily used. Most of these agencies have received little, if any, use in traditional nursing programs.

With respect to the facilities within the college itself, few additions are necessitated by the nursing program. Since the nursing students share all courses except those in nursing with all other students, few special laboratories or classrooms are needed. Most of the cooperating colleges have had to add a nursing laboratory. A few were able to adapt laboratories previously used in practical nursing programs. Most of these nursing laboratories are equipped with only those items necessary for fundamentals of nursing. There has been no attempt to duplicate a hospital situation. In one institution the nursing laboratory is a very flexible classroom. It can be equipped with beds when necessary, the beds being rented from a hospital equipment company. Usually it has only one patient unit (including bed, bedside table, and chair). In addition, this room has easily movable tables and chairs. A folding door between it and another classroom increases the uses of both rooms. Linen is secured when needed from a linen rental company, thus reducing cost and also the need for extensive storage space. Another institution equipped its nursing laboratory with only those items which might logically be found in a home, depending upon the hospital situation itself to teach those nursing skills using hospital equipment.

Whatever the specific plans of individual colleges, all have found a simple nursing laboratory sufficient. This means that a very small capital investment is needed when a college decides to offer a nursing program.

Teaching Methods

The changes which the new nursing programs effected in content, in organization, and in the learning experiences engaged in by the student necessitated corresponding changes in teaching methods. Some of the traditional methods have been and are being used, but even these have been somewhat altered. The line between theory and practice has been a very flexible one; actually it is scarcely a line at all with theory and practice considered as inseparable parts of the whole. Therefore, there has been no distinction made between the more formal classroom activities and those which take place in the patient situation. The student has had instruction in the care of specific types of patients while she has been actually caring for these patients.

All the pilot programs made extensive use of a _labora-tory period_, which means the opportunity to give patient care of designated length and with specific objectives. One way of making the laboratory periods more effective has been adopted by all the pilot programs. At the beginning of the laboratory period, the students are given specific assignments in a group session. At this time they are briefed about the particular needs and problems of the patients they are to care for, and about the nursing care to be given. Each student then makes a plan for caring for the patient or patients for whom she is responsible. The plan provides for demonstration of new procedures by the instructor; for help with those procedures that may be difficult, even though not new; and for other help that is anticipated by both student and teacher. After approval of the plan, the student proceeds to carry it out. The teacher plans to be with each student at a specified time, and is available to be

called on at other times. Thus the student is given responsibility for the care of patients while having the teacher
available for help. The amount and timing of the teaching for
each student during the laboratory period is determined by
both teacher and student.

In the latter part of the laboratory session, the students are again brought together for a group discussion of the
patients and of the care they have given these patients. A
resource person is often invited to participate in this discussion in order to amplify or clarify a particular problem.
The physician is frequently asked to indicate the medical re-
gime and nursing care needed for the patients under consideration. Thus each laboratory experience consists of three parts
-- the assignment and briefing, the planning and doing, and the
discussion and evaluation of the care given.

It can be seen that much of the teaching takes place in
the laboratory session, in the actual patient situation. The
emphasis on teaching in the actual situation is described by
one instructor as follows:

> In planning my teaching I go from the less
> serious to the more serious types of de-
> viation and behavior. For example, I speak
> about the psycho-neurotic illness at first
> and go into the psychotic condition, giving
> the student an opportunity to go from those
> patterns that she might have seen in her own
> home, in her own community, to those that
> are the extreme deviations that we see in
> a mental hospital. The student's ability to
> detect the subtleties in the behavior that
> describes schizophrenia does not come very
> readily. It comes only if the instructor is

there to interpret them for the student in
the form that is manifest in the patient.
The students very often have difficulty in
seeing this, so the teaching that takes
place is in the clinical area. It is not
unusual for the student during psychiatric
nursing to spend a few hours with a patient
in order to observe, to explore with the
patient certain areas of behavior. The
opportunity to get to know the patient --
and that might be underlined -- is something
that the student definitely is assigned to
and is helped with in the clinical area.

From this statement it can be seen that the student's need to
learn is paramount, and that what the student does is determined by her needs. When the student is not responsible for
nursing service, the assignments can more effectively meet the
learner's needs.

The use of resource persons in addition to physicians
has been found desirable. One instructor stated:

One of the opportunities which has been ours
as a part of a junior college is that of
using experts from its various departments
to assist in our nursing classes. Nutrition
is discussed by a home economics instructor,
child development by the instructor in that
area. To introduce the subject of spiritual
needs of the patient, we have used a panel
composed of leaders of the various religious
faiths found in our area.

Another instructor reported the close cooperation between nursing instructors and other instructors in the college
who teach courses in which nursing students are enrolled. She
stated:

> Before the September classes began, the
> college instructor who teaches the science
> course the nursing students take and I sat
> down to preplan the approach each of us would
> take during the teaching of our respective
> courses. To correlate and integrate those
> aspects of our courses that were related and
> to avoid undue repetition, we decided to
> synchronize our teaching as much as possible.

At all times, of course, it is the nursing instructor who is

responsible for the nursing course and all its parts.

The group discussion method has been used extensively,

with the students involved in the planning and conduct of the

discussion to a considerable degree. The discussions most

frequently center around a problem which the students have met

in the course of carrying out patient care. In one of the

colleges, tape recordings of these discussions are frequently

used, both to permit other groups to share a particular ex-

perience and as a tool for evaluation. The faculty has also

used the recordings to compare the merits of oral and written

reports of certain learning experiences.

The reliance on time-spent units as the major, if not

the only, criterion for determining the assignment of students

has been referred to earlier. The instructors in the pilot

programs used many ways to deepen and broaden the learning ex-

periences the students had even though the time spent on them

might be very short. The following example shows how a single

observational experience may be effective in students'

learning.

As a part of learning to care for patients with medical-surgical conditions, the students spent one day in a tuberculosis hospital. The experience was planned by the two nursing instructors in cooperation with a physician and the director of nursing service at the tuberculosis hospital. It was planned as part of a unit on the care of a patient with an infection of the respiratory tract, and was aimed particularly at understanding of long-term illness.

Six patient histories were presented by the physician and the nurse to twelve students and two instructors as they sat in an informal conference room. Discussion and questions by the group identified the physical and emotional effects of tuberculosis on the patient and the social and economic impact of the disease on the patient and his family. The students then observed surgical dressings done on several patients, who told the students about their experiences with tuberculosis, especially what the nurses at the hospital had taught them. The wife of one of the patients was also present and told how she had been taught to do the dressing at home and how to plan her food purchases to get the essential foods on her limited budget.

One patient described in vivid detail how he had been treated as almost an "untouchable" while he was in a general hospital; how worried he had been about surgery lest he be neglected entirely after the operation, when he would be unconscious and unable to call for help. The implications of this attitude were later discussed, and the physician quoted statistics concerning the chances of the nurse's contracting tuberculosis from a diagnosed well-taught patient against the chances of contracting it from an undiagnosed patient.

The director of nursing conducted a tour of the physical facilities of the hospital. She discussed how a patient is referred to the hospital, what he has to pay, and how the patient is followed after discharge. She told of the satisfactions of working with patients with long-term illness.

Other aspects of the learning experience included demonstration of the teaching function of the nurse and selected aspects of asepsis; discussion of desirable attitudes toward patients with communicable disease; and exploration of the community facilities available for the prevention, care, and rehabilitation of the tuberculosis patient. The effectiveness of this experience was judged, in addition to the comments by students, by paper-and-pencil tests and by observation of the care given to the tuberculosis patient in the general hospital.

Another example of a one-day observation has been described by an instructor as follows:

> In the study of normal growth and development of well infants, a day's observational study is planned for the nursing student in an infant orphanage. The babies available in this agency for study range in age from one month, proceeding monthly, through eighteen months of age.

The purposes of this learning experience:

1. To validate the significant "facts" of normal growth and development of well infants;

2. To develop skills in observing and recording behavior patterns of well infants;

3. To observe some of the effects of maternal deprivation on the growth and development of well infants.

Prior to the observational study, the teacher and the nursing students discuss, in the classroom, the neuro-muscular development of normal infants during the first year of life. Each nursing student then selects a baby whose month-age is of particular interest to her. Some direction in the selection of babies is given by the teacher to insure consideration of each level of development during the period of infancy.

Each nursing student plans and provides care for "her baby," based on the individual needs of the baby. She observes and records the behavior patterns of "her baby" during bathing, feeding, sleeping, and playing.

A seminar is planned and conducted in the orphanage. The infant supervisor is utilized as a resource person as the students present and discuss their anecdotal records. The teacher gives some direction to the group discussion, to illustrate "Growth coming from within, reaching out."

Observation by students was found useful if some type of direct experience had preceded it. Perhaps the best example of this is in the operating room. Instead of being assigned to the operating room for a specified period, the student is assigned to a patient who is to undergo surgery. She gives the patient preoperative care, accompanies the patient to the operating room, observes the surgery, and then gives the patient immediate postoperative care. This experience may be repeated several times, depending on the student's needs. The reaction to this method has been favorable by both instructors and students. One first-year student's statement gives a typical reaction:

> I think the following represent the major aspects of my learning experience. Although as my experience in nursing builds up, I find other things in the operating room more meaningful, as of now this is the most helpful aspect of my observation. No matter how many pictures I see or descriptions I read, these never are so revealing and enlightening as the actual sight of working anatomy. I've adjusted my concepts of tissues, blood vessels, the size and shape and color of organs and the relationship of organs to each other and have come to appreciate the variations from person to person.
>
> I have come to appreciate better the continuity of the patient's experience -- the relationship of the illness calling for surgery, the patient's mental approach to the situation, and the patient's experience -- the trauma inherent in any surgery as well as the specific disruption of function -- and the patient's physical and mental state following surgery. In this I would also include several items mentioned in our class discussion, such as better ability to answer the patient's pre-operation questions and fears; more understanding of doing each nursing procedure correctly -- seeing how many other steps follow from it or are hampered by incorrect performance.
>
> I would also include an appreciation of the detail involved in aseptic technic and of how easily one small step can undo hours of work or cause extremely serious consequences....

Planning for the experiences of the student, whether in the more formal classroom situation or in the laboratory, is of utmost importance. The teaching load of faculty members must take this need for planning into account. In addition to planning by individual instructors, frequent meetings of the faculty group are desirable to keep all informed of the students' activities and progress.

The selection of teaching methods, like the selection of content and learning experiences, depends on the objectives to be achieved. The teaching methods used in one pilot program have been described as follows:

> During the first year, in the curricular area of common learnings, the lecture-demonstration method is used. Class discussion, centered around a problem situation, is also used. These are simple problems relating to nursing-care needs of patients as distinguished from the complex problem situations dealt with in the second year.

> During the second year the discussion method is used to advantage. In the area of identified student needs, students discuss the problems encountered in their daily care of patients. The students state the problems encountered, discuss the relevant facts and principles, recall known information, determine what additional information is needed, secure this information, then decide possible courses of action, select the most reasonable plan of action, and, when in the actual situation, carry out the plan and then evaluate the outcome.

There is still much to be done in the development of effective teaching methods. For example, the teaching of larger groups of students, both in the classroom and in the laboratory, is necessary if nursing programs grow in size to keep pace with the demand for nurses. Further identification of what can be learned only through participation and what may

be learned as effectively through another educational technic
is essential. The faculties of the several pilot programs believe they have made only a beginning in the development of new
teaching methods and in the adaptation of the methods now in
common use.

Role of the Faculty

That the development of the curriculum was the responsibility and privilege of the faculty was accepted from the
beginning of the Cooperative Research Project. The state
boards of nurse examiners' regulations have really deprived
the faculty of a nursing program of one of its rightful and
important functions. With the waiving of existing regulations
in these experimental programs the opportunity and the need
arose for the faculty to plan and carry out a curriculum. The
curriculum of each institution was developed by the faculty of
that institution, using the agreed-upon principles as a foundation. The similarities among the curricula are due to these
principles, to common objectives, and to the working together
of the several faculties in annual workshops. It was also considered essential to have the total college faculty involved in
the nursing curriculum. In several of the institutions this
cooperation has been outstanding. In others it has developed
more slowly. It seems safe to say that where such cooperation
began early and continued to grow the progress in curriculum
development was more rapid and where this kind of effort was

slow to start the progress of the curriculum was more slow.

In addition to being responsible for the nursing curriculum, representatives of the nursing faculty have served on
the all-college curriculum committee. As they have expected
others to share in the development of the nursing curriculum,
so have they expected to take their part in developing the
total curriculum of the institution.

The nursing faculty assumed complete responsibility for
teaching the nursing courses. This means teaching students
wherever their learning experiences are found. Instead of turning over part of the teaching function to those outside the
educational institution, the faculties in the pilot programs
have done the teaching regardless of the agency used to provide
learning experiences.

Workshops

In each of the five years of the Cooperative Research
Project a workshop was held for all the faculty members of the
pilot programs. The purpose of these workshops was to provide
an opportunity for the entire faculty group to work on the
problems inherent in developing a new curriculum. In those
held in 1953 and 1954 it was possible to include representatives
of state boards of nursing and faculty members who taught other
than nursing courses. As the pilot programs increased both in
size and in number, it was necessary to restrict attendance to

the nursing faculty only. In 1953, 1954, and 1957, the over-all problems of the curriculum were considered; while in 1955 and 1956 the workshops concentrated on the problems of evaluation. These latter workshops were directed by Dr. Elizabeth Hagen, Assistant Professor of Education at Teachers College.

The workshops provided a way of keeping the several curricula moving in the same general direction. Although there was no attempt to regiment or in any way standardize the curricula, it was important to keep the objectives of the project clearly in mind. Perhaps the most important result of the workshops was to give a sense of common purpose to the group and to give encouragement to each faculty member as she struggled to develop and teach new nursing courses. It must be remembered that these individuals were charting a new nursing curriculum. They were not infrequently subject to questioning and criticism because they were doing something new. During the workshops they were able to work with individuals sharing the same interests and problems, and through this came new ideas, new energy, and new courage. Each year the curriculum showed changes which could be considered a result of the workshop

Summary

The general characteristics of the nursing programs are: first, both general and specialized education are included; second, the courses have been reorganized and placed in a different sequence; third, many facilities which provide health services are used; fourth, the length of the program is two years; fifth, the program is college-controlled and financed; sixth, all faculty members are selected, appointed, and paid for by the college; and seventh, the students enjoy the same status as all other students in the college.

The curriculum was considered to be the responsibility of and an opportunity for the faculty. Each college took the responsibility for developing its own curriculum. There are variations in the programs which are the logical outcome of allowing each curriculum to be developed by the faculty. There has been no desire or attempt to standardize the course.

The length of the new program has received so much emphasis that it has taken on unusual significance. While shorter than the traditional program, the length is less significant than the underlying philosophy and the methods employed in implementing it.

The control of the educational program by the college made possible the selection of learning experiences regardless of where they were provided. These experiences were determined by the objectives to be met. A variety of agencies were used by each college in providing the learning experiences.

The teaching methods used included the more traditional methods but even these have been altered somewhat. New uses of the usual methods were tried. The faculties of the several pilot programs believe they have made only a beginning in the development of new teaching methods and in the adaptation of the methods now in common use.

CHAPTER VI

THE STUDENTS

This chapter is devoted to describing some characteristics of the 811 students who enrolled in the eight pilot programs during the five years of the Cooperative Research Project.
The policies for the selection of the students in each program
were determined and administered by the individual schools.
The outline of the Cooperative Research Project states:

> The students will enjoy the same status as all
> other students in the college. They will be
> eligible for all activities of the college and
> will be held to the same standards of admission,
> graduation, etc., as all other students.[1]

This does not mean that all of the students in each college are held to the same standards of admission. In junior
and community colleges, selection policies depend upon the particular curriculum. Public junior colleges may be required to
admit any resident who has a high school diploma, but this does
not mean that the individual will be accepted for the program
of his choice. For instance, higher standards might be

---

[1]Institute of Research and Service in Nursing Education,
Teachers College, Columbia University, "Cooperative Research
Project in Junior and Community College Education for Nursing,"
(Unpublished), November 6, 1953, p. 2.

113

required of a pre-engineering student than of an engineering technology student. Using studies of the California junior colleges, Dressel points out that there is a "wide range of abilities (found in the student body) in an institution, provided that a variety of programs is available."[2]

In considering the admission policies of the pilot programs, it should be noted that in two schools final administrative approval to initiate the pilot programs was not granted until immediately prior to the fall semester. Consequently the administration was more concerned with assembling the initial class than with establishing selection policies.

The students in each program have been classified according to age, sex, marital status, socioeconomic background, residence, general intelligence, withdrawal rate, and reasons for entering the pilot programs. These data were obtained from the files of the Cooperative Research Project. From the beginning of the experiment, the pilot program staffs have cooperated with the project staff in collecting data on the students and their progress.

Age

At the time they began their program, the median age for the 811 students was 18.8 years. The lowest median is 18.0,

---

[2]Paul L. Dressel, "Educational Demands Arising from Individual Needs and Purposes," in The Public Junior College, Fifty-fifth Yearbook of the National Society for the Study of Education, Part I (Chicago: The University of Chicago Press, 1956), p. 59.

TABLE 11

AGE DISTRIBUTIONS, MEDIAN AGES, AND PERCENTAGE OF STUDENTS 26 YEARS OR OLDER ENROLLED IN THE EIGHT PILOT PROGRAMS

Age	Pilot Programs[a]								Total	
	A	B	C	D	E	F	G	H	N	%
16.0-17.9	11	23	4	12	39	19	7	11	126	16
18.0-19.9	44	66	59	105	105	38	19	17	453	56
20-22	10	8	9	8	17	5	5	4	66	8
22-24	10	2	5	3	9	0	3	3	35	4
24-26	4	1	4	2	3	0	0	1	15	2
26-28	5	2	3	1	3	0	1	1	16	2
28-30	4	4	1	0	1	1	0	1	12	1
30-32	2	3	2	1	2	0	0	1	11	1
32-34	0	1	3	2	2	1	2	1	12	1
34-36	2	2	4	2	2	0	1	1	14	2
36-	19	2	6	6	11	0	2	0	46	6
Unknown			3	1	1				5	1
Totals	111	114	103	143	195	64	40	41	811	100
Median	20.1	18.7	19.3	18.7	18.6	18.4	18.0	18.9	18.8	
% 26 or older	29	12	19	8	11	4	13	12	14	

[a]The individual pilot programs will hereafter be referred to in the tables and text by their code letters, A to H. This identification of the programs by their code letters is not provided.

while the highest is 20.1. The youngest student was 16.7 years old, while the oldest was over 59. More than 75 per cent of the entire group entered before reaching the age of 21.

One hundred and eleven (14 per cent) were 26 years or older. Only 4 per cent of those who started at one school were 26 years or older, compared with 29 per cent of those at another. The smallest program was at a private junior college with residence facilities, while the largest was at a public college with no residence facilities.

All of the programs enrolled some older students. Some have a larger proportion than others, which indicates that certain types of junior and community colleges may have access to a wider age range of students.

Sex

Twenty-one (3 per cent) of the 811 students who enrolled were males. Less than 1 per cent of the admissions to diploma nursing programs in 1954 were males.[3] Of the males, 16 (76 per cent) were veterans of the armed forces. Of these, 10 (48 per cent) had been hospital corpsmen.

Marital Status

Ninety-four (12 per cent) of the students were married at the time they started the programs (Table 12). Twenty-one

---

[3] 1957 Facts about Nursing, p. 66.

(3 per cent) were either separated, divorced, or widowed (the
"other" category). Sixty-nine (8 per cent) had children.

TABLE 12

MARITAL STATUS OF STUDENTS

Program	Number of Students	Single		Married		Other	
		N	%	N	%	N	%
A	111	86	78	19	17	6	5
B	114	102	89	11	10	1	1
C	104	84	81	18	17	2	2
D	143	130	91	8	6	5	3
E	194	167	86	22	11	5	3
F	64	60	94	3	5	1	2
G	40	33	82	7	18	0	0
H	41	34	83	6	15	1	2
Total	811	696	85	94	12	21	3

In contrast to the number of pilot-program students who
were married, the Michigan League for Nurses' recruitment study[4]
showed that none of the 245 first-year nursing students in the
sample were married. One hospital school of nursing in New
York admits married women and permits them to live at home.
At this school, married students are expected to fulfill the
same academic and service requirements as the other students.

---

[4]Michigan League for Nursing, Nurse Recruitment in
Michigan (Lansing: Michigan League for Nursing, 1956), p. 6.

In the last ten years, the total enrollment at this school has been over 1,000 students; of these, only 2 were married at the time they entered, and neither chose to live at home except temporarily, during periods of family need.

These data suggest that junior and community college nursing programs enroll certain married women who would not otherwise enter nursing. Unfortunately, systematic data concerning the number of students who married while in the pilot programs were not collected. However, some students did marry and did continue in the programs.

Socioeconomic Background

The occupation of the father is generally accepted as the best single indicator of the socioeconomic status of the family. Anne Roe's recently proposed classification scheme for occupational levels was selected as suitable for this study. The levels of occupations are determined by "the degree of personal autonomy and the level of skill and training."[5]

One hundred and sixty-one (20 per cent) of the 811 fathers were not classified. Eighty students wrote only "deceased" and no other information in the space for father's occupation; 17 wrote only "retired." When "deceased" or "retired" and the occupation were given, the occupation was

_____

[5]Anne Roe, Psychology of Occupations (New York: John Wiley and Sons, 1955), pp. 149-50.

TABLE 13

OCCUPATIONAL LEVEL OF PARENTS OF PILOT-PROGRAM STUDENTS

Level	A N	A %	B N	B %	C N	C %	D N	D %	E N	E %	F N	F %	G N	G %	H N	H %	All Eight Programs N	All Eight Programs %
1. Professional and Managerial	1	1	4	4	5	5	0	0	9	5	1	2	1	2	0	0	21	3
2. Professional and Managerial	7	6	15	13	10	10	20	14	36	18	12	19	11	28	1	2.5	112	14
3. Semi-professional and small business	24	22	40	35	19	18	57	40	52	27	26	41	5	12	6	15	229	28
4. Skilled	30	27	23	20	25	24	42	29	39	20	10	15	9	22	11	27	189	23
5. Semi-skilled	12	11	7	6	12	12	12	8	15	8	5	8	3	8	10	24	76	9
6. Unskilled	4	4	4	4	3	3	4	3	1	1	0	0	0	0	7	17	23	3
Deceased	20	18	11	10	13	13	5	3	16	8	5	8	5	12	5	12	80	10
Retired	6	5	1	1	4	4	2	1	4	2	0	0	0	0	0	0	17	2
Unclassified or no answer	7	6	9	8	12	12	1	1	23	11	5	8	6	15	1	2.5	64	8
TOTAL	111	100	114	101	103	100	143	99	195	100	64	101	40	99	31	100	811	100

classified. In 64 instances, there was either insufficient or
no information on which to make a decision concerning the level
of occupation. In most of the 31 instances of insufficient evidence, the name of the business concern was given -- for
example, Ford Motor Company -- but no additional information
was provided.

The largest percentage (28) of the 811 fathers were
classified in Level 3 -- Semi-Professional and Small Business.
The lowest percentage (3) of the parents were classified in
the highest level, Professional and Managerial, and in the
lowest, Unskilled. The range by schools for the Semi-Professional and Small Business level is from 40 to 12 per cent.
The range for the Professional and Managerial levels, when Levels
1 and 2 are grouped, was 23 to 2.5 per cent.

The distribution of occupational levels for one of the
pilot programs, a Negro school, deviates sharply from that of
the other seven. This program has 40 per cent of the parents
classified in Levels 5 and 6, and 2.5 per cent in Levels 1 and
2. These data are consistent with the low socioeconomic status
of the Negro -- especially the southern Negro. This distribution and general knowledge about the occupational status of the
Negro suggest that the classification of five farmers in Level 3
should be questioned. It is likely that several of them are
tenant farmers, a Level 5 classification. However, on the
basis of the information given, the individuals had to be placed
in Level 3.

Although the distribution for the Negro school adds considerably to the ranges, there were variations among the other seven programs. Almost one of every three (30 per cent) of the Program G students had parents who were Professional or Managerial, while less than one of every ten (7 per cent) of the Program A students had parents in those levels.

In general, the occupational data are not inconsistent with the findings of other studies. For example, Anderson and McManus[6] found that the fathers of nursing students in their sample tended to be engaged in trades or manufacturing rather than professions.

Birdwhistell concluded that:

> Although all of us could name exceptions, nursing tends to recruit its students from one general class area. In terms of W. Lloyd Warner's system, the nurse comes from the top of the upper lower class and the bottom of the lower middle class. To be somewhat more traditional in terms of parental occupation, she tends to have parents who were skilled workers: plumbers, railroad workers, skilled craftsmen, government employees, skilled factory workers, or farmers who were semi-successful or successful.[7]

In analyzing the family backgrounds of the nurses involved in their study, Sledge and Rohrer found that

---

[6] M. H. Anderson and R. L. McManus, "Interests of Nursing Candidates; the Patterns of Interests and Activities of 800 Pre-Nursing Students," Amer. Jour. Nurs., 1942, p. 562.

[7] R. L. Birdwhistell, "Social Science and Nursing Education: Some Tentative Suggestions," in Fifty-fifth Annual Report of the National League of Nursing Education (New York: Livingston Press), p. 322.

> ... primarily the nurses' fathers were engaged
> in farming or the skilled occupational groups.
> In the case of approximately 25%, both parents
> had completed high school. These character-
> istics suggest that nurses are drawn from
> lower-middle-class stratum, although there are
> variations in the cases of individual nurses.[8]

The analysis of the student bodies of the pilot programs indicates variations from program to program. On the basis of his knowledge of the eight institutions in which the programs exist, the author believes that the backgrounds of the student bodies in the pilot programs conform to the enrollment patterns in the junior and community colleges in which the programs are offered.

This section would not be complete without pointing out that 13 (2 per cent) of the fathers were doctors; 1 was a hospital administrator; and 38 (5 per cent)of the mothers were registered nurses.

Residence

Students in diploma nursing programs traditionally have been required to live in dormitories adjacent to the hospital. One prominent characteristic of the junior and community college movement is that students live at home. Of the eight pilot-program schools, five have no dormitory facilities at all.

---

[8]Sarah H. Sledge and John H. Rohrer, "Role Perceptions and Conceptions among Graduate Nurses," in Leonard Reissman and John H. Rohrer, Change and Dilemma in the Nursing Profession (New York: G. P. Putnam Sons, 1957), p. 66.

Only one is considered a residential school. At another program, the hospital,which is used for most of the clinical experience, has a nurses' residence where some of the students live. This number has decreased to an almost negligible one and plans are under way to discontinue the residence.

The permanent residences of 596 (74 per cent) of the pilot-program students were located within a twenty-five-mile radius of the educational institution (Table 14). Twenty-five miles was selected as a distance which did not prohibit commuting.

TABLE 14

PERCENTAGE OF NURSING STUDENTS WHOSE PERMANENT
RESIDENCE IS WITHIN COMMUTING DISTANCE (25 MILES)
OF THE PILOT PROGRAM ATTENDED

| School | Living within 25 Miles | |
	Number	Per Cent
A	89	80
B	96	84
C	96	93
D	67	47
E	172	88
F	22	34
G	26	65
H	28	68
TOTAL	596	73

In two schools, over half of the pilot-program students did not live within the twenty-five-mile commuting distance.

Both schools are located in sparsely populated areas. One is
the only residential school among the pilot-program schools.
In general, the pattern of home residence for the nursing students in the pilot programs tended to fit the pattern of the
colleges in which the programs were located.

General Intelligence

The American Council on Education Psychological Examination for College Freshmen[9] was taken by 708 of the pilot-program
students. The whole first class at School D, and individuals
in each program, did not take the examination. The results reported here are based on raw scores on the 1952 edition. Since
most of the schools used this edition, the scores on the other
editions were translated into equivalent 1952 scores.

TABLE 15

MEDIAN A.C.E. PERCENTILE RANKS
(NATIONAL FOUR-YEAR COLLEGE NORMS)

Program	Number	Percentile Rank of Median
A	109	27
B	79	42
C	79	37
D	93	37
E	192	52
F	58	30
G	39	55
H	41	7
TOTAL	708	39

[9]The American Council on Education Psychological Examination for College Freshmen will, hereafter, be referred to as the
A.C.E.

The median for the applicants to 536 schools of nursing that used the 1954 edition of the A.C.E. was at the thirty-fourth percentile of the four-year college norms. The medians for five of the pilot programs (Table 15) were at a higher percentile than the median applicant to nursing schools; three were below. It is important to remember, however, that the median for nursing schools is for applicants, not for those accepted.

Most junior and community colleges offer both transfer and terminal programs. Transfer programs prepare the student to transfer to another institution for the last two years of baccalaureate work. For example, a student might obtain an associate degree in a pre-engineering program from a junior college and transfer to a four-year college for his last two years. Although nurses who graduate from pilot programs can continue their education, as some already have, the programs are essentially terminal. Bressel reports differences between students in transfer and terminal programs in California junior colleges. In one college the median A.C.E. scores of various groups of transfer students ranged from the fortieth to the fifty-third percentile on the four-year college norms, while for groups in terminal programs the medians ranged from the twenty-fourth to the twenty-ninth percentile.

The medians for the pilot program located in California, and for the pilot programs as a whole are more nearly like the medians of students in transfer programs. These comparisons are gross, and it should be remembered that gross comparisons obscure important regional and cultural differences which may transcend even the type of program being offered.

Withdrawal

The present analysis of the rate of withdrawal from the pilot programs is limited to those pilot-program classes that had graduated by August 1956. This fact completely excludes two of the project schools, which will be graduating their first classes in 1957.

TABLE 16

PERCENTAGE OF STUDENTS WITHDRAWING
FROM PILOT PROGRAMS

Program	Number Entered	Number Withdrawn	Percentage Withdrawn
A	61	21	34
B	58	18	31
C	43	13	30
D	71	14	20
E	81	24	30
F	22	8	36
TOTAL	336	98	29

The coordinators of the project nursing programs were requested to supply the reasons for the withdrawal of students from the programs (Table 17).

TABLE 17

REASONS FOR WITHDRAWAL FROM PILOT PROGRAMS

Reasons	Number
Academic failure	30
Transfer to other programs	23
Marriage	21
Health problems	11
Personality problems	6
Family and financial difficulties	5
Dislike of nursing	1
Falsified records	1
TOTAL	98

The rate of withdrawal computed above is based on withdrawal from the nursing program, not from the college. Twenty-three (7 per cent) of the group transferred to other programs within the college. From the viewpoint of the college, these twenty-three students would certainly not be classified as withdrawals. Of those who transferred within the college, five transferred to technologies, such as X-ray specialist and laboratory technology, and two transferred to medical secretarial. Although the seven have withdrawn from nursing, they are still in the health field. One special aspect of the pilot programs is that it represents just one curriculum among many. This fact makes it possible to counsel a student who might otherwise fail academically to take another curriculum in which she may be successful.

Five who withdrew because of marriage or for financial reasons indicated that they intended to return to the program.

The national rate of withdrawal for student nurses has not been below 32 per cent since 1950. The percentage of general withdrawals from junior-community colleges is well over 40 per cent. The rates of withdrawal for the students in the nursing programs are more nearly similar to withdrawal rates from nursing schools in general than to those from junior-community colleges.

In considering the low rate of withdrawals in comparison with the general rates in junior and community colleges, one should remember that the nursing student is in a curriculum that is organized to include a clear occupational goal. It is doubtful that most students attending junior-community colleges have such a clearly defined occupational goal. In a study of junior college freshmen, Todd[10] found that 19 per cent lacked a vocational choice, while as many as 40 per cent of those having an occupational goal indicated doubt about working in the field they had chosen.

Selection of the Pilot Programs by Students

One consideration in using junior and community colleges as the setting for the education of nurses has been the hope

---

[10]Lindsey O. Todd, "Meeting the Needs of Junior College Students," Unpublished Doctoral Dissertation, George Peabody College for Teachers, 1943, p. 156.

of recruiting individuals who might not otherwise enter nursing.
One hundred and sixty-four (20 per cent) of the 811 students who
entered pilot programs reported that they would not have
selected nursing if such a program had not been offered in the
junior college.

The percentage of students who reported that they would
not have selected nursing if the pilot programs had not been
offered was found to be related to the age, marital status,
and sex of the student:

> Of the 111 students who were twenty-six or older, 48
> (43 per cent) would not have selected nursing;
>
> Of the 94 students who were married, 40 (43 per cent)
> would not have selected nursing;
>
> Of the 21 male students, 11 (52 per cent) would not
> have selected nursing.

All the entering students were asked why they had chosen
the pilot programs. Their reasons related to (1) the geographic
location of the program; (2) characteristics of a college environment; and (3) specific attributes of the pilot programs.

The reasons most commonly given involved the location
of the college. Most of the students commented on the opportunity to live at home and commute to school. In some instances,
the reasons were related to family and financial considerations.
Some married students stated that they could only attend a program which enabled them to stay at home with their families.

The characteristics of a college environment which
attracted the students were (1) the opportunity to combine

becoming a nurse with taking college courses; (2) the social life on the campus; (3) the atmosphere of a small college; and (4) free weekends.

The specific attributes of the pilot programs that interested the students most were (1) the length of the program and (2) the opportunity to be part of an experimental program.

Summary

Analysis of specific characteristics of the pilot-program students revealed that the pilot programs enrolled a considerable proportion of students who were over twenty-six years old, were married at the time they started the programs, and were living within commuting distance of their programs. Three per cent of the students were males. Almost half of these had been hospital corpsmen.

The majority of the fathers of the nursing students were engaged in semi-professional and small business occupations, or were skilled laborers. The variation in the occupational backgrounds of the fathers by program was illustrated by the range -- from 2.5 to 23 per cent -- of fathers engaged in professional and managerial occupations.

The median on the A.C.E. was at the thirty-ninth percentile of the four-year college norms. The level of intelligence for the whole group, as measured by the A.C.E., was slightly higher than that of applicants to all nursing schools.

There is evidence to suggest that the intelligence level of the pilot-program students was more nearly like that of transfer than of terminal students in junior colleges. Again, there was considerable range from program to program.

When transfer to other programs within the college was considered as withdrawal, the rate of withdrawal (29 per cent) for the pilot programs is similar to the national rate for schools of nursing. When such students are not considered withdrawals, the rate is reduced to 22 per cent.

Of the 811 students, 20 per cent stated that they would not have selected nursing if the pilot programs had not been offered. There is some evidence that the selection of such programs was related to age, marital status, and sex. Of the 111 students who were twenty-six years or older, 43 per cent would not have selected nursing. Of the 94 students who were married, 43 per cent would not have selected nursing. Of the 21 males, 52 per cent would not have selected nursing.

PART II

CHAPTER VII

INTRODUCTION TO THE EVALUATION STUDY

Evaluation was considered an essential part of the Cooperative Research Project in Junior and Community College Education for Nursing from the time of the first meeting of the
advisory committee in March 1952.

The concept of continuous evaluation by the individual
programs was encouraged through workshops sponsored by the
Cooperative Research Project. Individual programs developed
instruments to help evaluate the effectiveness of teaching and
learning, particularly in the area of nursing skills. Individual programs instituted follow-up studies of their graduates
to obtain suggestions from the students and hospital personnel
for improving the educational program. The Cooperative Research
Project itself sponsored several studies to increase basic
knowledge concerning junior and community college nursing programs.

Although the research projects referred to above involve
important contributions to understanding of the Cooperative
Research Project programs, the ultimate criterion for the success

132

or failure of the project is the nursing performance of the graduates. The project's concern with the nursing performance of the graduates is illustrated by the performance rating forms that have been mailed to employers since 1954, when the first class graduated (Appendix G). The results of the ratings were generally favorable (Appendix H).

However, a broader and more systematic evaluation study was considered essential. The immediate importance of such a study stems from the nationwide interest of nursing and junior-community college personnel in the experimental programs. Many colleges and citizen groups have become interested in sponsoring nursing programs in junior and community colleges, and they require a thorough report of the experiment in order to reach a decision. The present evaluation study represents one part of the report these schools are awaiting.

Definition of Terms

Several terms require definition in order to make the following discussion clear. These terms include the following:

"Graduates of pilot programs" refers to the nurses who graduated from the six pilot programs that had graduated nursing students by September 1956.

"Staff nurse" and "general-duty nurse" are the terms used interchangeably to describe the nursing position of first-level graduate nurses in hospitals. The two terms are commonly accepted by hospital personnel to describe the first-level graduate nurse. However, as will be made clear in this chapter and later in the study, what the staff nurse does varies from service to service and from hospital to hospital.

"Graduates of other programs" refers to staff nurses who have graduated from diploma or degree programs.

Purpose of the Evaluation Study

The purpose of this study is to test the following hypotheses, derived from the aims identified by the advisory committee of the Cooperative Research Project:

1. The graduates of the pilot programs qualify for the registered nurse license on the state board licensing examinations.

2. The graduates of the pilot programs are prepared for staff nurse positions (under supervision and, if possible, in situations where in-service training is available).

3. Given some work experience, the graduates of the pilot programs perform the functions of the staff nurse as well as graduates of other types of programs.[1]

Objectives of the Evaluation Study

1. The first objective was to determine the nursing roles being assumed by graduates of the pilot programs.

2. The second objective was to determine whether or not pilot program graduates require in-service education different from that of graduates of other types of programs.

---

[1]Two parts of this hypothesis, "some work experience" and "the functions of the staff nurse" require extensive qualification and elaboration, which will be provided later in the study.

3. The third objective was to compare the nursing performance of graduates of the pilot programs with graduates of other types of programs.

The Data

Data involving the graduates of six pilot programs were used to test the hypotheses of this study. The six programs are located at Fairleigh Dickinson University, Henry Ford Community College, Orange County Community College, Weber College, Pasadena City College, and Virginia Intermont College. The pilot programs at the Norfolk Division, Virginia State College and Monmouth Memorial Hospital could not be included since they did not have graduates by September 1956.

The first hypothesis was tested by using the State Boards Test Pool Examination scores. The scores of the graduates of the pilot programs were compared with the national results of diploma-program graduates for the year 1954. The examination remained the same for the years 1954, 1955, and 1956.

The second and third hypotheses were examined by using data gathered in interviews with graduates of the pilot programs, graduates of other programs, head nurses, and directors of nursing services. Ratings of the nursing performance of graduates of pilot and other programs were obtained from the head nurses in the interviews.

Some Problems in the Evaluation
of Nursing Performance

The major obstacle to evaluating the nursing performance of the graduates of the pilot programs was the absence of a yardstick that can be used to measure the quality of nursing performance. In speaking to the Conference on Nursing Education in Junior and Community Colleges, Spaney described the problem of evaluating the graduates of junior and community college nursing programs. She described the problem in terms of the need for an instrument with nationally usable norms:

> ... we do not yet have a nationally usable instrument with norms at different levels of experience which can be used to describe performance of either students or graduates in behavioral terms. At the present time there are several groups at work on such an instrument. The National League for Nursing has at least two committees and three departments working on various aspects of this problem. The Committee to Formulate More Definite Criteria for Accreditation has identified critical behaviors which are essential in the effective nurse. The Committee on Records, together with the staffs of the Department of Diploma and Associate Degree Programs, the Department of Baccalaureate and Higher Degree Programs, and the Department of Hospital Nursing, has evolved a behavioral rating device in the critical areas defined by the former committee. This device represents a beginning; it needs refinement, tryout, and norming in terms of types of educational program and experience level.[2]

---

[2] Emma Spaney, "Evaluation, Interpretation, and Implementation of Associate Degree Programs in Nursing," Nursing Education in Junior and Community Colleges (New York: American Association of Junior Colleges Cooperative Research Project, National League for Nursing, 1956), p. 32.

Although the device referred to by Spaney does represent a beginning, it has not even been given a preliminary trial to see whether norms could be established.

The development of a yardstick of nursing performance requires a basic knowledge of the practice of nursing. However, little research has been done on nursing practice. The Committee on the Function of Nursing[3] has pointed out the failure of nursing research to contribute in general to the growth of a systematic body of nursing knowledge. Henderson[4] has suggested that research in nursing has focused on the practitioner and not on the practice of nursing. Since 1951, nurses have invested a total of $400,000 in research on nursing functions.[5] These studies bypass the problem of quality of nursing care. In the preface to one of the studies of nursing functions, the authors explicitly state:

> This research is concerned with what the nurse does, and not with how well or how poorly she may do it. Thus this is not a study of nursing proficiency, important as proficiency may be in the determination of the function.[6]

[3]Committee on the Function of Nursing, A Program for the Nursing Profession (New York: The Macmillan Company, 1948), pp. 90-95.

[4]Virginia Henderson, "Research in Nursing Practice-When," Nursing Research, February 1956, p. 99.

[5]American Nurses' Association, Nurses Invest in Patient Care -- A Preliminary Report on a Five-Year Program of Studies of Nursing Functions (New York: American Nurses' Association, 1956), p. 5.

[6]Donald D. Stewart and Christine E. Needham, The General Duty Nurse (Fayetteville, Arkansas: University of Arkansas, 1955), p. 1.

This statement applies to all of the American Nurses' Association's studies of nursing functions that have thus far been published.

In reviewing the literature on evaluation procedures for nursing practice, Bailey states:

> Nursing educators, psychologists, head nurses, and student nurses have frequently expressed dissatisfaction and concern in relation to evaluation procedures.[7]

Bailey goes on to point out that "rating scales for student and graduate nurses seem to have been devised on the assumption that the raters are familiar with behavior that characterizes skilled nursing,"[8] that nursing students are dissatisfied with their clinical evaluations, and that "personal qualities such as 'emotional maturity' and 'good adjustment,' which often appear on rating scales, are too high on the ladder of abstraction to warrant commonality of meaning for the raters, or the subjects."[9]

Bailey's own study, which employed the critical-incident technique, was concerned with behaviors that are observed in practice. The purpose of her study was:

> First, to identify, objectively, behavioral criteria of the effective or successful

---

[7] June Teig Bailey, "The Critical Incident Technique in Identifying Behavioral Criteria of Professional Nursing Effectiveness," Nursing Research, October 1956, p. 53.

[8] Ibid.

[9] Ibid.

professional graduate staff nurse by means of
the "critical incident" technique recently
described by Flanagan; and, second, to investigate to what extent patients and the medical
team, i.e., doctors, head nurses, and clinical
instructors, vary in their judgments relative
to professional nursing effectiveness.[10]

The analysis of 419 incidents collected from nursing supervisors,
patients, and doctors identified twenty-seven behavioral criteria of professional nursing effectiveness under seven major
areas. The 419 incidents were analyzed to check the agreement
among doctors, nursing supervisors, and patients. Bailey con-
cludes:

Of these 27 behaviors, doctors, nursing
supervisors, and patients demonstrated
agreement on only 2 behaviors, "Giving
medications and treatments on time," and
"Talking about subjects of interest to the
patients."[11]

Bailey's study demonstrates that different levels of personnel
use different criteria to evaluate nursing performance. The
nursing behaviors she did isolate have not been tested, as she
herself points out.

Although the primary factor complicating the evaluation
of the nursing performance of the pilot-program graduates was
the absence of a yardstick and of norms for measuring quality of
nursing performance, other factors influenced the nature of
the study:

---

[10]Ibid., p. 52.

[11]Ibid., p. 63.

1. The time limit for completing the study;
2. The dispersion of the sample;
3. The fact that the class of 1956 had already graduated;
4. The possibility of bias influencing the evaluations;
5. The discrepancy between the preparation of the pilot-program graduates and job demands in present nursing practice.

Time Limit to Complete the Study

The Cooperative Research Project ended on July 1, 1957, after five years of experimentation. The evaluation study had to be completed by that time. A period of one year was set aside for the design of the study, the collection and analysis of data, and the writing of the study. The time was short, especially since it required that the researcher familiarize himself with the field of nursing. Meeting the deadline of completing the report meant that graduating classes for only three years could be considered. Effects of program changes made in 1956 and 1957, therefore, could not be shown in the findings.

Dispersion of the Sample

The pilot-program graduates are employed in hospitals all over the United States. If only one or two hospitals had been involved, a more rigorously controlled evaluation procedure would have been feasible. However, there were compensating advantages to the broader sampling required by the number of hospitals employing pilot-program graduates.

Class of 1956 Had Already Graduated

The pilot-program graduates of 1956 had already been at work a minimum of three months by the time data collection began. Accounts of initial experiences as staff nurses were obtained in retrospect. It is important to note, however, that these accounts were vivid, and that what the pilot-program graduates did recall indicated some similarity of experience. The ratings were obtained after the graduates had had at least three months of nursing experience.

Possibility of Bias Influencing
the Evaluations

Since head nurses and directors of nursing services were the primary judges of the competence of staff nurses, it becomes necessary to examine the educational experience of the judges as a possible factor influencing their evaluations.

Most head nurses and directors of nursing services have had their basic nursing education in diploma schools of nursing. Traditionally, the training of nurses in diploma schools includes giving service, which constitutes part of the training and helps pay for it. Brown has described what the experience of giving service is like in the typical hospital:

> In the typical school the first six months are
> devoted to classroom work in the physical,
> biological, medical, and social sciences, and
> in nursing and allied arts. What the high-school
> graduate acquires, other than intellectual in-
> digestion, from so many subjects thrust at her
> in six months' time is something most educators
> would not like to contemplate.

> Thereafter begins the clinical experience, if we
> may dignify with that term the supervised nurs-
> ing service that the great majority of students
> are still expected to render the hospital. It
> has been consistently assumed that through
> "practice" -- even if the supervision of that
> practice were often quantitatively and qualita-
> tively inadequate, and prior classroom instruc-
> tion were extremely deficient -- the student
> would emerge at the end of three years a com-
> petent nurse. If practice made perfect, much
> could be certainly expected. In the typical
> school it runs to thirty-three hours a week
> during the remainder of the first year after the
> student finishes her preclinical training.
> During her second and third years, in more than
> two-thirds of the schools, practice (exclusive
> of time spent for planned clinical instruction,
> classroom work, study, and meals) is between
> forty-one and forty-eight hours weekly.[12]

During the many hours of giving service, student nurses
perform the job of the nurse before they have graduated. Much
of the service they give is without supervision. For example,
most nursing students have been in charge of a floor at night.
This may or may not mean that they had been adequately prepared for or oriented to the responsibilities this entails.
Student nurses assume the role of the nurse in a variety of
situations, in many services, and usually in more than one hospital. Not only do they learn nursing, but they learn the
organizational and social systems of the hospital and what it
means to be a member of the hospital community, which includes
learning the jargon of their occupation.

At the time of graduation the diploma-school graduate
has had considerable experience as a worker. Nurses with such

---

[12]Esther Lucille Brown, <u>Nursing for the Future</u> (New York
Russell Sage Foundation, 1948), pp. 49-50.

experience have had many opportunities to practice nursing skills, procedures, and techniques. At graduation most diploma-program graduates can be considered fully prepared practitioners in the hospital in which they received their training.

In contrast to the students in the diploma school of nursing, the students in the pilot programs have not been workers. When they have played the role of the nurse, they have done this for only a few patients and under the close supervision of their instructors. They have not given care without supervision. They have not had a wide range of experience with hospital procedures and hospital personnel. They have not given patient care under the pressure of a large work load.

As has been pointed out, most of the nurses evaluating staff nurse performance are steeped in the tradition of giving service during training as a necessary prerequisite to becoming a full-fledged nurse. It is only natural for a person who has undergone an intense experience to tend to evaluate that experience as "the only way" for a learner to reach the same status. This expectation would obviously influence, if not bias, the evaluation of nurses prepared in a program radically different from their own. At the same time, it is necessary to recognize that evaluators "sold" on the pilot programs' educational approach may be influenced by their convictions in evaluating individual nurses.

Discrepancy between Preparation of Pilot
Program Graduates and Job Demands in
Present Nursing Practice

In order to understand the nature of the discrepancy
between the preparation of nurses in the pilot programs and
present nursing practice, it is necessary to understand the
functions for which the graduates of the pilot programs were
prepared.

The preparation of nurses in the pilot programs was
based on McManus' analysis of the functions of nursing.[13]
McManus has described a spectrum-like continuum of nursing
functions, which were divided into three levels. At each of
these three levels were personnel with preparation appropriate
to that level. The levels that make up the continuum are:

(1) Simple functions based on common knowledge;
(2) Intermediate functions requiring skill and some
    judgment;
(3) Complex functions requiring expert skill and
    judgment.

McManus specified that the preparation for the simple
functions is on-the-job training; for the intermediate functions, technical training; for the complex functions, professional education.

The individual trained on the job performs simple and
routine activities and assists the physician or nurse. This

_____

[13]Mildred Montag, The Education of Nursing Technicians
(New York: G. P. Putnam's Sons, 1951), pp. 4-8.

person works under the supervision of the nurse with professional

preparation. At the other extreme, the nurse with professional

preparation performs complex functions which include directing

the nursing team. The preparation of this nurse would legiti-

mately be carried on within the university or college and lead

to a baccalaureate degree. In discussing the preparation of

the professional nurse, the Committee on the Function of Nursing

stated:

> We agree with the leaders of the nursing pro-
> fession who hold that the professional nurse
> should be college-trained -- in short, that
> she should receive an education similar to that
> of teachers, engineers, and others.[14]

The nurse with college training, according to the Committee on

the Function of Nursing, directs the nursing team:

> The "team approach" places full responsibility
> for the planning of the nursing function and
> the primary responsibility for its proper
> execution on the most mature and competently
> trained individual, the professional nurse, and
> leaves to her the assignment of specific duties
> among others less competently trained. The
> allocation of these duties is the beginning, not
> the end, of the relationship between the pro-
> fessional nurse and her associates; as head of
> the team she provides professional counsel and
> retains supervisory responsibility.[15]

The functions that make up the middle range of the con-

tinuum of nursing functions would be performed by the nurse

---

[14]Committee on the Function of Nursing, op. cit.,
p. 56.

[15]Ibid., p. 40.

with technical training. This nurse performs functions that
involve both skill and judgment but works "under the direction
of the nurse with professional preparation or the physician."
The graduates of the pilot programs were prepared to perform
these functions. The assumptions made by the advisory committee
were that the graduates would "perform technical (or semi-professional) functions," "be prepared for beginning practitioner
positions with supervision," and "be prepared to become competent practitioners."

The pilot-program graduates, in other words, were prepared to be members of the nursing team, not its leaders. If
team nursing is practiced, the pilot-program graduate works
under the supervision of the team leader. If team nursing is
not practiced, this nurse would expect to work under the supervision of the head nurse. With this supervision, the pilot-
program graduate is expected to develop into a competent practitioner.

This conception of the pilot-program graduate as a staff
nurse is at variance with the description of the supervision
staff nurses received in practice. In 1951 the nursing profession, with the help of social scientists, focused its attention on the what of nursing practice in order "to provide a
scientific basis for steps to improve nursing services and
patient care." The studies carried out reveal "variations as
to what she (the general-duty nurse) does, the amount of supervision she receives, the amount of responsibility she is called

on to assume."[16]

Variations in "what the nurse does" begin with the amount of <u>direct nursing care</u> she gives. By "direct nursing care" is meant those activities performed by the nurse in the presence of or at the bedside of the patient. The studies of nursing functions generally distinguish between two types of <u>direct nursing care</u>: "direct patient care" and "medications, treatments and procedures." The studies show generally that nurses spend up to 50 per cent of their time giving <u>direct nursing care</u>.

However, the amount and type of <u>direct nursing care</u> given by the general-duty nurse are dependent on a variety of factors. Stewart and Needham found that:

> ... the function of the general duty nurse is associated with variation in (a) the general structure of the nursing service of the hospital in which she is employed in terms of the size of the hospital, type of control, and similar variables; (b) the place of the nurse in this structure in terms of nursing service, shift, number of patients for which she is responsible, and number of auxiliary nursing personnel as assistants; (c) individual differences in the nurses such as those associated with age, motivation, and similar matters.[17]

It is reported in <u>Nurses Invest in Patient Care</u> that:

> ... Variations in the functions of nursing personnel are, of course, also due to methods of work assignments which prevail in each hospital. The field notes in one study showed that the functional method of work seemed to

---

[16]<u>Nurses Invest in Patient Care</u>, p. 31.

[17]Stewart and Needham, <u>op. cit.</u>, p. 98.

predominate in ten of eleven hospitals, in
that medications and treatments were usually
assigned to one general duty nurse who performed functions related to those procedures
to the exclusion of patient bedside care.[18]

Reissman and Rohrer found in their studies of one large
urban hospital that this movement toward specialized functions
was at the heart of important changes that have taken place in
the role of the general-duty nurse.

She is no longer responsible for the "total
care" of the patient, for she now has many more
patients, all with specific illnesses, and she
has had to relinquish other duties. She is no
longer responsible for the environment of the
patient, because others now wash the floors,
make the beds, and cater to the patient's wishes.
Indeed, as described in Chapter II, a separate
department has assumed the housekeeping functions in the hospital on an assembly line basis.
She is no longer the individualist maintaining
the control she once held, for she must now fit
into the routine of a large bureaucratic administration. Her day is now divided into specific
tasks which she administers to all patients
rather than to one, as the observer noted in
one of the studies; hypodermics are begun at
one end of the ward and given to all requiring
them at one time. All these facts are evidence
that the nurse's role today is at wide variance
with what it once may have been.[19]

When no other general-duty nurses are on the ward except
the one on functional assignment, practical nurses and aides
give most of the "direct patient care." However, when general-
duty nurses are available, they do have a group of patients to

---

[18]Nurses Invest in Patient Care, p. 32.

[19]Leonard Reissman and John H. Rohrer, Change and Dilemma
in the Nursing Profession (New York: G. P. Putnam's Sons, 1957),
pp. 13-14.

whom they give total patient care, usually with the exception
of medications. The difference between the assignment of the
general-duty nurse and the practical nurse under these circumstances usually rests in the condition of the patients whom
they are assigned. The staff nurse is given the critical or
sicker patients.

It has been mentioned that there is considerable variation in the amount of supervision the nurse receives. "In one
study of 107 general duty nurses in 10 hospitals, only 28 of
them -- all located in one of the hospitals -- fit the definition of a general duty nurse as 'a professional nurse working
under the supervision of a head nurse.'"[20] In such circumstances, the only supervision that the staff nurse received
usually occurred when the supervisor or head nurse made her
rounds.

Research findings stress another condition of the work
of the general duty nurse -- the responsibility she assumes.
This is not just a matter of the direct responsibility for
patients. It is the responsibility for managing patient care
and delegating tasks to others. Kreuter stated that the management of auxiliary nursing personnel by the staff nurse started
during the 1940's:

> During the labor shortage of the 1940's more and
> more of the hospital nurse's time was taken by
> other than those involving nursing practice, and
> many untrained persons were employed and trained

---

[20]Nurses Invest in Patient Care, p. 31.

by nurses to give nursing care to the patients.
The concept of nursing came to include the
training and supervision of these workers.
This decade marked the beginning of the de-
cline in the professional status of the nurse
practitioner in hospitals.[21]

In their study of one hospital, Reissman and Rohrer

found that the general-duty nurse:

> ... is responsible for the management of a
> team of personnel under her authority: student
> nurses, practical nurses, and aides.[22]

In the nursing literature, the nurse who manages "a team

of personnel" is usually referred to as the team leader.

Although the quoted studies indicate that staff nurses

often work without supervision, this does not mean that the

nurses consider this proper. In one study,[23] 51 per cent of

the graduate nurses stated that the supervision they received

was insufficient or inadequate. They felt that those in charge

gave no instructive criticism or praise. Many felt that the

fault was one of omission rather than commission. There was

further evidence in this study that nurses often assumed super-

visory or administrative responsibilities without being trained

in these functions.

---

[21]Frances Kreuter, Minutes of Conference of the Council
of Member Agencies of Dept. of Baccalaureate and Higher Degree
Programs, National League for Nursing.

[22]Reissman and Rohrer, op. cit., p. 13.

[23]Carrol E. Izard and Douglas Courtney, The Hospital
Nurse in Greater Cleveland (Philadelphia, Pa.: Research Associates, 1955).

The conflict that has been defined is a discrepancy
between what nurses in the pilot programs are trained to do
and what nurses do in practice. It is important to note that
graduates of other programs feel that they need more adequate
supervision and that they are asked to take supervisory and
administrative responsibilities for which they have not been
prepared.

Method of the Evaluation Study

Spaney described what would be done to evaluate the
graduates if a nationally normed behavioral instrument existed:

> If a basic behavioral instrument were devised
> and nationally normed in terms of selected
> graduates of basic associate-degree, diploma,
> and baccalaureate-degree programs, at meaning-
> ful time intervals after the graduation, each
> local institution might then attack the problem
> of securing local norms for its graduates in
> somewhat the following way:
>
> 1. Follow up a sample of graduates to see where
>   they have found employment.
> 2. Orient the employers to the problem, and
>   seek their cooperation.
> 3. Have all graduate nurses who are on a staff
>   level rated by the head nurses or super-
>   visors. (This will get data about graduates
>   of various types of programs.)
> 4. Repeat this procedure as necessary over a
>   period of time long enough to get sufficiently
>   large groups, at desired experience levels.
> 5. Analyze the data so obtained in terms of type
>   of program and experience level.[24]

---

[24] Ibid., p. 33.

Although no instrument with norms at different experience levels was available, the procedure of the present study
essentially followed Spaney's outline.

1. A large sample of the pilot-program graduates were followed up to see where they
   had found employment.

2. The employers were oriented and their
   cooperation sought.

3. Graduate nurses on a staff level were rated
   by head nurses (or supervisors).

4. The data were analyzed.

Although the general procedure suggested by Spaney was
followed, the method of the present study deviated from it in
several ways:

1. No nationally normed instrument was available.
   Instead, a revision of the behavioral rating
   form devised by members of the Cooperative
   Research Project staff under the guidance of
   Professor Elizabeth Hagen was used. The
   original instrument was the one previously
   used to collect data about the graduates by
   mail. (Appendix G)

2. All graduate nurses on staff level were not
   rated. However, graduate nurses from other
   than pilot programs were rated on the same
   instrument by the same head nurses who rated
   the pilot-program graduates.

3. Repeated ratings over a period of time were
   not obtained. Single ratings of nurses were
   obtained on visits to individual hospitals.

4. The instrument was revised to include four
   behaviors pertaining to organizing the giving
   of patient care and ward work. The wording
   of the instrument was changed so that nurses
   were rated as nurses rather than graduates of
   pilot programs (Appendix H, Part C).

Several additions were made to Spaney's suggested
approach so that the evaluation was not based on a single instrument administered to a single occupational group. Nursing
knowledge was evaluated by means of State Boards Test Pool
Examination. Evaluation of nursing performance and preparation
in the work situation was obtained through interviews with head
nurses, with graduates of the pilot and other programs, and
with directors of nursing services.

Ratings by head nurses who observed the nurse on the
job were obtained as part of their interviews (Appendix H).
The interviews were also used to define:

1. The context of the ratings: What is expected
   of nurses in each hospital situation?

2. The reasons for the ratings: What kinds of
   incidents and explanations does the rater
   use to justify the rating?

The ratings do not represent an index of quality of
nursing performance. Instead, they allow a comparison between
the performance of pilot-program graduates, as individual
nurses, with the performance of other nurses working in similar
hospital situations. The performance of other nurses observed
by the head nurses was used as the standard for comparison.
Such a comparison does not represent an index of the quality of
nursing performance, since each rater's standard is relative to
her own experience.

Graduates of the pilot programs were interviewed to
find out:

1. What kind of orientation program and supervision they received when they started working at their hospitals.

2. The nature of their jobs as staff nurses.

3. Their opinion of the adequacy of their preparation for their present nursing jobs.

The interview guide for these nurses is provided in Appendix I.

The directors of nursing services of the hospitals were interviewed to determine their opinion of the employability and performance of the graduates of the pilot programs.

Collection of the Data

The data were collected between November 1956 and February 1957. Various local trips were made to hospitals in New York and New Jersey, and three trips were made to more distant parts of the country. On one trip, a week was spent in Utah and a week in California. During the week in Utah, several days were spent in Ogden, Salt Lake City, and Provo. In California, all of the time was spent in Pasadena. The second trip was to Michigan. All of the hospitals visited were in or around Detroit. The third trip included visits to hospitals in Bristol, Tennessee; Charlestown, West Virginia, and Richmond, Virginia.

The initial contact with the hospitals employing graduates of the pilot programs was made through a letter from Dr. Montag. This letter to nursing-service administrators

requested their cooperation in the evaluation study and identified the investigator (Appendix J). In local situations this
letter was followed up by a telephone call from the investigator to the director of nursing services to arrange for the
time and date of the visit and to work out some of the details
of scheduling the interviews. In non-local situations,
Dr. Montag's letter was followed by a letter from the investigator. This letter included information about the study and the
approximate dates for the visit to collect the data.

Upon arriving at the hospital, the investigator went
immediately to the director of nursing services. Whenever possible, she was interviewed first in order to obtain some idea
of particular aspects of the hospital situation that might influence the other interviews. It was found that some knowledge
of the orientation program was of particular help in conducting
the interviews. All interviews were recorded on tape.

The Sampling

All the interviews and rating data were obtained from
twenty-five hospitals. The selection of the hospitals began
with an examination of the lists of graduates and the hospitals
in which they were working. It was observed that the graduates,
although working in forty-nine hospitals, were clustered in
institutions located in the geographic area where they had gone
to school. The hospitals in the six school areas were used as
the centers for collecting the data. Approximately half of

the hospitals employing graduates of each program were visited (Table 18).

TABLE 18

NUMBER AND PERCENTAGE OF HOSPITALS VISITED

Program	Number of Hospitals Employing Graduates	Hospitals Visited N	%
A	13	6	46
B	12	6	50
C	8	6	75
D	10	5	50
E	2	1	50
F	6	3	50
Total	51[a]	27[a]	53

[a]The number of employing hospitals and visited hospitals are fifty-one and twenty-seven, respectively. In the preceding text the respective numbers reported are forty-nine and twenty-five. The disparity between the pairs of numbers is accounted for by the fact that two of the hospitals visited each employed graduates of two pilot programs.

All of the graduates of the pilot programs who were working in the hospitals in these six areas were rated, with the following limitations:

1. Graduates who were working so far from the six educational centers that the time and expense of obtaining the data became prohibitive were not interviewed or rated.[25]

_____

[25]A legitimate question can be raised concerning the possibility of bias resulting from sampling only hospitals located in the vicinity of the pilot-program schools. In these areas there may be greater awareness of the pilot programs than in areas where a single pilot-program graduate is employed and the administration is not familiar with her radically different

2. When many graduates were clustered in a single
hospital, the number rated and interviewed
was affected by time and scheduling problems.
In such hospital situations priority was given
to those pilot-program graduates who were
working with graduates of diploma programs who
had approximately the same amount of graduate-
nurse experience.

The forty-nine hospitals employed 167 pilot-program
graduates. Of these 167, 85 (51 per cent) were rated by their
head nurses. For only one of the programs were less than 50
per cent of the graduates rated. This occurred when 49 of the
50 nurses were located in one hospital. Ratings of 16 nurses
from the one program was considered adequate representation of
the graduates of that program and that hospital.

TABLE 19

NUMBER AND PERCENTAGE OF GRADUATES RATED

Program	Number of Graduates Working in Hospitals	Graduates Rated N	%
A	22	11	50
B	24	14	58
C	19	14	74
D	39	23	59
E	50	16	32
F	13	7	54
Total	167	85	51

preparation. It is possible that this awareness of the nature
of the pilot-programs influences the rating and assimilation
of the pilot-program graduates. The present study in no way
provides an answer to this question.

Many of the forty-nine head nurses who rated graduates
of pilot programs were also working with recent graduates of
other programs. They rated the graduates of other programs
when these had nursing experience comparable to that of the
pilot-program graduates. Initially, it had been planned to
have each head nurse rate as many graduates of other programs
as graduates of pilot programs, leading to a matched sample.
It was not possible to obtain a matched sample, however, since
many head nurses working with pilot-program graduates were not
also working with graduates of other programs who had less
than three years of graduate-nurse experience. However,
50 graduates of other programs were rated. Eighty-eight per
cent of these nurses graduated from diploma schools of nursing
(Table 20), and 88 per cent of the schools they graduated from
were either fully or temporarily accredited by the National
League for Nursing (Table 21).

TABLE 20

DISTRIBUTION OF THE 50 GRADUATES OF OTHER PROGRAMS
BY TYPE OF PROGRAM ATTENDED

Type of Program	Number	Per Cent
Diploma	44	88
Degree	4	8
Unknown	2	4
Total	50	100

TABLE 21

DISTRIBUTION OF THE 50 GRADUATES OF OTHER PROGRAMS
BY THE ACCREDITATION STATUS OF THE NURSING
PROGRAMS ATTENDED

Accreditation Status	Number	Per Cent
Fully Accredited	24	48
Temporarily Accredited	20	40
Not Accredited	3	6
Unknown	3	6
Total	50	100

The majority of the nurses rated graduated in 1956
(Table 22). In the analysis of the ratings, the 1954 and 1955
graduates were combined into a single group.

TABLE 22

DISTRIBUTION OF GRADUATES BY YEAR OF GRADUATION
FROM NURSING SCHOOL

Class of	Pilot Programs		Other Programs	
	N	%	N	%
1956	58	68	32	64
1955	24	28	10	20
1954	3	4	8	16
Total	85	100	50	100

The majority of the nurses rated had from three to seven months of graduate-nurse experience at the time they were rated (Table 23).

TABLE 23

MONTHS OF GRADUATE-NURSE EXPERIENCE
AT TIME OF RATING

Months of Experience	Graduates			
	Pilot Programs		Other Programs	
	N	%	N	%
3- 7	58	68	33	66
8-12	6	7	6	12
13-17	18	21	5	10
18-22	1	1	3	6
23-27	2	2	1	2
28-32	0	0	2	4
Total	85	99	50	100

The median A.C.E. for all the pilot-program graduates who took the State Boards Test Pool Examination was at the fortieth percentile of the national four-year college norms for 1952.[26] The median A.C.E. for the pilot-program graduates rated was at the thirty-ninth percentile (Table 24). For the students enrolled in the programs, the median A.C.E. was also at the thirty-ninth percentile. However, all of the

---

[26]More detailed information concerning the A.C.E. is contained in Chapter VI.

entering students had not taken the A.C.E. Of those pilot program graduates who took the State Boards Test Pool Examinations,
147 (77 per cent) had taken the A.C.E. Of the 85 who were
rated, 67 (79 per cent) had taken the State Boards. The medians
were computed on the basis of those who had taken the A.C.E.
The medians in Table 24 suggest no differences between the
A.C.E. scores of those pilot-program graduates who took State
Boards and those who were rated.

Examination of the A.C.E. medians by programs for the
pilot program graduates taking the State Boards Test Pool Examinations indicated that one program deviated markedly from the
others (Table 24). The median A.C.E. for the first class
graduating from Program E was at the seventieth percentile of
the national four-year college norms.

TABLE 24

MEDIAN A.C.E. PERCENTILE RANKS (NATIONAL FOUR-YEAR
COLLEGE NORMS) FOR PILOT PROGRAM GRADUATES WHO TOOK
THE STATE BOARDS TEST POOL EXAMINATIONS AND FOR
PILOT PROGRAM GRADUATES WHO WERE RATED

Program	Graduates Taking State Boards		Graduates Rated	
	Number	Percentile Rank of Median	Number	Percentile Rank of Median
A	39	30	11	27
B	34	40	14	42
C	20	37	14	39
D	24	42	23	40
E	18	70	16	62
F	12	21	7	24
Total	147	40	85	39

A.C.E. scores were not available for graduates of other programs who were rated.

Of the 85 pilot-program graduates rated, 45 were interviewed. Of the 50 graduates of other programs, 18 were interviewed. The selection of nurses to be interviewed was based on their availability.

Twenty-three directors of nursing services were interviewed. Two assistants to the director were interviewed because the directors were at conferences.

Application of the Findings

The reader must remember that the present study is concerned with the graduates of six junior and community college programs that were part of the Cooperative Research Project in Junior and Community College Education for Nursing. As members of the Cooperative Research Project, the programs have several common features. Among the common features, the most important are:

> The advisory committee for the project established criteria to serve as a guide in the selection of the pilot programs. These programs meet the criteria.

> The pilot programs were in general agreement concerning certain aspects of the educational curriculum and the type of nurse that they were interested in producing.

On the other hand, there are important differences among the pilot programs. A superficial examination of the six programs involved in the study reveals differences ranging from the lengths of the program to the selection of the students. Also, when the graduates of the pilot programs went to work, they did not go into equivalent situations.

This study does not, therefore, pertain to all junior and community college nursing programs. Nursing educators or junior college personnel interested in interpreting the results must understand the educational programs being tested, the differences among them, and the importance of relationships with hospital personnel.

CHAPTER VIII

THE GRADUATES QUALIFY FOR NURSING

This chapter is concerned with testing the hypothesis that "the graduates of the pilot programs qualify for the registered nurse license on the state board licensing examination."

The Licensing Examination

In 1955 the American Nurses' Association Special Committee of State Boards of Nursing reported that nursing is "the only profession to develop a tool that is used throughout continental United States to appraise those who wish to enter its ranks."[1] The State Board Test Pool Examination[2] has been used since 1950 for licensing professional nurses in all of the forty-eight states, the District of Columbia, Hawaii, and two Canadian provinces. This examination tests knowledge considered important by "qualified nurses from the various

---

[1]American Nurses' Association Special Committee of State Boards of Nursing, "Studying State Board Test Scores," American Journal of Nursing, 9:1093 (September 1955).

[2]The State Board Test Pool Examination will hereafter be referred to as the SBTP.

jurisdictions"[3] in which this test is administered.

The examination has distinct limitations. It does not test performance in the actual situation nor measure potential for growth. These limitations should be kept in mind when interpreting the results of the examination. The examination provides information about what a person knows, not about what she will do.

This examination is a standardized instrument which permits schools of nursing to compare the scores of their graduates with the scores of other graduates from their state and from the whole country. The norms referred to in this analysis are derived from the State Board Test Pool Examination, Series 154, for 1954. The comparison of the performance of graduates of the pilot programs with that of graduates of diploma programs has been simplified because Series 154 was used for 1954, 1955, and 1956, the three years that pilot-program graduates took the SBTP examination.

The results of the examination are reported in standard scores. The standard-score scale used for the SBTP uses 500 to represent the mean, and 100 standard score units are equivalent to one standard deviation. An individual whose standard score is 400, which is one standard deviation below the mean, exceeded 16 per cent of those originally tested. One who earns

---

[3] American Nurses' Association Special Committee of State Boards of Nursing, "Studying State Board Test Scores," American Journal of Nursing, 9:1093 (September 1955).

a standard score of 600, which is one standard deviation above
the mean, exceeded 84 per cent of those originally tested.
An important attribute of standard scores is that an individual's standing on one test can be compared with the same
individual's standing on another test when both tests have been
given to the same group of individuals. For example, consider
an individual who made the following scores on the five sections of the SBTP:

Medical Nursing   500
Surgical Nursing   610
Obstetric Nursing   371
Nursing of Children   545
Psychiatric Nursing   435

The scores above have been obtained on five different
sections. It is possible to make direct comparisons between
a nurse's scores on the different sections. On the Medical
Nursing section, she scored at the mean of all those who took
the examination. On the Surgical Nursing and Nursing of
Children sections, she scored above the mean; on Obstetric
Nursing and Psychiatric Nursing, she scored below the mean.

Not only do standard scores permit making quick comparisons of scores in relation to the mean, but they enable
the direct comparisons of deviations below and above the mean
since the score units for each test are the same. The score
of 610 on each of the sections represents the same standing in
relation to all those who were given the examination.

If the state in which this individual took the test
used a standard score of 350 or above as the passing score,

this individual would qualify for licensure, since she scored 350 or above on all five sections. In a state using 400 or above as the passing grade, this individual would not qualify for licensure, since she scored 400 or above on only four of the five parts.

Scoring 500 or above on all five parts of the SBTP licensing examination is particularly important because the ANA Subcommittee on the Preparation of More Flexible Standards to be Used as a Guide by State Boards of Nursing has recommended:

> ... that any candidate for interstate licensure who receives a score of 500 or above (on all five sections) be granted a license upon state verification of the original license and such other things as the statutes require without further investigation of the nursing program or secondary education.

Although the SBTP examination is a standardized instrument administered throughout the United States, the actual testing and licensing are controlled and administered by the individual states.

Analysis of the test-score results by states indicates a tremendous range. The percentage of individuals scoring 500 or above on all five sections is as high as 88 per cent for one state but as low as 18 per cent for another.[4] In two states, 100 per cent of those taking the examination scored

---

[4] _Ibid._, p. 1095.

350 or above on all five sections, while in another state only 72 per cent scored 350 or above on all five sections.

SBTP Examination Results for the Pilot-Program Graduates

One hundred and ninety-two of the 234 pilot-program graduates have taken the SBTP examination. Of the 42 graduates who have not taken the examination, 39 are from the Class of 1956 of Pasadena City College. The California State Law required that nursing programs must be at least three years in duration. A third year, designated the practicum, had to be completed before the Pasadena pilot-program student was permitted to take the examination. However, the California State Senate has recently amended the Business and Professional Code to permit the licensing of graduates at the end of two years. Three 1956 graduates, one each from Programs A, B, and C, have not yet taken the examination.

Of the 192 pilot-program graduates taking the examination, 176 (91.7 per cent) qualified for licensure the first time they took it. Of the 16 graduates who failed, 14 have retaken the examination. Thirteen (93 per cent) passed on the second trial. One repeated the examination a second time before she qualified.

The percentage of pilot-program graduates qualifying and failing to qualify for licensure are similar to the results for graduates of all programs for 1954 and 1955 (Table 25).

TABLE 25

NUMBER AND PERCENTAGE OF GRADUATES OF PILOT
AND OTHER PROGRAMS PASSING AND FAILING STATE
BOARD TEST POOL EXAMINATIONS ON FIRST TRIAL

Type of Program	Number of Candidates		Percentage of Candidates	
	Passing	Failing	Passing	Failing
Pilot Program	176	16	91.7	8.3
All Programs (1954)	27,009	2,835	90.5	9.5
All Programs (1955)	27,363	2,542	91.5	8.5

Of the pilot-program graduates taking the examination,
98 per cent scored 300 or above on all five sections (Table 26).
Each of the programs had more than 90 per cent of its graduates
score over 300 on all five parts. None of the graduates of
Program E had any scores below 400; none of the graduates of
Programs C and D had any scores below 350. Each of the schools
had at least 90 per cent of its graduates scoring 350 or above
on all five sections.

Thirty-seven per cent of the pilot-program graduates
scored 500 or above on all five sections. This would qualify
them for inter-state licensure according to the recommendations
of the Subcommittee on the Preparation of More Flexible Standards. The differences in test results by schools are illustrated
by the range of percentages -- 15 to 83 -- of those scoring
500 or above on all five parts. Differences of this magnitude
are also found in the test pool results by states and types of
nursing programs. For example, the percentage of diploma-school

TABLE 26

PERCENTAGE OF INDIVIDUALS MEETING OR EXCEEDING SPECIFIC STANDARD SCORES ON ALL FIVE SECTIONS OF THE STATE BOARD TEST POOL EXAMINATION, PILOT AND DIPLOMA PROGRAMS

Type of Program	Number of Graduates	Number of Candidates Examined	Percentages of Individuals Whose Standard Scores on ALL Five Sections of the SBTP Examinations Were:			
			300 or above	350 or above	400 or above	500 or above
Pilot Programs						
A	40	39	95	82	64	15
B	39	38	97	89	87	26
C	28	27	100	100	93	52
D	57	57	100	100	88	40
E	18	18	100	100	100	83
F	13	13	92	85	69	31
Total	195	192	98	94	83	37
Diploma Programs						
Fully accredited		8,565	99	96	89	46
Temporarily accredited		14,776	96	89	74	29
Not accredited		2,209	89	73	54	15
Non-participating		536	83	69	47	16
Total		26,086	96	90	77	33

graduates scoring 500 or above on all five parts of the examination ranges from 15 to 46 by the accreditation status of the school (Table 26).

The percentages of the total group of pilot-program graduates exceeding specific standard scores are larger than those for all diploma programs and are more nearly similar to the fully accredited diploma school percentages than to the others (Table 26). The percentages for the graduates of Programs C and E are greater than the percentages for the fully accredited diploma programs.

The means for the 192 pilot-program graduates are higher on all of the five sections than the means for all the graduates of diploma programs (Table 27). When the means for the entire group of pilot programs are compared with those of the diploma programs, they are found to lie between the means for the fully and the temporarily accredited programs, with the exception of the Obstetric Nursing mean, which is a few points higher than the mean for the fully accredited diploma programs.

The comparison of the means by individual pilot programs and the means by accreditation status gives results similar to the previous comparison of percentages of individuals exceeding certain standard scores.

The variation in the scores of the graduates of the six pilot programs raised the question:

> Can these differences be attributed to sampling variations, or are they indicative of significant differences between the graduates of the six programs?

TABLE 27

MEANS OF INDIVIDUALS ON THE FIVE SECTIONS OF THE STATE BOARD TEST
POOL EXAMINATION FOR PILOT AND DIPLOMA SCHOOLS

Type of Program	Number of Candidates Examined	Medical Nursing	Surgical Nursing	Obstetric Nursing	Nursing of Children	Psychiatric Nursing
Pilot Programs						
A	39	477	471	475	505	531
B	38	573	490	543	525	573
C	27	560	554	575	568	590
D	57	534	530	537	553	536
E	18	656	607	612	635	636
F	13	455	495	518	504	536
Total	192	526	518	537	540	559
Diploma Programs						
Fully accredited	8,565	545	548	533	559	561
Temporarily accredited	14,776	506	510	499	524	525
Not accredited	2,209	458	464	454	486	486
Non-participating	536	443	455	452	477	480
Total	26,086	517	517	505	531	533

The appropriate test is an analysis of variance on each of the five sections of the SBTP examination. The last steps of the computation for one of the sections are shown below (Table 28).

TABLE 28

ANALYSIS OF VARIANCE FOR COMPARING THE SCORES
ON THE MEDICAL NURSING SECTION OF THE STATE BOARD
TEST POOL EXAMINATION FOR THE GRADUATES OF THE
SIX PILOT PROGRAMS

Source of Variation	Sum of Squares	Degrees of Freedom	Mean Square	F	F.001
Total	3,798,939	191			
Between the Program Means	531,890	5	106,378	6.06	4.01
Within the Programs	3,267,049	186	17,565		

The observed value of F is 6.06. The probability that an F of this size might occur merely by chance is less than 1 in 1,000. The idea that the differences in test results are due to chance must be rejected.

In the previous chapter, emphasis was placed on the independence of the institutions, which were deliberately selected to represent a variety of junior and community colleges, to select their own student bodies in accordance with their own standards. The impact of these different policies was observed in the variation from school to school on those characteristics analyzed in the previous chapter. Therefore, it is not very surprising to find that these differences also affect the results of the licensing examination.

Summary

The hypothesis that the graduates of the pilot programs are able to qualify for licensure on the SBTP examination is supported by the test results. Of the pilot-program
graduates taking the examination, 91.7 per cent qualified on
their initial attempt for licensure in the states in which they
took the examination; in 1954, 90.5 per cent of the graduates
of all types of programs -- that is, including degree and
diploma graduates -- qualified on the first attempt.

The results of the test scores for the pilot-program
graduates as a group resembled the results for the fully
accredited diploma programs. Examination of the results indicates that they vary significantly from one pilot program to
another. The graduates of two programs scored higher as a
group than the graduates of accredited diploma programs, while
the graduates of another program as a group made scores that
fell between the scores of graduates of temporarily and non-
accredited diploma programs.

It has already been pointed out that the pilot programs differ. They differ in their student bodies, in their
faculties, and in the curricula developed for the nursing program. The fact that they are all two-year programs participating in the Cooperative Research Project does not eradicate

these differences. Their impact was found in the significantly
different levels of achievement of the graduates of the six
pilot programs on the several parts of the SBTP examination.

However, regardless of the differences between scores,
almost all of the graduates of the pilot programs qualified
for licensure on the SBTP examination.

CHAPTER IX

THE GRADUATES GO TO WORK: SETTINGS

This section is devoted to describing the types of nursing positions and the hospitals in which the graduates are working.

New graduates in nursing are restricted to hospital nursing jobs or jobs in which they receive supervision until they have passed their licensing examinations. The examinations are usually taken a few months after graduation. The instructors in the pilot programs have encouraged their graduates to continue their hospital experience for at least one year before branching into other areas of nursing service.

Nurses on maternity leave and part-time employees were not included in the working population, with the exception of one nurse, who had been employed by the hospital for over a year and is now working part-time while attending school.

Information concerning the work status of the graduates was obtained in October 1956 from the directors of the pilot programs. In general, the graduates have maintained close contact with their instructors and their colleges. That most of this information was current and accurate was validated in the visits to the hospitals. If the nurse was no longer at the

176

hospital at the time of the visit but had been working there three weeks before the visit, she was included in the working population. If the hospital was not visited, the work information remained as reported by the nursing directors.

Types of Positions

One hundred and ninety-one (81 per cent) of the 234 graduates were working as nurses. One hundred and sixty-seven (71 per cent) were employed as general-duty nurses in hospitals. The 40 in the Unclassified category were primarily married women of whom many had recently become mothers. Some of them were part-time hospital employees. The remaining few were unemployed for health or family reasons, or had moved and had not yet established contact with their programs. More information about the activities and whereabouts of those in the Unclassified group would undoubtedly add to the number working.

TABLE 29

POSITIONS HELD BY GRADUATES OF THE PILOT PROGRAMS

| Position | Pilot Programs | | | | | | All Programs | |
	A	B	C	D	E	F	No.	Per Cent
General duty	22	24	19	39	50	13	167	71
Doctor's office		1	3	5	3		12	5
Public health	2	4		1			7	3
School	1	2					3	1
Private duty	2						2	1
Other than nurse		1		2			3	1
Unclassified	13	7	6	10	4		40	17
Total	40	39	28	57	57	13	234	99

Almost all of the graduates work initially in hospitals. In 1956, 125 nurses graduated from the pilot programs. One hundred and fourteen (91 per cent) of the 125 were working in hospitals. Seven were not working and four were working in doctors' offices. Those who were employed as public health, school, and private duty nurses graduated in 1954 or 1955. One of the graduates had obtained a degree in psychology and was teaching that subject in a college. Another had returned to teaching elementary school, was working in a hospital summers, and was planning to prepare for teaching nursing in a pilot program. A third had been working as an airline stewardess until she married. She planned to return to hospital nursing.

The Hospitals

The 167 graduates were working in 49 hospitals. Thirty-nine (80 per cent) are fully accredited by the Joint Commission on Accreditation of Hospitals. Five (10 per cent) are temporaril accredited, while five (10 per cent) have not received full or temporary accreditation. Of these five, one (an extremely small hospital located in a mining community in West Virginia) is not even listed.

The 49 hospitals may be described in terms of their ownership, service, and size. Over one-half (51 per cent) of the hospitals are of the nonprofit, nonsectarian type of control (Table 30); 40 (82 per cent) are general in service

(Table 31); and 30 (61 per cent) have fewer than 300 beds
(Table 32). Of the 6,956 hospitals in the United States,
34 per cent are of the nonprofit, nonsectarian type of control; 78 per cent are general in service; 86 per cent have
fewer than 300 beds.

TABLE 30

OWNERSHIP OF HOSPITALS EMPLOYING GRADUATES
OF PILOT PROGRAMS

Type of Ownership	Number	Per Cent
Nonprofit	34	69
Church-operated	6	
Church-related	2	
Other than church	26	
Governmental	14	29
State	4	
County	4	
City or Municipal	5	
City-County	1	
Proprietary	1	2
Individual	1	
Total	49	100

Twenty-one (43 per cent) of the 49 hospitals are located
within twenty-five miles of the pilot programs. These 21 hospitals employed 124 (74 per cent) of the 167 pilot program
graduates working in hospitals.

Six hospitals employed five or more graduates of the
pilot programs. They are located in the vicinity of the

pilot-program schools and, moreover, were the primary sources
for the clinical experiences of the students. The six hospitals employed 102 (61 per cent) of the working graduates.

These statistics suggest that at least in the initial
years, the graduates of the programs are employed primarily in
local hospitals. How time will influence the distribution of
these workers cannot yet be determined.

Included in this report are various references to the
problems of nursing in specialized services. Those hiring the
pilot-program graduates should recognize that their education
has emphasized the general principles of nursing and that their
total experience in both general and special areas of nursing
is limited. Some of the graduates have gone to work in specialized hospitals, but most (82 per cent) are employed in
general hospitals.

TABLE 31

TYPE OF HOSPITALS EMPLOYING PILOT-PROGRAM GRADUATES
AND NUMBER OF GRADUATES WORKING IN THOSE HOSPITALS

Type of Service	Hospitals		Graduates	
	No.	Per Cent	No.	Per Cent
General	40	82	155	92
Mental and Allied	3	6	5	3
Tuberculosis	2	4	3	2
Children	1	2	1	1
Orthopedic	1	2	1	1
Other	2	4	2	1
Total	49	100	167	100

Both type of service and hospital size can be mislead-
ing classifications. In medical centers, which are classified
as general service, the organizational structure is often such
that the individual services resemble small hospitals. Such
services may be located in a separate building, have their own
administrative head, and their own admissions. Under these
circumstances the nurse may be working in a specialized hospital except that it is called an institute. The general atmosphere and network of communications, except for the over-all
relationship to a larger institution, might more resemble a
typical small hospital.

TABLE 32

NUMBER AND PERCENTAGE OF HOSPITALS EMPLOYING
PILOT-PROGRAM GRADUATES BY NUMBER OF BEDS

Number of Beds	Hospitals	
	Number	Per Cent
0 - 99	8	16
100 - 199	9	18
200 - 299	13	27
300 - 399	2	4
400 - 499	0	0
500 - 599	2	4
600 - 699	2	4
700 - 799	1	2
800 - 899	1	2
900 - 999	1	2
1,000 -	9	18
Unknown	1	2
Total	49	99

The Hospitals Visited

Analysis of the characteristics of the twenty-five hospitals visited to collect data indicates that they are similar to the forty-nine employing hospitals. Twenty-one (84 per cent) of the visited hospitals are fully accredited; 19 (76 per cent) are general; eleven (44 per cent) are non-profit, nonsectarian; fifteen (60 per cent) have fewer than 300 beds.

The twenty-five hospitals visited employed 143 (86 per cent) of the pilot-program graduates working in hospitals.

Summary

More than four out of five of the pilot-program graduates were employed as nurses. They were employed in a variety of nursing positions, but primarily they were working in hospitals as general-duty nurses, the type of position toward which their education had been directed. They were employed, however, in all types of hospitals. Most of them were employed by hospitals in which they had received some of their clinical experience.

It is too early to draw long-range conclusions concerning the geographic distribution of the pilot-program graduates as hospital employees. At this time, however, the data suggest that a large proportion of the graduates who receive their train ing in their own communities work as nurses in their own communi

CHAPTER X

THE GRADUATES GO TO WORK: BEGINNINGS

This chapter is concerned with the experiences of the graduates of the pilot programs in going to work as staff nurses in hospitals. The materials in this chapter can be examined with respect to two different criteria, each of which has its own special implications. The first one concerns the relationship between the experiences of the graduates and the basic assumptions of the Cooperative Research Project. The second involves the implications for nursing service in orienting and utilizing new personnel.

Two threads are found woven through the materials presented in this chapter: (1) The orientation provided most of the staff nurses interviewed was unplanned and subject to service demands; (2) The conception of the full responsibility of the job of the staff nurse included acting in a supervisory capacity.

These findings are particularly important because they are in conflict with certain of the assumptions on which the pilot programs were based. The assumptions stated that the graduates would "perform semi-professional functions," "be prepared for beginning practitioner positions (under supervision),"

183

and "be prepared to become fully competent nurses."

The question of the competence of the practitioner at the time of graduation was considered an important issue in Shields' study of the goals of the three-, four-, and five-year programs. The respondents were asked to check one of the following statements:

> At the time of graduation from the basic professional program, the nurse should have acquired the preparation in necessary intellectual, physical and emotional skills which will enable her <u>gradually to become</u> an accomplished practitioner as she gets additional experience.
>
> or
>
> At the time of her graduation from the basic professional program, the nurse <u>should already be</u> an accomplished practitioner; whatever will come within the range of her responsibility has already been experienced repeatedly and practiced to the point of easy performance.[1]

Of the 3,008 nurse respondents, 73 per cent felt that the graduate gradually becomes an accomplished practitioner while only 13 per cent felt that the nurse should already be an accomplished practitioner.

The experiences of the pilot-program graduates as staff nurses in hospitals are described in three sections:

1. The factors that influence taking over the full responsibility of the job of the staff nurse;

2. The interpretations of the meaning of the full responsibility of the job of the staff nurse;

---

[1]Mary R. Shields, "A Project for Curriculum Improvement," <u>Nursing Research</u>, October 1952, p. 28.

3. The orientation that staff nurses receive in starting on a new job.

Factors That Influence Taking the Full Responsibility of the Job

Forty-one (91 per cent) of the 45 pilot-program graduates and 15 (88 per cent) of the control group graduates interviewed felt that it takes more than two or three days to take over the full responsibility of the job of the staff nurse when going to work in a new hospital. The questions which elicited the data in this section can be found in Appendix I, p. 416. The reasons given for feeling that it takes more than two or three days to take over the full responsibility were classified into three categories: (1) becoming acclimated to the new work situation; (2) the demands of the job; (3) personal feelings. The majority of the responses involved becoming acclimated to the new situation.

Several questions were asked concerning the kinds of problems nurses face on a new job. Although these questions were asked about nurses in general, many of the responses were worded in terms of personal experience. Those interviewed were also asked about their own difficulties in first going to work as graduate nurses.

Becoming Acclimated to the Work Situation

The emphasis in the responses to the different questions was similar -- nurses have difficulty at first because they are

not acclimated to the situation, which includes: where things
are; the routine of the ward; the procedures of the particular
hospital; and the patients. Becoming acclimated to the hospital situation is influenced by such things as previous
familiarity with the hospital, the size of the hospital, and
hospital organization.

> You don't know where the equipment is. It takes
> several days to know the physical setup. It's much
> easier to get started on the job if you have an
> orientation before you take the whole job. (PP 56)[2]

> I think she should have a period of orientation.
> Particularly in the operating room it takes such
> a long time to get to know where things are and
> the same is true of OB (Obstetrics). I don't
> think on the second day (a person is ready to take
> over the whole job). In the delivery room we have
> two people on the shift and it is hard on the regu-
> lar girl if she has to orient the new girl plus
> take care of things. (PP 56)

> I think that the whole setup is new and different.
> The hospital has its several divisions divided up
> according to kinds of patients and the nurse has
> to get familiar with it as well as with the equip-
> ment, medicines and other things. The nurse
> doesn't find all that out the first day. She has
> to get to know the patients and the other nurses
> and the rules of the hospital. (PP 55)

> It was confusing -- that's all I can say. The
> doctor would say get something quick -- and I would
> run all over trying to find it. Everyone was so
> busy, and I felt so embarrassed to have to ask them
> where things were. (PP 55)

----

[2]"PP 56" refers to a pilot-program graduate who
graduated in 1956. Pilot-program graduates quoted in this
study will be identified by PP and the year of graduation.
When graduates of other programs are quoted, they will be
identified as graduates of either diploma or degree programs
and by the year of graduation.

> If something wasn't there, you just didn't know
> where to go and get it. You have to wait to ask
> someone and find out what kind of form you had
> to fill out and that took up a lot of time. (PP 56)

> I think she really takes part of the job until
> she gets to know the hospital and the routine of
> the hospital and how they work -- until she really
> gets the swing of the doctors and the books on
> that hospital's procedures. (PP 56)

Graduates of other programs made similar responses concerning
getting used to the work situation:

> You have to be there to get adjusted to the
> situation -- the people on the floor, the type of
> routine. (Degree 56)

> In a new hospital she has to adjust to their way
> of doing things. I think it takes at least a week
> to adjust to the floor. (Diploma 55)

> Just finding things ... procedures. She doesn't
> know anyone. She doesn't know the personalities.
> She doesn't know who to ask to answer the ques-
> tions briefly. Every hospital has its own tech-
> niques. (Diploma 56)

The graduates were asked to rank "not knowing where
things are," "not knowing hospital procedures," "not having
enough supervision," and "too many patients" in their importance as problems a nurse faces on a new job. Both the graduates of pilot programs and the graduates of other programs
ranked them in the same order. "Not knowing where things are"
and "not knowing hospital procedures" were ranked as the most
important problems a nurse faces on a new job.

The pilot programs are school-centered and the students
spend only a limited time in the hospitals, in comparison with

students in diploma schools. But some of the pilot-program
graduates who went to work in hospitals where they had had some
of their field experience felt that the time they had spent in
the hospital influenced their job readiness:

> It really wasn't too new. I was here as a stu-
> dent and I knew the people and I knew the general
> idea. Some of the floors I had worked on more
> than others. I started on a new floor, and it
> was a little strange. The routine was different
> than the other floors. It was just getting into
> the swing of things. (PP 56)

But knowing where things are is only part of the problem. When a nurse knows where things are, other things assume
importance:

> Now I knew where things were because I trained
> in women's surgery here. If I had been in a
> different hospital I think that would have been
> the problem. Here we are so short they put you
> right on and expect you to work. They don't give
> you enough supervision. (PP 55)

Graduates of other programs who went to work in the
hospital they trained in commented on the value of this experience:

> When I first started training, not knowing where
> things were was difficult, but as a graduate nurse,
> it was no problem since I was working in the same
> hospital. (Diploma 56)

> Right off. I had my training here, and in our
> training we had three months on each division so
> they figured that I had enough. (Diploma 55)

Another who went to work in the hospital in which she trained
commented that none of the four types of problems she was asked
to rank were problems for her "because I'm used to this

hospital." She went on to mention that she still had a lot to
learn about nursing:

> The only difference is that it's a little dif-
> ferent working as a graduate. When you're an
> R.N. you really begin to find out what nursing
> is like. Many things came up on the 3 to 11
> shift. (Diploma 56)

Nurses become familiar with the hospitals in which
they go to work in ways other than by going to school. Some
worked as aides before they went to school:

> Well, I worked here as an attendant and I knew
> some of the procedures. I knew a lot of the
> employees. I knew where things were kept.
> I went to a new ward but the ward to which I
> went was quite similar to the one I was working
> in before. (PP 56)

Another had worked in the hospital during her vacations:

> I can't say that any one of them was a problem
> because ... well, because in the first place,
> during vacations I worked in Pediatrics. (PP 56)

A graduate of a collegiate program stated that she had
worked weekends while a student in the hospital in which she
was now employed. It was not the hospital with which her
school was affiliated.

Many nursing schools are attached to small hospitals
in small communities. The graduates of these schools have
not been exposed to large urgan hospitals. A pilot-program
graduate who went to work in a medical center after working
in a small hospital said:

> Well this is the first place -- I'd never worked
> in a hospital larger than about two hundred and
> fifty beds and when I came down here, of course,

> this section is small, but you get the idea
> that you are in a large medical center, the
> bigness of it ... and I was lost, completely
> lost, really. I didn't know a soul. I didn't
> know my way around. I didn't even know how to
> find my way to the hospital. I didn't know
> anything of the way the hospital was run. Nothing.
> I was just lost. But I found my way around after
> a while. (PP 54)

A graduate of a diploma school attached to a small hospital

stated:

> ... This hospital was quite large to me because
> I had come from a 150-bed hospital. I ran into
> obstacles because of the number of wards. Once
> I was told to bring a patient to the first floor
> and I got lost ... not knowing where to go, but
> after a time I got accustomed to it all.
> (Diploma 56)

Many individuals commented on the differences in

routine and location of equipment from floor to floor. This,

of course, varies with hospitals. One of the nurses already

quoted mentioned that from her experience as an attendant

she knew where things were even though the floor she worked on

was different. One pilot-program graduate found that going

to work in a newly built hospital made finding things easier:

> In this hospital, since it's new, it's easy to
> learn where things are. There's a place for
> everything and things are neat, located func-
> tionally. The locations are the same on each
> floor -- that I've been on -- at least almost
> the same. (PP 56)

Another nurse found going to work on a newly organized ward

"confusing" because there was no established procedure:

> T.B. here was routine and you do the same things
> as in other hospitals but Polio was completely
> different. They started the same time that I

> started and it was confusing as to where things
> were to be kept, and as to the procedures which
> they were going to follow since they hadn't made
> them up yet. They made up the procedures as
> they went along. (Did they just start the Polio
> unit when you started here?) Yes, when I started
> in August of '55. (PP 55)

Demands of the Job

The problems nurses face in beginning a job pertain to more than the situation in which they work. The nurses interviewed reported difficulties that arose from: (1) working without supervision; (2) the work load; and (3) taking supervisory responsibility. Broadly, these might be labeled as "the demands of the job." Some of the responses referred to the particular difficulties of being graduates of the pilot programs. Although the frequency or degree of these problems might well be related to the type of preparation, similar incidents were reported by graduates of other programs.

Working without supervision. In some of the quotations already given, reference has been made to the lack of supervision. Two graduates of the pilot programs described having to get used to working without the supervision of their instructors:

> For about a week it just seemed like that just
> trying to find things and knowing just exactly
> what to do were the big problems. As a student
> you had your instructor to sort of follow you
> around to see that things were done. The super-
> visors were nice in helping us to show us where
> things are and how to do things. But the first
> few days you just sort of stay lost. You are

> scared to start with and you're trying to get people to accept you and find out who the people are. (PP 56)

> You are working with a new set of people and you have to get used to them. As a student, you can always fall back on your instructor where you now have the full responsibility. Just the general things, too, like on any job -- where things are, not knowing the patients. (PP 56)

Another mentioned having to work without the security of supervision:

> As a student you don't have as much responsibility as you do as a graduate nurse. When you are in training, you have the security of supervision, but now you are on your own. (PP 56)

Although graduates of other programs did not mention their instructors, they did mention working without supervision. The nurse whose comments follow was in charge of the nursery at night:

> We had the day nurse but we never saw the supervisor except perhaps in the morning. O.B. (Obstetrics) used to be one separate division and I don't know what happened but since I've been here we don't have a supervisor -- just the head nurse and the people down here. If a baby dies, it's really confusing. You have all these forms and the supervisors on the divisions don't want to be bothered. They figure it's a separate unit and we should do it. But if it's a separate unit, we ought to have a supervisor. That was the biggest problem except times we were overloaded with patients and we didn't have enough help. Most of the married nurses don't want to work any more and they have an awful time trying to find part-time help that will come in an emergency. (Diploma 55)

> I worked the 3-11 shift from the beginning when I first started and I would go days without seeing anyone. They left me alone for a long time. I

wish they would have looked in once in a while
in case I needed help. (Diploma 55)

Work load. During their training, the pilot-program
students had only a minimum amount of experience in caring for
a group of patients.

> In our education, we were used to being assigned
> to a small number of patients because we were to
> learn the method of treatment, and we were given
> patients who were interesting. On the first
> floor staff work was a problem during the first
> couple of weeks. After a few weeks, it was pretty
> clear. We knew where everything was and the
> nursing instructor was on the floor at the hos-
> pital and we could get in touch with her if we
> wanted any supervision. (PP 55)

With the shortage of personnel, a nurse may have a large
complement of patients. Some nurses commented on the difficulty of giving care under these circumstances:

> I trained here. I knew pretty well the hospital
> procedures, where things were and things like that.
> So I think it was too many patients. You cannot
> give the patients the care they deserve if you
> have too many patients. You can't spend the
> necessary time with each one. I remember one
> morning I had eight bed baths and a few (of the
> patients) were absolutely adrift, couldn't turn
> or anything. You can do it, but you lose some-
> thing. It was a rugged morning. (Were there many
> mornings like that?) Not too many. (With experi-
> ence does this become easier?) Uh-huh. (PP 56)

This nurse pointed out that there were also ward responsibilities beyond the increased number of patients:

> During our student days, we were accustomed to
> having just two patients assigned to us and as a
> graduate there are anywhere from five to ten
> plus many other things. As a graduate you more
> or less take care of the entire ward in addition
> to your assignment. There are always little things

that you can do for others and as students we
didn't do this. (PP 56)

Taking supervisory responsibility. Not only did
graduates of pilot programs have to become used to working
without supervision, but they had to supervise other nursing
service personnel.

The strongest arguments for gradualness in taking over
the full job came from pilot-program graduates who were required
to act as head nurses or team leaders almost immediately:

> I feel that way because responsibility was thrust
> upon me. When I began, I worked for one day and
> then the head nurse was off for two days. I
> didn't know what to do if a patient died or how to
> summon doctors or who they were or anything.
> (PP 56)

> Had I gone to B (the hospital), where I had some
> of my training, I would feel differently, but
> here all our routine is different, and different
> ways of handling things, and besides, I had been
> trained in individual patient care where we give
> medications as well as care for the patient.
> Here, I had one day of orientation, and the next
> day I went to work and there was no one on the floor
> except the head nurse and I, and I was given the
> responsibility of medications as well as team
> leadership for about 40 patients, and it was be-
> wildering. (Would you describe what it was like?)
> Well, medications that were to be given at 10
> o'clock were given at 12, and I never did get to a
> student conference. I wasn't familiar with all
> the medications, naturally, and I didn't know
> where the rooms were. I didn't know any of the
> patients. This was the second day I was in the
> hospital, and I don't think it is the only hos-
> pital -- but others also because there is a short-
> age of nurses. (PP 55)

The shortage of nurses at this nurse's hospital was particularly
acute during the summer when she started working.

Some of the nurses interpreted the full responsibility of the job as including charging, or taking over for the head nurse. They described why they were not ready for this responsibility:

> I think that it would be better to be a gradual process. I know when I first came here, I didn't feel that I was ready to take over. (Is there some particular reason that you feel this way?) Well, I wasn't because I'm a two-year nurse. I just didn't have any charging responsibility on a floor and until I got acquainted with this hospital and where things were and the routine ... I mean it was much better for me to start gradually. (PP 55)

> I believe it is the latter (gradually taking over the full job) because I didn't feel capable right at first when I went to surgery. I didn't think we were prepared to take right over. We are prepared for bedside nursing and not charge nursing in our program but we are forced into that position because of the lack of nurses.... Course it doesn't take very long. (PP 56)

Graduates of pilot programs are not alone in feeling that they are not prepared for the responsibilities of the head nurse. A graduate of a diploma program stated:

> I think in two or three days, she should be accustomed to the floor and be able to take full responsibility, that is, if she is working as a general-duty nurse -- not as a head nurse or anything like that. If they just graduated from school, however, I think she would need a little more time (than the two or three days).
> (Diploma 54)

One graduate of a pilot program who worked in a situation which involved many patients and supervisory responsibility for other personnel commented on the changes being made in her

program to prepare pilot-program graduates for supervisory
responsibility:

> It is different in my case because I'm from a
> two-year program and I wasn't ready at all. I
> needed a lot more orientation than I got. Well,
> our program is being revised to include more super-
> visory work and more of what the general-duty
> nurse is expected to do. I came in rather green
> when I first came here. It took me two weeks be-
> fore I began to catch on. It takes a month or
> longer to be any good. (PP 56)

The new director of nursing in this hospital stated:

> ... it is obvious to me there has been absolutely
> no orientation of new personnel.

A graduate of a diploma program indicated that the time
involved in taking charge of the floor was influenced by going
to work in a new hospital:

> This is only the second hospital in which I have
> worked and we just graduated in September. This
> hospital is quite a bit different from the one that
> we trained in. I would say that it took three
> weeks or so to get used to actually taking charge
> of the floor -- taking over for the head nurse.
> (Diploma 56)

Being Accepted as a Graduate Nurse

Some of the graduates felt unsure of themselves when
they first started. For two of them this uncertainty was related to their concern about being accepted as graduates of
two-year programs:

> There are always interpersonal relationships --
> how well you are accepted. This was particularly
> a problem with me because I'm from a two-year
> school. For me it was a matter of getting self-
> confidence. The problem in any new job is

> learning to fit into the schedule. I felt a
> little insecure in the beginning but I think
> all new graduates do. (PP 56)

What is most interesting about this person's being worried about

being accepted "because I'm from a two-year school" is that she

went to work in the hospital in which she had had most of her

clinical experience. That the attitudes of some of the workers

and even administrators in the hospitals become known to pilot-

program nurses is illustrated in the next quotation from a nurse

who was also concerned about working with polio patients:

> I think my problem may have been a little dif-
> ferent from the others, you see you are worried
> about the contagion. The first day I got a polio
> (patient) I was worried to death but after that
> it was o.k. Then there was the fear that we
> wouldn't be accepted because we were from a two-
> year program. The nurses I worked with on Polio,
> Mrs. G. and Mrs. P., were very nice and never
> questioned my authority or anything else. They
> were very good. On T.B., it was a little dif-
> ferent. Most of the nurses would ask if I had
> done this or that when they found out I was part
> of the group (two-year program). Mrs. C. (the new
> director of nursing services) doubted the two-year
> program very much. (PP 55)

Any investigator who has tried to squeeze responses

into categories has faced situations in which the quality of

the incident overshadowed the classification scheme. The fol-

lowing response from a nurse who felt that lack of supervision

was her biggest problem when she first went to work and who

now acts in a supervisory role herself is a revealing example

of the pressures that can be put on a new nurse:

> I was a graduate of a two-year program and of
> course when we first came here, there was little

knowledge of this new program. We were treated
as full graduate nurses with full responsibility
and a tremendous amount of patient care. We also
weren't clear on procedures as we weren't taught
what was being done here at the hospital at the
time. If we would have received supervision and
help from the supervisor, there wouldn't have been
as much confusion and tension cropped up about
the two-year graduates. One of the big questions
when we came here was what our status was. There
was also a misunderstanding in pay. The two-year
graduates thought they were receiving the same
amount of pay as the other graduates and we found
out later through the grapevine that we were not.
There was very little knowledge of the two-year
program and what to expect of a girl who is a
graduate of the two-year program. We should be
treated a little differently than the graduate of
the three-year program. We didn't have as much
clinical experience. (PP 54)

This nurse was in one of the first graduating classes.
Perhaps this fact accounts for the complete confusion in the
policy of the employing agency. The nurse's experience illus-
trates the kinds of problems involved in integrating pilot-
program graduates into nursing service.

Taking the Full Responsibility of the Job of the Staff Nurse

The graduates were asked how long it took them to
assume the responsibility for their jobs as staff nurses.
Specifically, the question was:

By the full responsibility of your job, I mean
having the same number of patients as the other
staff nurses and the same responsibility for the
patients as the other staff nurses. How long was
it before you took the full responsibility for
your job as a staff nurse?

The wording of this question is particularly appropriate for the bedside nurse. This description was selected in consideration of the emphasis on bedside nursing in the preparation of the pilot-program graduates. The question assumed that the staff nurse job can be defined in these terms of bedside nursing. If the nurse has a functional assignment, such as giving medications, the question is less appropriate.

The responses to the question asked were further complicated by the interpretations given to "the full responsibility of the job of the staff nurse." In the initial part of the question what is meant by "the full responsibility" is defined. But, as so often happens with questions, the respondents used their own interpretations. Regardless of the different interpretations, however, 81 per cent of the graduates of pilot programs interviewed responded that assumption of such responsibility occurred within the first three weeks (Table 33); 90 per cent of the graduates of other programs interviewed concurred that the same thing happened to them within three weeks.

The interpretations of "the full responsibility of the job" were not explored uniformly. Originally the question, "When or how did you know that you had reached this 'full responsibility'?" was not asked. When the investigator became aware, from the responses he was obtaining, of the implications of the respondents' frame of reference in answering this question, the extra question was included.

TABLE 33

LENGTH OF TIME TO TAKE OVER FULL RESPONSIBILITY
OF THE JOB OF STAFF NURSE, AS STATED BY GRADUATES
OF PILOT AND OTHER PROGRAMS

Time	Pilot Programs N	Pilot Programs %	Other Programs N	Other Programs %
Less than one week	22	49	12	67
Between one and two weeks	7	16	3	17
Between two and three weeks	7	16	1	6
One to two months	4	9	2	11
Two to three months	2	4		
One year	1	2		
Unspecified	2	4		
Total	45	100	18	101

The types of interpretation given to "the full responsibility of the job" included: assuming the role of the bedside nurse, assuming the role of the functional nurse, assuming the role of the nurse-manager, feeling fully responsible,
and working without supervision.[3]

One distinction between the pilot program graduates
and graduates of other programs involved five graduates of
other programs who went to work in the hospitals in which they
trained. When these five responded that they took the responsibility from the beginning, they indicated that they had been

----

[3]The terms "bedside nurse," "functional nurse," and
"nurse-manager" are defined in Chapter XI. Broadly, these
terms parallel the three types of assignment -- case, functional
and team leader.

doing the same things on the same floors with the same people when they had been student nurses.

Assuming the Role of the Bedside Nurse

Several of the nurses referred to being responsible for the patient care of a group of patients:

> Right as soon as I graduated. They didn't give me any really difficult people but I was responsible for the ones I had. I didn't do meds (medications) for about a week. (PP 55)

> From the beginning, although we have the team system and could always ask the team captain. (PP 55)

> They gave us a couple of weeks of orientation -- we were taken on more or less as extra help. After these two weeks were up we went on regular shifts and took our patients just the same as everyone else. (PP 55)

Another pilot-program graduate referred to a two-week orientation period. A question on what happened after the orientation brought an interesting response:

> They gave us two weeks of orientation. (And right after that you had the full patient load?) I got that from the start, the same as everyone else. I started out with that the first day I came. (How could you get your orientation and at the same time have a full patient load?) I didn't get a good orientation. (PP 56)

A graduate of a diploma program felt that having the responsibility for her patients was a new experience:

> Three days. (How did you know that you had reached this "full responsibility"?) There were only two besides the head nurse on the floor and I did have the responsibility for my patients and I knew I had it. It was a new experience. (Diploma 56)

Another diploma graduate felt that taking the full responsibility for a group of patients depended on the condition of
the patients:

> It depends on the condition of the patients so
> you can't really define it. You may be only
> able to do 8 criticals in a day, and someone
> else will be able to do 8 convalescents in half
> that time. It's more important what you do for
> the patients. (How long did it take you to do
> what the other staff nurses were doing for the
> patients?) I would say it would be a week for me.
> (Diploma 55)

Assuming the Role of the Functional Nurse

Other nurses referred to the first time they were required to give medications. One of the nurses who had had the
practicum referred to the gradual increase in responsibility
in consideration of individual readiness:

> We did mostly patient care during the practicum
> period and worked up to giving medications and
> other things. It depended when the individual
> was ready. (How long was it before you gave
> medications?) About a month. (PP 55).

> One thing I want to explain is that practical
> nurses do most of the bedside care. We have a
> nurse to pass medications, a nurse in the treat-
> ment room. (How long before you passed medica-
> tions or worked in the treatment room?) The
> second day I gave the medications. The first
> day I was there they let me read the procedure
> manuals and showed me where the medicine cabinet
> was and what medicines were to be given and how
> many patients they had and so on. They were very
> nice. There was adequate orientation. Everything
> was fine, and then on the second day one of the
> girls didn't show up and I had to pass the medi-
> cine to the whole ward, and that was difficult
> because there were a lot of patients with menin-
> gitis and I wasn't used to measuring out medica-
> tions. But that was a personal problem. (What

was a personal problem?) Maybe every nurse
that starts in that way had difficulty with it,
but it takes time to know exactly where things
are and how to measure them. (How many patients
did you have this for?) Oh, medications for the
whole floor. About fifty patients. (PP 56)

Right away. The first two weeks was an orientation period where we were assigned to many different things so that during those two weeks we
got accustomed to everything. We had medications
one day and treatments another day, and so on.
(How did you know that you had reached this
"full responsibility"?) When I knew my two weeks
were up and my orientation period was over. (PP 56)

The third day I was here. For two days I had someone to acquaint me with the patients. The third
day I gave medications and I knew the patients
quite readily. (PP 56)

None of the eighteen graduates of other programs used

giving medications or treatments as the criterion for taking

the full responsibility of the job.

Several graduates made reference to being members of

the nursing team in a way that indicated that they were assum-

ing the role of the bedside or functional nurse:

We work on a team system here where we don't
assume the full responsibility for the individual
patient. It depends upon what part of the team
you are on -- if you are treatment nurse or medications nurse or patient care. Therefore, it takes
the whole team to assume the full responsibility.
I feel that I was capable of carrying my end of the
load from the very beginning, having trained here.
The first day I didn't really carry the full load
because there were procedures I wasn't familiar
with. However, the second day I got on very well
on my own. (PP 56)

Another pilot-program graduate distinguished between

taking the responsibility for medications and treatments and for being in charge of the floor:

>Before I came, they just had one head nurse on
>each floor and I took the responsibility of being
>medication nurse and treatment nurse, and after
>about two weeks I was taking full responsibility
>of that. I imagine it was about a month before
>they let me charge the floor. (PP 55)

Assuming the Role of the Nurse-Manager

The most common referent, especially among the graduates of other programs, was to assuming the role of the nurse-manager. In the responses to other questions, references have been made to graduates being placed in charge of a floor or acting as team leader.

Taking charge of the floor is sometimes seen by the graduates as related to the shortage of nurses:

>I began working on the third floor and just
>recently I moved down to the medical floor. I
>actually was put in charge of the third floor
>on my second week here due to a shortage of
>nurses here, but I had liked OB (Obstetrics) in
>my training so I knew more about it than anywhere
>else. (So in the second week you were in charge
>of the floor. Would you describe what it was
>like?) I had two aides and I was in charge. I
>was always on call if they needed help. As soon
>as they could, they got another nurse to be re-
>lief. (PP 56)

>I think I worked four days and went on nights
>without supervision. I had never been on nights
>and I charged on the first night. I was very
>frustrated. I had people to talk to in the day-
>time. I was worried about the routine but the
>night supervisor said, "Don't worry about it."
>But you have to worry about it. There are cer-
>tain things that just have to be done and I was
>lucky to have a good aide, and she oriented me.
>The second night it was all right. (Was there a
>particular reason that you were put in charge so

suddenly?) What happened was the lady quit who
was working nights. They just said I was going
to do it and I had to. (Did you go back on days
soon?) No, I rotated the first few weeks. I was
taught to be a team leader and then I went on
nights and was on 3 to 11 for a while. (PP 56)

Six weeks, not even that, five weeks actually. I
worked four weeks on days, one week on nights, and
then I was put in charge. (Was there a particular
reason that you were put in charge?) The head
nurse was off. (Did you do this regularly?) No.
We had a reinforcement of staff and then I didn't
have to take it.... (PP 55)

In one hospital, taking charge of the desk was included

in the orientation of new personnel:

Actually the first three weeks on the Medical floor
could be considered orientation. First I had fewer
patients, less complicated ones, no dressings, and
then one week in the treatment room where all
the treatments are done for the entire day. Working these is important. About a week on medications and a week at the desk being in charge.
(Does this mean that you were acting as head
nurse?) Yes. I was acting as head nurse. I
observed the first day and then the rest of the
week I did it. (PP 56)

In another situation the orientation was less formal:

I worked about two weeks and then I took over the
11-7 shift, but the nurses told me ways that
helped them to organize and do their work. (PP 56)

The graduates of other programs were more matter of

fact about assuming the responsibility of the head nurse or

team leader. One who was acting as an assistant head nurse

stated:

About a month later (after she started) I assumed
the responsibility I have now. (Diploma 56)

A diploma graduate who had had some graduate experience before coming to work in this hospital stated:

> I would say, functioning as a team leader,
> approximately one week if I recall correctly.
> I feel that this was an adequate time. (It was
> adequate?) Yes, I think it was. I feel that
> I had a greater amount of supervision than some
> other people who had recently been employed on
> a particular unit where I was working due to
> the personnel that was on the unit at that time.
> (Was this orientation you received systematically
> organized? ... involving classes?) No, it
> wasn't under any organized system. (Would you
> explain what you meant by "more than others?")
> Probably because I was put on a particular unit
> where people were conscientious, they gave me
> perhaps more of their time and attention than
> say someone who was put on another unit at the
> corresponding time. (Diploma 55)

Another nurse who used taking over when the head nurse was absent stated:

> Five days before I could take care of the floor
> when the head nurse was absent. (Diploma 56)

However, some graduates of diploma programs find assuming the responsibility of the head nurse difficult:

> Three days. Of course that wasn't continuously.
> Three days after I came, the head nurse went on
> vacation. You just don't feel adequate.
> (Diploma 55)

Several of the nurses responded that they had the full responsibility when they "felt comfortable" or "felt secure." This type of criterion is based on an internal rather than an external definition of job responsibility. For instance, a nurse might have the responsibility for giving medications although she did not feel thoroughly competent in handling that responsibility. When she felt competent, then she would respond

that she had the full responsibility. Individual differences

were observed in the length of time it took to feel "secure."

> Until I got used to the hospital routine. Maybe
> two days. (How did you know that you had reached
> this "full responsibility"?) You can feel it
> within yourself. You feel confident, as though
> you can handle anything that comes up. You have
> responsibility. (PP 56)

> About a week. (How did you know?) I just felt it
> myself. I felt secure. At first you're scared
> really. You don't know where to start. Later I
> knew what I was doing and how I was going to do
> it. (PP 56)

The feeling that you "can do it" did not come as quickly

for some as others:

> I think about two or three months before I actually
> felt that I could do it. (Actually when were you
> given the full responsibility, though?) Oh, right
> along, but I didn't feel right in it. I felt very
> uncomfortable. (PP 56)

Another used organizing her work as well as feeling

confident:

> By the end of two or three weeks we were taking
> full responsibility. (How did you know that you
> were taking full responsibility?) I felt like I
> was giving good nursing care. I was able to or-
> ganize my work well enough to give good care.
> (PP 55)

> About a month. (How did you know?) You feel
> capable in doing something. You are meeting the
> needs of the patient. (PP 56)

Graduates of the diploma programs also made reference to

"feeling responsible":

One or two weeks. (How did you know that you had
reached this "full responsibility"?) I more or
less felt it. It's hard to describe. (Degree 56)

About two weeks. About two weeks until I was sure
of myself. (Diploma 56)

The Orientation of the Staff Nurse

This section is devoted to an analysis of the orientation given pilot-program graduates. Such an analysis is particularly important since one study objective was to determine
whether the graduates of the pilot programs require an orientation different from that of graduates of other programs.

The information in this section utilizes interviews
with the graduates of the pilot and other programs, with head
nurses, and with directors of nursing services.

The importance of the initial orientation for staff
nurses going to work in new hospital situations has already
been established in this chapter. In general, staff nurses
starting on a new job feel that a gradual introduction, taking
more than two or three days, is required. They feel that they
need to become acclimated to the hospital situation. In explain
ing the need to become acclimated, many of the graduates pointed
out that the orientation they had received did not provide
time to become acclimated to the job.

Informal and Formal Orientation Programs

Orientation approaches found in the twenty-five hospitals visited can be classified broadly into two types --
informal (unstructured) and formal (structured). In some hospitals, the graduates of the pilot programs received special
orientation -- that is, orientation different from that ordi-
narily given to new staff nurses. The special orientations
also fit into the informal and formal types.

What is most characteristic of an informal orientation
is that it has not been planned. No written outline exists of
what the staff nurse ought to know about working there.
There is no schedule of meetings to accomplish orientation
objectives. The members of nursing service have not met to
decide what constitutes an adequate orientation.

Informal orientation is usually an individual orientation. More typically it is found in small hospitals. Often
it consists of an interview with the director of nursing services. It might include an hour tour of the hospital to point
out the various services. After the tour, the nurse is taken
to the floor on which she will work and introduced to the head
nurse. On the second or third day she will be working as a
regular staff nurse. What occurs from the time she reaches the
floor is completely in the hands of the head nurse. Such an
approach is best described as incidental teaching -- that is,
when and if the head nurse has the opportunity to instruct the
new nurse, she does.

The quality of the informal orientation is dependent upon the floor personnel with whom the nurse works. In a small hospital, such an orientation seems sensible. The number of personnel and the patients to become acquainted with are reasonably limited. The lines of communication are informal. All of the personnel, including the director of nursing services, are readily observable and available.

What is most characteristic of the formal orientation is that it has been planned. There is an outline of what the staff nurse is expected to be told as a new employee. It includes a schedule of meetings. In one hospital, part of the orientation included seeing films which described the special types of surgical patients common to that particular hospital.

Formal orientation is usually a group orientation. Usually it is found in large hospitals. Although it includes a tour of the hospital, it also includes an explanation of the organization of the hospital. While the director of nursing services might participate by discussing her place in the hospital and her views about nursing service, the entire program would probably be run by the educational director, who is in charge of the entire in-service educational program.

Although the nurse may be working on the floor part of the time during the first week on the job, she usually works in the capacity of a learner -- getting used to the hospital routine. Such work is considered a part of her orientation and she works as an extra person. Although she may give some service during this period of time, her work is secondary to becoming acclimated.

After the orientation has been completed and the nurse goes to her floor, her orientation to the floor is in the hands of her head nurse, who may or may not have some formal scheme for orienting the worker to the floor. What is most important about a formal orientation is that it is not supposed to be dominated by service needs.

The Orientation of the Graduates of Pilot Programs

Many of the graduates of the pilot programs received informal orientation, the same as that provided all new staff members.

One pilot-program graduate who went to work in a seventy-bed hospital described her orientation as follows:

> (When you started working in the hospital, were you given any special introduction to the job?)
> Yes.
> (What did this consist of?)
> Mrs. M. (the director of nursing services) showed me the different departments of the hospital.
> Showed me around and introduced me to the personnel in the departments.
> (Were you oriented to the rules and regulations of the hospital?)
> Yes. Mrs. M. did this in my interview.
> (What about the specific aspects of working on your ward?)
> Over a period of two weeks or a month I got acquainted with the different things as I worked.
> (PP 55)

The orientation this nurse received was the same as that of any new graduate in the hospital.

A diploma-program graduate who went to work in a seven hundred-bed hospital found her informal orientation inadequate:

> (When you started working in the hospital, were you given any special introduction to the job?)
> Yes.
> (What did this consist of?)
> I was told where the wards were and things like that. It was just a general introduction given by the head nurse. It was just a brief introduction as far as I was concerned.
> (Were you oriented to the rules and regulations of the hospital?)
> No. I would have appreciated a two-hour orientation at least for the rules and regulations and what could be expected.
> (Just what do you mean by "what could be expected"?)
> Well the things that they expected of the nurse working here and the kinds of things that happen in a large hospital like this.
> (Diploma 56)

In contrast with the orientations above, a pilot-program graduate who went to work in a two hundred-bed hospital described his orientation (the orientation given all new employees):

> (What did this orientation consist of?)
> Working half days at first. They had lectures, films, a tour of the building.
> (What topics did the lectures cover?)
> Hospital pay, policy, sick leave, vacation. We were given material on the responsibility of the staff nurse, and were shown books and pamphlets on cancer.
> (How long did your orientation last?)
> More than a week. For the first couple of weeks I had fewer patients, less complicated ones, no dressings. (PP 56)

On the floor the orientation included spending a day at the desk working with the head nurse, a day acting as head nurse under the observation of the head nurse, and three days of assuming the role of the head nurse without direct supervision. In the last phase the head nurse was on the floor.

In two of the hospitals the investigator was presented with mimeographed copies of the plan for orienting new personnel. One of the plans provided for a two-hour conference every week for five weeks for all newly employed graduate nurses. Also, the nurse received orientation on the floor, and monthly in-service meetings were scheduled.

The other mimeographed orientation sheet included an outline for the orientation on the unit, to be given by the head nurse. The outline included a description of the new employee's job and the relationship of her service to the other departments of the hospital. In describing the orientation program, the director of nursing services stated:

> We have a very complete program, we think, which was developed by our office and the nursing staff. The nurse is oriented on the unit. In the nursing office we give two days to our part of it, and the rest of it is given on the unit.

The head nurses who were asked to rate the graduates of the pilot programs were asked about the orientation that all new nurses received.

Of the 49 head nurses, 39 (80 per cent) felt that they made special arrangements to start new courses on the job. Of the 39, only a few mentioned using anything like a check list as a guide in orientation. One head nurse made use of a folder that contained materials she felt were important for a nurse working on her floor.

The orientation by the head nurse usually lasted one
or two days and was influenced by service demands. For example,
one head nurse stated:

> I usually have an outline. I have an orientation
> program the first day. I orient her to the floor
> set-up and the routine. I have her read some of
> the procedures in the book. As different things
> occur, I try to assign her and go with her or have
> a graduate go with her.
> (Does it include any special supervision?)
> Yes, but most of the time it isn't possible.

Other head nurses referred to the discrepancy between
the orientation the nurses were supposed to receive and what
they actually did receive.

> We try to, but it isn't always possible. We try
> to orient them to our situation -- the way we do
> our orders, our charts and medications, and our
> procedures. If we can for the first week, we
> give her special orientation. I like to get her
> so she knows the hospital, knows where the dif-
> ferent departments are located as well as where
> the medications are located. She should start
> giving medications right after she is located.
> She should start giving medications right after
> she is oriented. We like to have it a week but
> it isn't always that long.

One head nurse described the orientation she gave the
new nurses as personal:

> It is personal. I go around with her and I answer
> anything she wants to ask and I tell her what I
> think is important. I write down things that are
> important to the floor, like the studies and the
> urines and such things. I always make it clear
> that if something isn't clear they should come to
> me and ask. We don't have a manual or anything.
> If the patient is on studies, the doctor makes
> an order up of what he wants and then each day I
> write it in the order book and we keep pretty
> close track of these things.
> (Then you do provide special supervision for the

new nurse?)
Yes. Just what I can give myself. However, if we
have several critical patients and a new nurse on
the floor there are situations which wouldn't come
up in other hospitals. We have an artificial
kidney or we may have an accident case such as bar-
biturate poisoning and we try to help but we are
very busy. Then there are private patients and the
little extra things you have to do that they expect.
(When is the new staff nurse usually given complete
responsibility for her job as a staff nurse?)
Immediately. I was when I first started out and
I was turned loose on the ward and I was expected
to take complete responsibility.

Evidently what the nurse meant by complete responsibility on the

research ward was acting as head nurse when she had her days

off. A pilot-program graduate working with her was placed in

charge of the ward on her second day in the hospital.

Another head nurse, who felt that individual differences

should be taken into account, stated that being placed in

charge was dependent on the needs of the floor:

There's the orientation program that the hospital
carries out for all staff nurses in regard to procedures throughout the hospital. I have a little
outline just for surgical procedures which I try
to use wherever it seems to fit in.
(Does this include any special supervision?)
It's not a formal type of supervision. Whenever
there is something new you approach her and offer
your help.
(When is the new nurse usually given complete responsibility for her job as a staff nurse?)
It varies considerably with what we consider her
ability and the needs of the floor. If you have
a number of staff nurses on the floor who have
been there a long time, naturally they are the
ones who are having the responsibility. Sometimes the turnover is such that a new nurse comes
on the floor and assumes responsibility within a
few weeks. We give them their patient load right
off, but I consider responsibility whether or not
I trust their judgment. There are some people who
have been here for years who I wouldn't trust to

be in charge, and there are others who have been
here six weeks, and I would feel confident that
they would do all right. It's usually dependent
on the needs of the floor as to when a nurse is
first put in charge and not when we feel the person is ready.

In one hospital a nursing supervisor described developing a new orientation program:

In orientation different people progress at different speeds, so for one week it is concentrated.
Now, that happens to be my pet right now and I am
working on it and trying to derive a good one.

She continued at length to describe the various people who
would be involved in such an orientation, the responsibility
of the head nurse in orientation, and the length of time it
took for a nurse to become used to a new hospital. The supervisor was asked, "How much of this have you been doing?" She
responded:

We are doing it right now, and we are having the
girls evaluate it so that they can tell us where
to find the loose ends.
(How long have you been giving this orientation?)
Well, about one month. What we had done prior to
this had not been as detailed, so that this is
actually a concrete orientation. We have everything planned for, and everyone is familiar with
what we are doing. The girl is told what she is
doing, we tell her that we want her to evaluate
the program to tell us what she thinks of it.

Certainly this supervisor was working to develop a
thorough orientation program. However, before the development
of "a concrete orientation" one graduate of a pilot program
was expected to be team leader and to give medications on her
second day of work in the hospital.

One director of nursing services, who had only recently
taken over her job, stated:

> As I told you, I am only here four months and it
> is obvious to me there has been absolutely no
> orientation of new personnel. They are just
> thrown into the job, on any shift, sink or swim,
> which is a very bad situation, and I think it
> would be very difficult for any nurse of any
> type of experience or of any type of preparation
> or any background to come in. Strangely enough,
> the nurses stay. Our turnover here I don't
> believe is any higher or as high as some of the
> hospitals that have the in-service and orientation
> programs. So I would say that any nurse, regard-
> less of what course she took, is certainly not
> oriented properly, and I think we should apologize
> to these people for not giving them a proper orien-
> tation. And, in another year, I am sure that I
> can change that picture 100 per cent.

A director of nursing services who felt that orientation was important found that she had to suspend the established orientation program when the educational director re-
signed:

> (What type of orientation program do you have
> for a new graduate?)
> It depends on the situation when they are hired.
> We did have a pretty good in-service program where
> they attended classes two or three times a week
> for several weeks, and we reviewed our procedures,
> our policies, the newest drugs, etc. This worked
> out pretty well for a while. Then the person who
> was doing the instruction resigned and went into
> the Air Force and about that time vacation started,
> and we had difficulty in continuing with these in-
> service programs. Right now, I am afraid, most of
> the time you get it on the floor in the work
> situation and that involves considerable pressure.

Special Orientation Programs for the
Graduates of the Pilot Programs

In most (76 per cent) of the hospitals visited, no
arrangements, other than those made for graduates of other programs, were made for the graduates of the pilot programs.
However, in some (24 per cent) of the hospitals, special
arrangements were made. The most complete special program of
orientation and in-service training was found in the practicum
period of the Pasadena program. After completing two years in
the program, the Pasadena students served on a special basis
as employees of Huntington Memorial Hospital for a year. They
worked thirty-seven hours a week on the floor, but once a week
they had a three-hour class taught by an instructor from the
pilot program. The person who taught the class had an office
at the hospital and could be called to the floor to help the
practicum nurses. The class included instruction in team
nursing. On the floor, the nurses received experience as team
leaders. During the practicum year the nurses were still considered students although they were paid employees and gave
the same care as graduates of other programs. The practicum
period included the experience of rotating services every two
or three months.

Now that the state law requiring registered-nurse programs to be three years long has been revoked, the practicum
period is no longer part of the Pasadena program. It is important to remember that in the collection of the data the

practicum students were considered and rated as graduates.

Over the past two years, one hospital that employed
most of the graduates of the local pilot program has been developing a special orientation program for the new graduates
of the pilot program. The first year the orientation consisted
only of periodic rotation every six weeks from service to
service. No one -- not the pilot-program graduates who were
rotating, not the head nurses who worked with the graduates
for the six weeks, and not the nurse who was directing the orientation -- was clear as to its purpose. Some of the pilot-
program graduates were reluctant to move after becoming
acclimated to the work situation on a floor.

The next year the new graduates received a week of
orientation to the hospital in general before being put on
the floor. Included in the orientation was a description of
the rotation plan, which involved rotating both shifts and services. The first time the pilot-program graduate went to work
on the 3-11 or 11-7 shifts, she went on as an extra person,
which incidentally is the policy for all new employees going
to work on these shifts.

The week's general orientation was provided only once,
for the major portion of the new graduates, who start working
in the hospital shortly after graduation. Those pilot-program
graduates who did not start working at the time the week's
orientation was given received the same orientation as graduates of other programs.

Two other hospitals encouraged rotation of services for the graduates of the pilot programs. In one hospital it worked out poorly. The director of nursing services described what happened as follows:

> When we knew that we were going to have them, we got together with the supervisors to talk about what we could offer them knowing that they have had a minimum of clinical experience. We agreed that for their benefit, and so that they would be the most use to us later, we would ask them to rotate through the four major services. So when the girls came in for their interviews, this program was presented to them. We were very pleased to find that they were delighted to have a chance to do this. We would have two of them begin in admitting, so that they would always have in mind that picture of what a patient goes through in admission. We couldn't have done anything worse, it turns out, because they weren't familiar with medications. They had very little practice in giving medicines. Our admitting and emergency go together. The doctor would ask for a medication, and of course they didn't see it written, eventually it would be written while they were carrying it out. So the poor girls made an awful lot of mistakes. Fortunately the patients didn't get the results of their mistakes, but they would go to the nurse that had the key to the medications cabinet and say, I need such and such, and it sounded rather odd so she would ask them why.
> (This experience in admitting turned out badly?)
> Well, we made a bad choice. We should have realized that these girls weren't ready for this kind of thing. As soon as we realized it we had a meeting and talked with the head nurse down there and found that it worried her terribly. We didn't want anything bad to come out of that so we immediately made reassignments.

When such an obvious mistake in placement of a pilot-program graduate was made, in spite of good intent, it seems appropriate to ask nursing service administrators, "is it wise to assign new graduates of any program immediately to a combined service like admitting and emergency?

One nursing service administrator who was particularly interested in the pilot program provided two pilot-program graduates with a special orientation that involved close supervision:

> We brought these people in and sent them to one of the surgical wards. Mrs. G, who is the supervisor, went on the floor and supervised these nurses just like we would do if they had been student nurses in our school of nursing. She spent about two weeks with them. We gave her that assignment because her service wasn't too busy at that time. She took the procedure books and went over them with them. These nurses made these adjustments as easily and quickly as the average diploma-program graduate from any other hospital in this state that we give. The thing that we found was that these students had had their clinical experience in an institution that was smaller. The first thing they were confronted with here was much equipment they hadn't seen, and many cases they hadn't seen -- such as neuro-surgery and heart cases. Well, this was of course quite interesting to these nurses, but it didn't seem to frighten them and they took to it just like anyone else did and certainly they were eager to learn.

The director of nursing services went on to point out that the two pilot-program graduates received supervision other new employees did not receive:

> Well, I'm sorry to say that we have never been in the position with help to make the arrangements that we should have made. Now in other words, these people come into our service and due to pressure we are not in a position to give them that orientation. These two graduates have never been left alone on afternoon duty and we always put the other graduates on in at least two or three weeks. Due to the fact that we were so anxious to make this program work, we did not require these people to take charge in the afternoon or evening. (When will you require these nurses to go on afternoons or evenings?)

> We are waiting six months. By that time we have
> every reason to believe that they will be prepared.
> Now if we could have that kind of orientation for
> all our nurses then the problem of nursing orienta-
> tion would be solved.

The supervisor who worked with the two graduates for
two weeks found that they were slow at first but picked up speed
quickly. Also, she felt that they were not very well acquainted
with some procedures.

With the exception of the Pasadena practicum period,
the special orientation that graduates of the pilot programs
received differed from the orientation of other graduates in
only two ways: being rotated from service to service and being
kept on days for six months.

Summary

Most of the graduates of pilot and other programs interviewed felt that new nurses should work gradually into the full
responsibility of their jobs as staff nurses. The primary
reason for taking the full responsibility of the job gradually
involved the time that it takes to become acclimated to the new
work situation. Becoming acclimated includes knowing where
things are, getting used to the hospital's procedures and the
routine of the ward, and getting to know the patients and the
other personnel. Other important aspects of taking the full job
responsibility involved the demands of the job and being accepted
as a graduate nurse. The graduates of the pilot program had to

become used to working without supervision, carrying a large
work load, and taking supervisory responsibility. Graduates of
other programs had similar problems, but there seemed to be a
difference in the intensity of the problems. Some pilot-program
graduates indicated that their initial problems involved concern about being accepted as nurses. In some cases they were
conscious of antagonistic attitudes toward the pilot programs
on the part of nursing service administrators. In others it
was a matter of confusion on the part of nursing service as
to the status of the graduates of these new programs.

Most of the graduates of the pilot programs felt that
they were taking the full responsibility for their jobs as
staff nurses within three weeks. As indications of taking the
full responsibility they used: being assigned to a group of
patients, giving medicines, or taking supervisory responsibility.
Some responded that they had the full responsibility when they
felt sure of themselves.

The orientation that new staff nurses received was often
unplanned. Planned or unplanned, the quality of the orientation
was influenced by shortage of personnel and service demands.
There is some evidence that hospitals have become more conscious
of the importance of formal orientation programs. In a few
hospitals, special arrangements were made to orient the graduates of the pilot programs.

CHAPTER XI

THE GRADUATES GO TO WORK: ROLES

Of primary concern in analyzing what the graduates of the pilot programs were doing is whether the graduates were assuming the role of the staff nurse working under supervision. If team nursing was practiced, the question is more appropriately worded, "Were the pilot-program graduates assuming the role of members of the team?" When functional assignment was used, the question might be worded, "Were the graduates giving medications or treatments or some combination of both under the supervision of the head nurse?" Looking at the problem from another point of view, the question might be worded, "Were the graduates of the pilot programs required to manage the ward and the giving of patient care?"

The answers to these questions are complex. Essentially the complexity of the answer rests in the fact that nurses do not seem to hold a nursing role but instead assume nursing roles. In terms of the primary role being assumed by the graduates of the pilot programs, the graduates are functioning as staff nurses under the supervision of the head nurse or team leader. This fact is important to establish -- this role existed in many of the hospitals visited. However, when the head nurse or team leader had her days off, the staff nurse generally relieved her.

The previous sections illustrated that the experience of relieving the head nurse might come shortly after the staff
nurse started to work in the hospital. In a few of the hospitals visited, there were assistant head nurses whose duties
included relieving the head nurse. In some hospitals the
director of nursing services stated that it was the responsibility of nursing service to prepare the staff nurse for supervisory responsibilities if these responsibilities were to be
assumed by staff nurses (Chapter XIV). The general practice
did not seem to be to provide such in-service training.

The Primary Roles Being Assumed by
Graduates of the Pilot Programs

The primary roles assumed by the majority of the pilot-
program graduates interviewed were roles which their programs
prepared them to assume (Table 34). However, one-third of the
pilot program graduates interviewed had primary roles which
included supervisory functions, for which they had not been
prepared in their educational programs.

The primary role was decided upon from the nurse's
description of her job. The primary role was the one usually
assumed. From the description, the nurse was classified into
one of three categories: bedside nurse, functional nurse, or
nurse-manager. The graduates of the pilot and other programs
were placed in the categories from their responses to questions
on their method of patient care and their working relationships

with auxiliary personnel.

TABLE 34

PRIMARY NURSING ROLE OF GRADUATES OF PILOT AND
OTHER PROGRAMS AT TIME OF INTERVIEW

Nursing Role	Pilot Programs N	Pilot Programs %	Other Programs N	Other Programs %
Bedside nurse	22	49	8	44
Functional nurse	7	16	2	11
Nurse-manager	15	33	7	39
Unclassified	1	2	1	6
Total	45	100	18	100

Broadly, the three designated roles parallel the most
common types of assignment: case, functional, and team leader.
Moreover, the descriptions of the roles that follow take into
consideration the findings of the American Nurses' Association's
functions studies and McManus' analysis of the three levels of
functions along the continuum of nursing functions (Chapter VII).
For each role, examples are given from the interviews with
graduates of pilot and other programs. The two unclassified
nurses were working in the operating room. Their roles did not
seem to fit into the three major categories.

The treatment of these data does not include direct
references to the variation in the services on which the graduates were working. Graduates of the pilot programs who were
interviewed were working on all services -- general, maternity,

psychiatric, obstetric, pediatric, and surgical. Nor does this
analysis consider the problem of nurses rotating shifts. Some
graduates of the pilot programs were working steady 3-11 or
11-7. In some cases, hospital policy required that all personnel rotate shifts. The services that they have been working
on have been somewhat influenced by the orientation programs
of some of the hospitals, which expected the graduates to shift
from one service to another every six to twelve weeks.

In interpreting references to the three types of roles,
the reader should recognize that none of them are found ideally
in practice. The bedside nurse does answer questions that are
asked by the aides, and she may direct the aides as they work
together in performing some treatments or procedures. Individual bedside nurses may even have a particular aptitude for
supervising other personnel. The functional nurse may pause at
the bedside and give direct patient care. Part of her job may
involve taking care of one or two critically ill patients as
well as giving medications and treatments. The nurse-manager
may, as the only staff nurse on the ward, give medications and
treatments as well as assign and supervise the work of other
personnel.

The Role of the Bedside Nurse

The job of the bedside nurse primarily involves giving
"direct patient care" to a group of patients. This is usually
described in nursing practice as giving total patient care with

the exception of medications or treatments, or both. In case assignment, which is a form of bedside nurse assignment, the staff nurse gives total patient care for her patients, including medications and treatments.

The responsibility for the assignment and direction of practical nurses and aides who may be working with her rests with the head nurse or team leader. When team nursing is being used, the bedside nurse is a member of the nursing team.

The preparation of the graduates of the pilot programs is most applicable to the role of the bedside nurse. The functions of the bedside nurse are included in the middle range of the continuum of nursing functions.

The nurses interviewed whose primary role was that of the bedside nurse usually had from five to eight patients whom they gave total patient care excepting medications. An illustration from an interview with a nurse working as a team member follows:

> (I am going to ask you some questions about what is expected of you in your work as a staff nurse on a medical floor. Approximately how many patients do you carry?) Five.
> (How do you go about seeing that they get the care they need?) Well, I give total care except for medications and sometimes treatments. The team leader helps you out. (PP 56)

A graduate of a degree program had a similar assignment but was not working with a person designated as team leader:

> (Approximately how many patients do you carry?) Five. (How do you go about seeing that they get the care they need?) Usually I look after the

> sicker ones first and then go on down the line,
> but I try to spend about as much time on each one.
> Get the routine work done first and try to make
> them comfortable. (Do you also give the medica-
> tion to these patients?) No, I give total patient
> care with the exception of medicines. (Diploma 56)

On such an assignment the number of patients may depend
on the number of personnel available:

> (Approximately how many patients do you carry?)
> It all depends on the personnel. If you have the
> personnel that is supposed to come in, you have
> four to five patients usually. If they don't come
> in, you have eight to nine patients. (How do you
> go about seeing they get the care they need?)
> First I find out which are my most seriously ill
> patients and then I check on my other patients and
> see just what has to be done for them. If they
> are not as seriously ill as the others, then I
> usually do them first so I can spend more time with
> the seriously ill. (Do you have auxiliary workers
> to help out?) Yes, but they don't have a time
> schedule. They just more or less come in when they
> have spare time at home. We have four or five aides
> working on the floor. (Do you direct the work of
> the aides?) No. The head nurse assigns them.
> (Diploma 56)

Some assignments are not clearly defined. One pilot-
program graduate described a highly informal approach to the
assignment of patient care:

> (Approximately how many patients do you carry?)
> That is hard to say. I didn't really get a spe-
> cific assignment. We (including the head nurse)
> just pitch in and help wherever we can. We are
> responsible for all our patients. (PP 54)

The Role of the Functional Nurse

The functional nurse's job primarily involves giving
medications or treatments. She may or may not give some "direct

patient care." The most extreme form of the functional nurse is the staff nurse with a single function, such as giving intravenous injections on all floors of the hospital. Like the bedside nurse, she is not responsible for assigning or directing the work of auxiliary personnel. She may be a member of a team if the conception of team nursing used includes one nurse's giving all the medications or treatments.

The preparation of the graduates of the pilot programs includes the role of the functional nurse. The functions of this nurse are included in the middle range of the continuum of nursing functions.

One pilot-program graduate who gave medications and treatments pointed out that most of the patient care was given by auxiliary workers:

> Usually we have a charge nurse and then we have a second nurse who acts as a medications and treatments nurse. Maybe thirty patients we have medications to give, but one about five or ten for treatments. (Do you have any auxiliary workers to help out?) Yes. They give all the bed baths and most of the patient care unless there is something like a special treatment. (When you are on medications, do you direct the aides or is that the job of the head nurse?) Well, if the head nurse is busy and the doctor is doing something else, I do. (PP 56)

Another graduate of the pilot programs described working as a medications and treatments nurse:

> (Approximately how many patients do you carry?) That's a little hard because the practical nurses and attendants do most of the patient care. (And you do the medications?) Yes, I give the medications and treatments to all that need it. (Approximately how many?) Well, on the first floor

> there's about fifty to sixty patients.
> (Were you expected to give any bedside care?)
> Very little except for critical patients. We
> usually try to put a registered nurse or practical
> nurse almost on special, you could call it --
> you'd be in there as much as you could. (PP 55)

A graduate of a degree program described working as a team leader. It is apparent that in practice her assignment was a functional one:

> (Approximately how many patients do you carry?)
> Between thirty-eight and forty on the floor.
> In the ideal situation, the floor is divided in
> half. We use the team concept with one nurse on
> one-half the floor and another on the other.
> Occasionally you have to take the whole floor.
> (Do you have any auxiliary workers to help?)
> It depends upon how busy you are as medications
> nurse. The team concept isn't too perfect on our
> floor yet. If you aren't too busy, then you can
> give help to the aides. (Degree 56)

The Role of the Nurse-Manager

The job of the nurse-manager includes the responsibility for assigning and directing the work of auxiliary workers and may also include supervision of staff nurses. She may be a team leader giving patient care. This classification includes individuals who perform the functions of the head nurse. Lambertson makes an important distinction between nursing management and institutional management. This distinction is not considered in designating a nurse-manager. As long as the nurse has managerial functions as an essential part of the assignment, she is considered a nurse-manager.

The preparation of the graduates of the pilot programs does not include this role. The functions that separate this role from the others are managerial, and belong in the upper range of the continuum of nursing functions.

One pilot-program graduate, acting as a team leader, described giving medications and supervising the auxiliary workers:

> (Approximately how many patients do you carry?) If we have our full quota of RNs on the floor, we are asked to carry about half, which is about twenty to twenty-two. (You act as team leader?) Yes. Most of the time there are two RNs, a team leader at each end of the floor, and the head nurse is at the desk. (How do you go about seeing that the patients are cared for?) Well ... it's my responsibility to give the patients their medications. Then it's my responsibility to supervise or see that the auxiliary help carry out their part of the work and answer any or all questions that they should happen to ask. I have to check to see that their work is done. (Have you found working with them difficult?) I haven't ever had any big problems with them. Maybe one or two individual problems, but nothing outstanding. I have gotten along very well with them. (PP 55)

Another pilot-program graduate, acting as team leader, had another registered nurse as part of her team:

> (Approximately how many patients do you carry?) Seventeen. (How do you see that they get the care that they need?) Well, the floor is divided in half. I have seventeen patients. I have one RN working with me and I have one or two aides at the most. (Is it your responsibility to tell these people what to do?) Yes. (Do you give medications?) Yes, if the other RN isn't there. (What about patient care?) I do as many of the patients as I possibly can. I don't like to see the aides taking care of critically ill patients but sometimes it is impossible to do otherwise. (PP 56)

In one hospital, which employed a large number of pilot-program graduates, a nurse described her experiences in going to work on a new floor:

> (Approximately how many patients do you carry?)
> I have around eleven patients in Psychiatry. It
> has been lower. I have been there about two weeks.
> In the evening I am charge nurse and there is no
> other RN. I went on days at first and the head
> nurse was with me for three days and the third day
> was my job to charge. The fourth day I went on
> nights and that time I had an RN to show me things.
> I like it very much. I despised it (psychiatry)
> when I was a student, but now I like it very much.
> I needed experience, I guess. (PP 56)

The hospital this nurse works in encourages the graduates of the pilot programs to rotate every six weeks to another service in order to broaden their experience. The nurse who described her experiences was given the responsibility of the floor on her third day, but on Psychiatry. However, on that day she was supervised, and when she went on nights, she worked with another person the first night.

Another nurse who was acting as charge nurse pointed out that charging was different from bedside nursing:

> (Approximately how many patients do you carry?)
> Well, it varies with the season, but I think most
> of the time we carry around eighteen. I think
> that is about capacity. It depends on the shift
> that I am working about how many I have respon-
> sibility for.... Like tonight I am charge nurse
> and am over the whole floor, the whole division.
> (How many persons do you have to help you?)
> I have two RNs or one undergraduate who comes and
> helps. (How do you go about seeing that the
> patients get the care they need?) It is my job to
> take the doctor's orders and carry them out, which
> consists of treatments, and the orders that the
> other girls have to do I assist with. We have to

> do the treatments and take care of the medicines
> and start the IVs (intravenous injections) and
> keep track of the different conditions.
> (How do you like doing all of these things?)
> I enjoy it. It is different from bedside nursing.
> It is hard when there is a full house and that
> keeps me hopping to do the things I have to do
> and my practical can't do. I don't have the time
> to do the bedside care I'd like to do. (PP 55)

One of the 1954 pilot-program graduates, who had taken further collegiate work in nursing, was assigned to a particularly difficult floor. She described her job, one involving considerable responsibility:

> (What is your present position at the hospital?)
> I supervise the RNs, aides, orderlies on the second
> floor. There are approximately 100 patients on
> the second floor. I am trying to improve patient
> care on the second floor. I am trying to do this
> by working with RNs and aides and orderlies --
> going along with them and teaching them. If you
> take an individual interest in each worker, they
> will gradually improve their patient care. Also
> there is quite a bit of disorganization on the
> floor. It is a big unit. There are many services
> on the floor and it tends to be quite a busy floor.
> I am also trying to groom a very young three-year
> graduate -- recent -- for a head nurse position on
> the floor. It isn't an easy job -- not at all.
> It takes a long time to try to improve and make
> changes but I like it and find it satisfying.
> (PP 54)

At this point the nurse, who was supervising graduates of diploma programs, was asked about the differences that she perceived between graduates of the program that she had gone to and diploma programs:

> (What differences do you find between graduates
> of diploma and two-year programs in your work with
> graduates of these programs?) First of all the
> graduate of the three-year program has had much
> more clinical experience than I had. The three-year

graduate, though, has not had the emphasis on total patient care. I think that they tend to look at the patient physically. I don't think they are as flexible in some situations. They feel that they must do it this way because they were taught this way. I think there is a little rigidity as far as giving total patient care, though they have had much more clinical experience. (PP 54)

Several of the nurses who described functioning as team members referred to acting as team leaders:[1]

(Approximately how many patients do you carry?) This is team nursing and we are responsible for ten to twenty patients in all, two or three of us working together. Usually, I take care of patients. When I'm team leader I give the assignments and they take complete care of the patient. I give the oral medicines and the IVs (intravenous injections) and I make rounds to see how long it takes. I see if there is anything the others can't do and then I help. (PP 56)

This type of assignment is common.

Assuming the Role of Head Nurse

Most of the graduates interviewed had assumed the role of head nurse. Thirty-three (73 per cent) of the pilot-program graduates and 16 (88 per cent) of the graduates of other programs responded "Yes" to the following question:

_____

[1]Nurses offer a variety of descriptions of the practice of team nursing. The investigator suggests that the term has become popular. While many nursing services have been conscientious in putting the concepts of team nursing into practice, it would seem that many have adopted the label but have not modified previous practices.

In a recent report on the functions of the general-duty nurse the following appeared, "When a head nurse is not on duty, a staff nurse assumes head nurse duties and continues with her own."

Have you assumed head nurse duties?

Most of the pilot program graduates who had not assumed head nurse duties were in the practicum. While they had assumed the role of the team leader, many had not been asked to take over for the head nurse.

Most of the nurses had taken over for the head nurse regularly -- that is, acting as head nurse was a regular but secondary role of the staff nurse.

Some had taken over for two weeks when the head nurse was on vacation; others acted as head nurse regularly on the head nurse's day off. Asked how often he relieved the head nurse, one pilot-program graduate responded:

> Quite a bit. I relieved the head nurse when she was on vacation for two weeks, plus weekends when she was off and I was on. There's only the head nurse and one other RN besides me. It's got to be one of us. (PP 56)

Almost all of the nurses liked assuming the duties and responsibilities of the head nurse. However, many who did had reservations. For example, one stated:

> I like it when I am adequately staffed and I know the work is going to be done. It's very difficult when you are short of help, but this doesn't happen too often. (PP 56)

Another pilot-program graduate stated:

> It depends. If it's an awfully busy day and you're rushed, I don't enjoy it. But if it's a pleasant day and you feel you are doing your job, I enjoy it. (PP 55)

One of the pilot-program graduates stated a preference
for bedside nursing:

> I would rather be at the bedside. I'd rather do
> things myself than have to tell others to do
> them. I enjoy bedside nursing. (PP 54)

Another pilot program graduate, with a similar preference,
stated:

> I liked it but you don't get much patient contact.
> I like patient contact. (PP 56)

Still another described similar feelings:

> I think it's wonderful. I enjoyed it. The patient
> care I like more. You don't have the time to take
> care of patients when you're in charge like that.
> (PP 55)

Several of the pilot-program graduates felt that once
they got used to acting as head nurse, it was good experience.
For example, one nurse said:

> At first, when it's new, you feel rather strange
> about it. After a while it's all right. I like
> the responsibility. It's good experience. (PP 56)

Another pilot program graduate described it as a
"headache":

> It's a headache until you get used to it. You
> can work it among your other work. It takes
> longer of course. (PP 56)

One pilot-program graduate emphasized the importance
of orientation to head nurse responsibilities:

> Very much. I had a good orientation. At first
> a little squeamish when on alone. You think of
> things you ought to take care of. But then you
> resign yourself that you can't account for every-
> thing that will come up. (PP 56)

One of the graduates of the pilot programs refused at first to take charge of the floor and other personnel. This situation will be described thoroughly in the next chapter.

The graduates of other programs responded positively about taking over the responsibilities of the head nurse. Only three had any reservations. One described her feelings:

> At first I drew back from it all. We never had to assume responsibility in the other hospital (the one in which she trained), but I like it now, and I feel that the head nurse should continue to give (patient) care although the wards are large. (Diploma 56)

A graduate of a degree program did not like assuming the duties and responsibilities of the head nurse:

> I don't mind. I really don't like it. In addition to your own responsibility you have the head nurse's. The pressure gets pretty rough. (Degree 56)

For the graduate of a degree program which does not include service to the hospital the kind of stress involved in taking the head nurse's responsibilities, as well as her own, is a new experience. Many diploma school graduates have experienced the stress of being in charge of the ward in training.

A graduate of a diploma program working in the hospital in which she trained stated:

> I like it if you have more time. It would be better if it were your regular job but stepping into it with almost no notice is difficult. (Diploma 54)

The issue which confronts many nurses who prefer bedside nursing but are expected to assume supervisory responsibilities was illustrated by the pilot-program graduate who stated:

> Not as well as I should. As a general-duty nurse
> I should be sort of the type who supervises well.
> (PP 56)

Summary

The primary roles in nursing assumed by the pilot-program graduates were those for which they had been prepared. These roles involved giving patient care or giving medications or treatments under the supervision of a head nurse or team leader.

However, nurses have secondary roles which they assume with some degree of regularity. For example, they relieve the head nurse when she goes on vacation or has her days off.

While most of the nurses like assuming the duties and responsibilities of the head nurse, they also have reservations about assuming that role. The reservations involve: getting used to taking over, having adequate staff when taking over, and being given adequate notice before being asked to take over.

Some pilot-program graduates described taking over for the head nurse as good experience. Several mentioned that they preferred giving patient care to assuming supervisory responsibilities.

CHAPTER XII

THE GRADUATES ARE EVALUATED

This chapter is concerned with the evaluation of pilot-program graduates by the head nurses who worked with them. The evaluations are treated in two sections. The materials for both sections came from the interviews with head nurses. The first section is limited to ratings of the performance of the 85 graduates on twenty-three nursing behaviors (Appendix H). The second section is limited to global ratings of the performance of the individual pilot-program graduates and the reasons given for the ratings.

Graduates from programs other than pilot programs were also rated. As in the previous chapter, this group will be referred to as "graduates of other programs."

The Ratings on Twenty-Three Nursing Behaviors

The raters were asked to "... evaluate each nurse by comparing her with graduate nurses of equal experience. As you make your comparisons, keep in mind nurses whom you have supervised and who have approximately the same length of experience as this nurse." Each nurse was rated on twenty-three nursing behaviors (Appendix H).

240

The ratings were made in three categories, with a fourth headed, "No opportunity to observe." The three rating categories are:

This nurse performs somewhat below most graduate nurses of equal experience.

This nurse performs about the same as most graduate nurses of equal experience.

This nurse performs somewhat above most graduate nurses of equal experience.

The rater compared each nurse with the rater's mental image of the performance of other nurses whom she had supervised. She rated nurses who graduated from a pilot program in comparison with this norm. When possible, she also rated a graduate of a diploma or degree program against this standard.

Since the head nurses, with this method, rated both graduates of pilot programs and graduates of other programs, two distributions were obtained:

(1) the distribution of ratings of graduates of pilot programs;

(2) the distribution of ratings of graduates of other programs.

These distributions were analyzed separately. After being analyzed separately, they were compared.

The Distribution of the Ratings of
Pilot-Program Graduates

The distribution of the ratings for the pilot-program graduates for one of the behaviors follows (Table 35):

TABLE 35

HEAD NURSE RATINGS OF GRADUATES OF PILOT PROGRAMS
ON BEHAVIOR 6: "MAKES ACCURATE NOTATIONS ON
PATIENTS' RECORDS"

Ratings	Graduates of Pilot Programs	
	N	%
Have not had opportunity to observe	0	0
Performs somewhat below most	4	5
Performs about the same as most	64	75
Performs somewhat above most	17	20
Total	85	100

Sixty-four (75 per cent) of the 85 graduates of the pilot programs were rated "performs about the same as most graduates of equal experience." Eighty-one (95 per cent) of the graduates of pilot programs were rated either "the same as most" or "above most."

On twenty-two of the twenty-three nursing behaviors, more than 4 out of 5 of the pilot-program graduates were rated either "the same as most" or "above most" graduates with equal nursing experience (Tables 36-37).

On one behavior, "Is sought by auxiliary workers for advice," only 63 per cent of the pilot program graduates were rated either "the same as most" or "above most."

TABLE 36

HEAD NURSE RATINGS OF 85 GRADUATES OF PILOT PROGRAMS AND 50 GRADUATES OF OTHER PROGRAMS ON 23 NURSING BEHAVIORS

No.	Nursing Behavior	Pilot Program				Other Programs			
		No.observ.	Above	Same	Below	No.observ.	Above	Same	Below
1.	Carries out nursing techniques	3	12	63	7	0	7	43	0
2.	Shows skill in lifting and moving	5	10	60	10	2	14	34	0
3.	Operates special equipment	5	11	52	17	1	13	34	2
4.	Plans care for patient as a person	3	28	45	9	2	15	27	6
5.	Reports observations to nurse in charge	0	29	46	10	0	19	25	6
6.	Makes accurate notations on patients' records	0	17	64	4	0	8	39	3
7.	Seeks opportunities to give direct care to patients	0	21	48	16	1	13	32	4
8.	Uses opportunities to talk to patients	6	19	53	7	4	14	29	3
9.	Explains procedures etc. in understandable terms	16	9	51	9	6	5	36	3
10.	Adjusts approach to kind and type of patient	10	13	56	6	2	12	33	3
11.	Puts patients' families and relatives at ease	10	17	54	4	6	11	30	3
12.	Requests supervision when not sure of techniques	1	38	39	7	3	8	38	1

TABLE 36 (Continued)

No.	Nursing Behavior	Pilot Program				Other Programs			
		No.observ.	Above	Same	Below	No observ.	Above	Same	Below
13.	Uses suggestions from other personnel to improve nursing	4	21	53	7	3	9	32	6
14.	Uses opportunities to increase knowledge	1	29	48	7	1	15	30	4
15.	Talks with doctors and social workers with ease	8	12	50	15	4	10	34	2
16.	Shows same courtesy and consideration for all workers	1	21	56	7	0	11	36	3
17.	Displays conduct appropriate to hospital situation	0	18	59	8	1	23	24	2
18.	Has good personal appearance	0	28	52	5	0	20	29	1
19.	Is sought out by auxiliary workers for advice	10	3	44	28	3	9	28	10
20.	Organizes her own activities	0	15	54	16	0	13	31	6
21.	Organizes her own activities and activities of auxiliary workers	3	15	48	19	2	11	32	5
22.	Keeps patients records so that they are organized and orderly	1	15	62	7	1	12	36	1
23.	Assists with up-keep of the ward	5	16	51	13	2	14	26	8

TABLE 37

HEAD NURSE RATINGS OF GRADUATES OF PILOT PROGRAMS AND GRADUATES OF OTHER PROGRAMS ON 23 NURSING BEHAVIORS -- BY PERCENTAGES

No.	Nursing Behavior	Pilot Program			Other Programs		
		Above	Same	Below	Above	Same	Below
1.	Carries out nursing techniques	15	77	8	14	86	0
2.	Shows skill in lifting and moving	13	75	12	29	71	0
3.	Operates special equipment	14	65	21	27	69	4
4.	Plans care for patient as a person	34	55	11	31	56	13
5.	Reports observations to nurse in charge	34	54	12	38	50	12
6.	Makes accurate notations on patients' records	20	75	5	16	78	6
7.	Seeks opportunities to give direct care to patients	25	56	19	27	65	8
8.	Uses opportunities to talk to patients	24	67	9	30	63	7
9.	Explains procedures etc. in understandable terms	13	74	13	11	82	7
10.	Adjusts approach to kind and type of patient	17	75	8	25	69	6
11.	Puts patients' families and relatives at ease	23	72	5	25	68	7

TABLE 37 (Continued)

No.	Nursing Behavior	Pilot Program			Other Programs		
		Above	Same	Below	Above	Same	Below
12.	Requests supervision when not sure of techniques	45	47	8	17	81	2
13.	Uses suggestions from other personnel to improve nursing	26	65	9	19	68	13
14.	Uses opportunities to increase knowledge	35	57	8	31	61	8
15.	Talks with doctors and social workers with ease	16	65	19	22	74	4
16.	Shows same courtesy and consideration for all workers	25	67	8	22	72	6
17.	Displays conduct appropriate to hospital situation	21	70	9	47	49	4
18.	Has good personal appearance	33	61	6	40	58	2
19.	Is sought out by auxiliary workers for advice	4	59	37	19	60	21
20.	Organizes her own activities	18	63	19	26	62	12
21.	Organizes her own activities and activities of auxiliary workers	18	59	23	23	67	10
22.	Keeps patients' records so that they are organized and orderly	18	74	8	25	73	2
23.	Assists with upkeep of the ward	20	64	16	29	54	17

Distribution of the Ratings of
Graduates of Other Programs

The distribution of the ratings for the 50 graduates of

other programs on Behavior 6 follows (Table 38):

TABLE 38

HEAD NURSE RATINGS OF GRADUATES OF OTHER PROGRAMS
ON BEHAVIOR 6: "MAKES ACCURATE NOTATIONS ON
PATIENTS' RECORDS"

Ratings	Graduates of Other Programs	
	N	%
Have not had opportunity to observe	0	0
Performs somewhat below most	3	6
Performs about the same as most	39	78
Performs somewhat above most	8	16
Total	50	100

Thirty-nine (78 per cent) of the 50 graduates of other

programs were rated "performs about the same as most graduates

of equal experience." Forty-seven (94 per cent) of the gradu-

ates of other programs were rated either "the same as most"

or "above most."

On all twenty-three of the nursing behaviors, more than

4 out of 5 of the graduates of other programs were rated either

"the same as most" or "above most" (Tables 36-37). The be-

havior, "Is sought by auxiliary workers for advice," had the

smallest percentage of graduates of other programs rated "the

same as most" or "above most." Stating the results inversely, this behavior had the largest percentage of graduates of other programs rated "below most." It is interesting to note that this same behavior had the largest percentage rated "below most" for pilot-program graduates, too.

The Distributions Compared

The ratings of the graduates by their head nurses indicate that most of the pilot-program graduates, when given at least three months of experience working in hospitals, are rated "the same as most graduates of équal experience" or "above most graduate nurses of equal experience." Nevertheless, it is important to see whether there are differences between pilot-program graduates' ratings and those of graduates of other programs.

The statistical test selected as most appropriate to measure the significance of the differences between the groups was chi-square (X^2), with a confidence level of 95 per cent. When a difference is labeled as significant, there is a probability of at least 95 per cent that the difference is not due to chance alone.

However, differences between ratings that are large enough to warrant the rejection of the null hypothesis must be examined to determine the nature of the distribution differences which bring about large X^2 values. The value of X^2 with 2 degrees of freedom for $C = .95$ is 6.0. Any distributions in this study which result in X^2 larger than 6.0 warrant the rejection of the hypothesis of no differences.

The following comparisons of the distributions of ratings were made:

(a) The total group of pilot-program graduates (N=85) with the total group of graduates of other programs (N=50);

(b) The 1956 pilot-program graduates (N=58) with the 1956 graduates of other programs (N=31);

(c) The pilot-program graduates who finished before 1956 (N=27) with the graduates of other programs who finished before 1956 (N=19);

(d) The pilot-program graduates who finished before 1956 (N=27) with the pilot-program graduates who finished in 1956 (N=58).

The total group of pilot program graduates (N=85) with the total group of graduates of other programs (N=50). The distributions on Behavior 6, which have been presented already, are used for illustration (Table 39). In testing for differences between the distributions, the category, "Have not had the opportunity to observe," is omitted.

TABLE 39

HEAD NURSE RATINGS OF GRADUATES OF PILOT AND OTHER PROGRAMS ON BEHAVIOR 6: "MAKES ACCURATE NOTATIONS ON PATIENTS' RECORDS"

| Ratings | Graduates of | | | |
| | Pilot Programs | | Other Programs | |
	N	%	N	%
Performs somewhat below most	4	5	3	6
Performs about the same as most	64	75	39	78
Performs somewhat above most	17	20	8	16
Total	85	100	50	100

A cursory inspection of these two distributions indicated that they were obviously similar. Therefore, it was a valid conclusion that there were no significant differences in charting accuracy between pilot-program and other program graduates working in similar hospital situations. This conclusion is based on the observations of head nurses working with graduates of both programs.

On eighteen of the twenty-three nursing behaviors described on the rating scale, the ratings of the head nurses warrant maintaining the hypothesis that pilot-program graduates, when given some experience, perform as well as graduates of other programs.

The five nursing behaviors which produced statistically significant differences were:

Number of Behavior	Description of Behavior	Chi-square
2	Shows skill in lifting and turning patients, getting patients up and making patients comfortable.	10.52
3	Operates special equipment, such as oxygen equipment, suction apparatus, irrigation equipment.	8.83
12	Requests supervision when she is not sure of procedure techniques, etc.	14.79
17	Displays conduct appropriate to hospital situation, for example, uses well-modulated tone of voice in speaking, enters room quietly, etc.	10.04
19	Is sought by auxiliary workers when they need advice or instruction.	9.14

The distributions on Behavior 3 illustrate one way in which significant differences in the distributions arose (Table 40).

TABLE 40

HEAD NURSE RATINGS OF GRADUATES OF PILOT AND OTHER
PROGRAMS ON BEHAVIOR 3:   "OPERATES SPECIAL EQUIPMENT..."

Ratings	Pilot Programs		Graduates of Other Programs	
	N	%	N	%
Performs somewhat below most	17	21	2	4
Performs about the same as most	52	65	34	69
Performs somewhat above most	11	14	13	27
Total	80	100	49	100

The percentage of graduates rated "the same as most" is
about the same for both groups. However, the percentage of
pilot-program graduates rated "somewhat above most" was smaller
than that of graduates of other programs, while the percentage
rated "somewhat below most" was larger.

The differences for Behaviors 3 and 19 arose similarly
from the smaller percentage of pilot-program graduates rated
"somewhat above most" and the larger percentage rated "somewhat
below most." It is important to note that for Behaviors 2 and
3 a very small percentage of the graduates of other programs
was rated "somewhat below most." The two behaviors involve
technical skills and might require longer experience for marked
proficiency.

For Behavior 17, the difference arose primarily from the large percentage of the graduates of other programs rated "somewhat above most." Since the graduates of other programs have had extended experience with hospitals, it is not surprising that their behavior conformed to the expectations of the head nurses.

For Behavior 12, the difference arose from the large percentage of graduates of pilot programs rated "somewhat above most" (Table 41).

The 1956 pilot program graduates (N=58) with the 1956 graduates of other programs (N=31) (Tables 41, 42). Six nursing behaviors produced statistically significant differences when only 1956 graduates were considered. The six were:

Number of Behavior	Description of Behavior	Chi-square
2	Shows skill in lifting and turning patients, getting patients up and making patients comfortable.	7.19
3	Operates special equipment such as oxygen equipment, suction apparatus, irrigation equipment.	7.70
12	Requests supervision when she is not sure of procedure techniques, etc.	6.25
15	Talks with doctors and social workers with ease.	6.13
17	Displays conduct appropriate to hospital situations, for example, uses well modulated tone of voice in speaking, enters room quietly, etc.	7.91
19	Is sought by auxiliary workers when they need advice or instruction.	7.52

TABLE 41

HEAD NURSE RATINGS OF 1956 GRADUATES OF PILOT PROGRAMS
ON 23 NURSING BEHAVIORS (N=58)

Nursing Behaviors	No oppor. to observe	Number of Ratings			Percentage of Ratings		
		Above	Same	Below	Above	Same	Below
1	3	7	42	6	13	76	11
2	5	4	43	6	8	81	11
3	5	7	33	13	13	62	25
4	2	22	28	6	39	50	11
5	0	19	35	4	33	60	6
6	0	11	44	3	19	75	5
7	2	13	34	9	23	60	16
8	5	10	39	2	19	74	7
9	11	7	34	6	15	72	13
10	7	10	37	4	20	73	8
11	7	10	39	2	20	76	4
12	1	22	30	5	39	53	9
13	3	11	37	7	20	67	13
14	0	19	35	4	33	60	7
15	4	5	39	10	9	72	19
16	0	16	38	4	28	66	7
17	0	14	38	6	24	66	10
18	0	19	35	4	33	60	7
19	8	2	27	21	4	54	42
20	0	8	41	9	14	71	16
21	3	8	38	9	15	69	16
22	0	10	44	4	17	76	7
23	4	10	35	9	18	65	17

TABLE 42

HEAD NURSE RATINGS OF 1956 GRADUATES OF OTHER THAN
PILOT PROGRAMS ON 23 NURSING BEHAVIORS (N=31)

Nursing Behaviors	No oppor. to observe	Number of Ratings			Percentage of Ratings		
		Above	Same	Below	Above	Same	Below
1	0	4	27	0	13	87	0
2	2	7	22	0	24	76	0
3	1	8	21	1	27	70	3
4	2	9	17	3	31	59	10
5	0	12	15	4	39	48	13
6	0	6	23	2	19	74	6
7	1	9	20	1	30	67	3
8	2	8	20	1	28	69	3
9	5	2	22	2	8	85	8
10	2	9	19	1	31	66	3
11	3	7	20	1	25	71	4
12	1	5	24	1	17	80	3
13	2	4	21	4	14	72	14
14	0	10	19	2	32	61	6
15	4	5	39	10	24	72	3
16	0	10	19	2	32	61	6
17	1	15	15	0	50	50	0
18	0	14	17	0	45	55	0
19	2	6	17	6	21	59	21
20	0	4	23	4	13	74	13
21	1	5	22	3	17	73	10
22	0	6	24	1	19	77	3
23	1	7	18	5	23	60	17

Five of these six behaviors were the same that produced significant differences when all of the graduates were considered. Behavior 15, which was the other behavior found to be significant, should be interpreted as "talking with doctors" and not "talking with doctors and social workers." A majority of the raters commented that their ratings applied to doctors, since staff nurses had little or no contact with social workers. The significant difference on this behavior arose from the smaller percentage of graduates of pilot programs rated "somewhat above most" and the larger percentage rated "somewhat below most."

The pilot-program graduates who finished before 1956 (N=27) with the graduates of other programs who finished before 1956 (N=19) (Tables 43, 44). When the groups considered were composed of nurses who had graduated over a year prior to the ratings, only one of the behaviors produced differences large enough to warrant the rejection of the hypothesis of no differences, and that was Behavior 12, the one involving the request for supervision. As in the previous instances with Behavior 12, the difference arose from the large percentage of pilot-program graduates who were rated "somewhat above most" on this behavior.

The pilot-program graduates who finished before 1956 (N=27) with the pilot-program graduates who finished in 1956 (N=58). These comparisons involved two groups of pilot-program

TABLE 43

HEAD NURSE RATINGS OF PILOT-PROGRAM NURSES WHO
GRADUATED BEFORE 1956 ON 23 NURSING BEHAVIORS
(N=27)

Nursing Behaviors	No oppor. to observe	Number of Ratings			Percentage of Ratings		
		Above	Same	Below	Above	Same	Below
1	0	5	21	1	18	78	3
2	0	6	17	4	22	63	15
3	0	4	19	4	15	70	15
4	1	6	17	3	23	65	12
5	0	10	11	6	37	41	22
6	0	6	20	1	22	74	3
7	0	8	13	6	30	48	22
8	5	2	17	3	9	77	11
9	5	2	17	3	9	77	13
10	3	3	19	2	29	62	0
11	3	7	15	2	29	62	0
12	0	16	9	2	59	33	7
13	1	10	16	0	38	62	0
14	1	10	13	3	38	50	12
15	4	7	11	5	30	48	22
16	1	5	18	3	19	69	12
17	0	4	21	2	15	78	7
18	0	9	17	1	33	63	4
19	2	1	17	7	4	68	28
20	0	7	13	7	26	48	26
21	0	7	10	10	26	37	37
22	1	5	18	3	19	69	12
23	1	6	16	4	23	62	15

TABLE 44

HEAD NURSE RATINGS OF OTHER THAN PILOT-PROGRAM NURSES
WHO GRADUATED BEFORE 1956 ON 23 NURSING BEHAVIORS
(N=19)

Nursing Behaviors	Number of Ratings				Percentage of Ratings		
	No oppor. to observe	Above	Same	Below	Above	Same	Below
1	0	3	16	0	16	84	0
2	0	7	12	0	37	63	0
3	0	5	13	1	26	68	5
4	0	6	10	3	32	53	16
5	0	7	10	2	37	53	11
6	0	2	16	1	11	84	5
7	0	4	12	3	21	63	16
8	2	6	9	2	35	53	12
9	1	3	14	1	17	78	6
10	0	2	15	2	11	79	11
11	3	4	10	2	25	62	12
12	2	3	14	0	18	82	0
13	1	5	11	2	28	61	11
14	1	5	11	2	28	61	11
15	2	3	13	1	18	76	6
16	0	1	17	1	5	89	5
17	0	8	9	2	42	47	11
18	1	6	12	0	33	67	0
19	1	3	11	4	17	61	22
20	0	9	8	2	47	42	11
21	1	6	10	2	33	56	11
22	1	6	12	0	33	67	0
23	1	7	8	3	39	44	17

graduates. One group of graduates had been out more than one year, all of them having had at least eight months of hospital experience. The other group had been out less than one year, no graduates having had eight months' experience.

Two behaviors produced significant differences:

Number of Behavior	Description of Behavior	Chi-square
15	Talks with doctors and social workers with ease.	6.22
21	Organizes her own activities and the activities of auxiliary workers so that her patients receive the nursing care warranted by their condition.	7.78

For Behavior 15, the difference arose from the small percentage of 1956 graduates rated "somewhat above most." For Behavior 21, the difference arose from a more complicated distribution difference, which is explained below (Table 45).

TABLE 45

HEAD NURSE RATINGS OF PILOT-PROGRAM GRADUATES WHO GRADUATED BEFORE 1956 AND IN 1956 ON BEHAVIOR 21: "ORGANIZES HER OWN ACTIVITIES AND THE ACTIVITIES OF OTHERS ..."

Ratings	Pilot Program Graduates Before 1956		1956	
	N	%	N	%
Performs somewhat below most	10	37	9	16
Performs about the same as most	10	37	38	69
Performs somewhat above most	7	26	8	15
Total	27	100	55	100

Even after a year's experience, a large percentage (37 per cent) of those graduating from pilot programs before 1956 was not judged to "perform about the same as most" in organizing the care of patients. At the same time, with a year's experience, a large percentage of the graduates performed "somewhat above most." On the other hand, after working less than eight months, a smaller percentage of the 1956 graduates were rated "somewhat below most" in organizing patient care than of those having more nursing experience. A smaller percentage of 1956 graduates were rated "somewhat above most."

The Global Ratings

The head nurses were asked to make global ratings of staff nurses in terms of their own standards of good nursing. The directions for rating were:

> On the basis of your own observations, would you say in general that this nurse: (a) is definitely superior to your standards of good nursing; (b) meets your standards of good nursing; (c) definitely fails to meet your standards of good nursing.

The Distributions of Global Ratings of Graduates of Pilot and Other Programs

Seventy-three (86 per cent) of the 85 pilot-program graduates either met or were superior to the nursing standards of the head nurse raters, while 46 (92 per cent) of the 50 graduates of other programs either met or were superior to the standards of the raters (Table 46). The similarity between the

two distributions warrants maintaining the hypothesis that,
given some work experience, the pilot-program graduates perform
as well as graduates of other programs.

TABLE 46

HEAD NURSE RATINGS OF GRADUATES OF PILOT
AND OTHER PROGRAMS

Ratings	Graduates of Pilot Programs		Graduates of Other Programs	
	N	%	N	%
Is definitely superior to your standards of good nursing	13	15	9	18
Meets your standards of good nursing	60	71	37	74
Definitely fails to meet your standards of good nursing	12	14	4	8
Total	85	100	50	100

The distribution of ratings by those who graduated before
1956 and in 1956 for the graduates of pilot and other programs
further supports the hypothesis that given some work experience,
the pilot-program graduates perform as well as graduates of
other programs (Table 47).

Reasons for Ratings

After placing the nurse in one of the three rating categories, the rater was asked:

Would you elaborate as to why you place her (him)
in this category?

TABLE 47

GLOBAL RATINGS OF GRADUATES OF PILOT AND OTHER PROGRAMS BY TIME OF GRADUATION

| Ratings | Graduates of Pilot Programs | | | | Graduates of Other Programs | | | |
| | Before 1956 | | In 1956 | | Before 1956 | | In 1956 | |
	N	%	N	%	N	%	N	%
Is definitely superior to your standards of good nursing	4	15	9	16	3	16	6	19
Meets your standards of good nursing	18	67	42	72	13	68	24	77
Definitely fails to meet your standards of good nursing	5	18	7	12	3	16	1	3
Total	27	100	58	100	19	100	31	99

The reasons provided by the head nurses for rating pilot-program graduates showed great variation. Similarly, the statements about graduates of other programs showed great variation. Although the statements of reasons did indicate some characteristics common to the pilot-program nurses, the comments tended to indicate great similarity between the two groups of graduates -- that is, given some work experience, the pilot-program graduates seem to most of the head nurses with whom they work to be like nurses trained in other programs. This statement is not meant to imply that certain differences between graduates from different programs might not exist. Other instruments, such as attitude scales concerned with specific aspects of nursing behavior, would have to be used to explore subtler differences. However, the statements of the head nurses indicate far more similarity than difference.

It should be remembered that the statements by the head nurse were not controlled for the frame of reference or for the observational sophistication of the rater. Certainly some raters are more objective and have more insight than others.

In evaluating nursing performance in their own words, head nurses mentioned most frequently such qualities and behaviors as: exhibiting interest in nursing and patients, knowing practice as well as theory, giving good patient care, being observant, asking questions when uncertain, learning rapidly, being able to work on one's own, being able to delegate responsibility, etc.

Three types of comments were repeated about the pilot-program graduates: comments related to interest in nursing, comments related to asking questions when they were not certain, and comments related to their lack of confidence when they first began working. Comments relating to these behaviors were also made by the raters about graduates of other programs, but less frequently.

As in previous chapters, many quotations are used; and, as in previous chapters, these quotations were selected to illustrate the wide variety of reactions to graduates of pilot and other programs. The statements quoted were selected to provide a cross-sectional view of all the rating statements.

Of general importance in the evaluation of job performance is the assessment of personality. Super claims that all specific ratings stem from a generalized conception of the worker as a person.[1] Certainly the statements by head nurses illustrate the importance of personality and human relations in the rating of job performance.

Description of Nurses Rated Superior

A characteristic that tended to be emphasized in the descriptions of pilot-program nurses who were rated "superior" was intense interest in nursing. For example, one head nurse

---

[1]Donald E. Super, "The Criteria of Vocational Success," Occupations, October 1951, pp. 5-8.

described as follows a graduate who worked in obstetrics:

> She has a great deal of interest in obstetrics.
> I don't know whether she has displayed such in-
> terest in other areas. She takes her patients
> and develops a little bit of teaching for them and
> stimulates their thoughts. She seems to like this
> area and fits in nicely with everyone. She co-
> operates well. All her patients get very good
> care. (PP 56)[2]

Another head nurse spoke of a 1956 pilot-program

graduate:

> Exceptional in her line of work. She started on
> the 7-3 shift and was put on 3-11 and she excels
> in pediatrics. She is a model of the nurse who
> loves children. She knows them. She performs as
> well as knows the book knowledge. (PP 56)

A head nurse on a surgical floor pointed out that the

pilot-program graduate showed "keen interest" and a willingness

to devote extra time to nursing:

> She has a keen interest in the work. She has good
> intelligence and is willing to devote a lot more
> time to this sort of thing than others do. She is
> willing to stay overtime and to come back on her
> days off. She really seems to want to. She is in-
> terested in the patients, seems to like them and
> to like working with them. (PP 56)

Others of those who were rated superior were commended

for their ability to go ahead on their own. One 1956 male

graduate was praised:

> Because he doesn't have to wait to be told anything.
> He observes and then he sees that things are carried
> out. If an emergency comes up in the treatment
> rooms, he goes back and pitches in and this is im-
> portant because we have quite a few patients who
> hemorrhage. He works right along with the treat-
> ment room girls until the doctor gets there.
> (PP 56)

---

[2]The system of notation is the same as that introduced in
Chapter IX except that the designation is for the nurse being
rated, not for the nurse speaking.

Of a 1955 graduate, one head nurse stated:

> She is extremely dependable. She helps others.
> She thinks ahead and sees things that are coming
> rather than just what is before her. She antici-
> pates. (PP 55)

One head nurse described the rapid development of a
pilot-program graduate in six weeks. The six-week period
referred to was part of the rotation plan for pilot-program
graduates in that particular hospital.

> Superior at the end of her six weeks. At the be-
> ginning she was a little frightened of the tre-
> mendous responsibility. She improved greatly and
> was a very good nurse. She has a personality that
> fits with psychiatric nursing. She is calm and
> friendly and she has the interest of the patient
> at heart. She is very sympathetic. She is firm
> and yet kind. (PP 56)

An interesting "superior" rating came from a head nurse
who first rated the nurse in terms of the program from which
she had graduated. Her statement indicated her general attitude toward two-year programs. The nurse being evaluated was
the only pilot-program graduate employed in the hospital at
that time.

> Considering that she is a two-year graduate, I
> would say that she is superior. As long as Mrs. N
> has been here, I have never heard one complaint.
> I really think for her two years training, she is
> superior. (What would you say in comparing her
> with graduates of three-year programs?) I guess ...
> she would still be superior. (PP 55)

Graduates of other programs were also rated superior by
the head nurses. For example, one head nurse said of a 1956
diploma-program graduate:

I think she is very observant. She is very well
able to carry out her assignments and is careful
about medicines. She sees things to do. She
doesn't stop as you hand out her assignments.
She gets to work and does them. (Diploma 56)

Another head nurse stated about a diploma graduate:

Miss B is one of the best nurses on the floor.
She gives excellent nursing care. She is an eager
person, very observant. She is loving and kind with
children and has a very responsive personality.
She is lovable. (Diploma 56)

Of a 1954 graduate, a head nurse stated:

She can take over in any emergency situation without
any question. She is able to handle the floor without any notice, so to speak. She seems to meet any
situation with poise. (Diploma 54)

In contrast with the pilot program graduates' need to

develop confidence, a diploma graduate was described as follows:

She works with a great deal of confidence. It
didn't take her long at all to know our procedures
when she first came. She fitted very well into
our pattern. (Diploma 55)

The importance of leadership and organization was empha-

sized in the superior rating of a degree-program graduate:

Theoretically she knows her nursing well. She shows
a definite ability for leadership and organizes very
well. She carries through very well. (Degree 1956)

Description of Nurses Meeting Standards

The majority of the pilot-program graduates were judged

to meet the standards of the head nurse. Examination of the

comments of head nurses in placing individuals in this category

indicated considerable range for both graduates of the pilot and other programs.

Four examples, two for pilot-program graduates and two for graduates of other programs, serve as an initial illustration of the variation included in the category "meets." One pilot-program graduate who met the rater's standards was described:

> She takes care of her patients well. She is well liked by her patients. I have had several patients comment on how they like to have her around. She is very cheerful, that the patients appreciate. She takes her assignments seriously. She is capable of doing whatever she is assigned to do. Sometimes, I think, she feels insecure in instances although she knows the procedures. If the situation changes a little bit, she isn't quite sure of herself. (PP 55)

Another pilot-program graduate was described as follows by her head nurse:

> At times she doesn't think things through. She tends to rush into things. She forgets minor points, especially her legal aspects. She is a little young and immature at times. She takes responsibility well one day and then the next she will be all fluttery. (PP 56)

The descriptions of the diploma-program graduates indicate the same type of range. An essentially positive rating of "meets" was the following:

> She has good spirits, she has good principles, gets along well with people. I don't think we can judge her personality because we all have different personalities. She has a very dry sense of humor and I don't think it an attribute or otherwise, because it is part of her make-up But as a nurse, she gets along well with her patients, she's very capable, very willing. When she first came here she never had the knowledge of delegating responsibility, she had to learn how to delegate.

> (Did she have any difficulty in learning to dele-
> gate responsibility?) Well, I wouldn't call it
> difficulty. She had to learn what was expected
> of her. (Diploma 55)

Another head nurse rating a nurse as meeting her standards stated:

> In between meeting my standards and failing to meet
> them. She needs help. She is new and she has per-
> sonality problems. (Diploma 56)

The statements about nurses who met the standards of
their head nurses are presented in four sections. The first
section contains comments about pilot-program graduates who
met head nurse standards with some distinction. The second contains statements about pilot-program graduates who met head
nurse standards in spite of strong criticism. The third section contains statements about graduates of other programs who
met head nurse standards with some distinction. The fourth
section contains statements about graduates of other programs
who met head nurse standards in spite of strong criticism.

Pilot program graduates who met head nurse standards
with some distinction. A head nurse stated about a 1954 pilot-
program graduate who recently went to work in a highly specialized institute:

> She does all that is expected of her very well and
> thoroughly. She does good patient care. She has
> had the opportunity to take charge of the ward
> for a day and managed very well. She seems to
> learn very quickly. She is very interested in new
> procedures and procedures that are new to her and
> she takes opportunities to observe these and to
> ask about them. (PP 54)

Several of the comments indicated that the rater was either tempted to place the nurse in the superior category or felt that she had the potential to develop into a superior nurse. For example, one head nurse rated a pilot-program graduate:

> In between meets and superior. She's a very satis-
> factory girl. She does very good nursing. She's
> definitely very alert and very good and I think
> she's a very fine nurse. I've had no occasion to
> doubt her judgment on the floor. She's very quick
> to pick up things and very cooperative with all
> the girls. (PP 55)

A rather unique comment from a head nurse about an "immature" girl who might develop into a superior nurse went as follows:

> I think that with time she is going to be superior.
> She has a beautiful way with patients. The patients
> like her ... but she is just immature. I don't
> know, maybe she won't outgrow that. She's still
> like a little child. She tells me about her mother.
> I mean she just hasn't grown up. But yet she has a
> beautiful way with patients. (PP 56)

Another head nurse who stated that a pilot-program graduate was "not superior yet" also described behaviors to be improved:

> I wouldn't say that she is superior yet. She may
> be with experience. She worked 3-11 and handled
> it quite capably. Once or twice there have been
> incidents where she neglected charting something
> important. She gives good patient care. Her
> patients seem contented. She needs a little more
> help with organization. Occasionally she lets the
> sicker patients go till later on in the morning.
> Other than that she is working out well, consider-
> ing that she is a recent graduate. (PP 56)

The head nurse quoted above seemed to expect recent graduates
to need help.

The next head nurse had worked with the pilot-program
graduate she evaluated for more than a year. In her evaluation,
she recalled the initial period in which the pilot-program
graduate became acclimated to hospital nursing:

> She uses good judgment. We had to work with her
> a little bit at the very beginning. If she
> doesn't know, she comes and asks. She is good at
> recognizing danger signs and reports them. She
> did patient care for about the first two or three
> weeks. After that she went right into medications.
> Also she relieved on head nurse days off, doing
> charge work. (PP 55)

A head nurse statement repeating the most typical characteristics of the pilot-program graduate as a worker follows:

> I feel that she needs more experience. She will
> always check with the proper people for anything
> that she is unsure of. What she does do is very
> good. (PP 56)

Some of the head nurses, in evaluating individual
pilot-program graduates, explicitly evaluated two-year programs
in general rather than the individual nurse. One head nurse
commented on the pilot-program graduates in general while
evaluating one graduate:

> I have had a number of these students from B when
> they were students, and Mrs. M was one of them. I
> do notice that after they became graduates that
> they really developed a great deal -- I mean in nursing
> procedures and leadership. I think there is a much
> greater security about the girls after they have been
> with us as graduate nurses for a time. Although I
> don't think that these girls are quite as prepared
> in comparison with three-year students. Just from

> observations and so on I believe that they need a
> longer period of time to become secure as graduate
> nurses. (PP 56)

One head nurse indicated a sharp difference between the
graduates of two- and three-year programs. A pilot-program
graduate whom she found superior in relation to the other
pilot-program graduates she had contact with met her standards
of good nursing. She stated:

> She meets them in a superior manner in relation to
> the two-year graduate. She is one of the more
> superior in that group. However, in speaking of
> graduates generally, I would say she meets. Her
> nursing skills are developed. She has good inter-
> personal relationships. (PP 55)

Pilot-program graduates who met head nurse standards in
spite of criticism. Several pilot-program graduates were
criticized for the kind of bedside care they gave. For example,
one pilot-program graduate was described as an:

> Extremely slow nurse in bedside nursing and I felt
> she resented it (giving bedside care). (PP 55)

Another pilot program graduate who met her head nurse's
standards was criticized for her general handling of patients
and uncertainty:

> Her procedures and techniques are completely satis-
> factory. Where I think she falls down, well, I
> don't like that ..., let us say where I think she
> is lacking to some extent is in her general handling
> of patients and meeting difficult situations and
> also in her own expressed feeling of inadequacy.
> She herself is doubtful about some medications,
> treatments, and some diagnoses. She has heard of
> the latter and she doesn't feel that she knows too
> much and she asks about them. (PP 55)

What is most pertinent about these two criticisms of speed and sureness is that both of the graduates had over one year of nursing experience.

Erratic performance was a factor that entered in several evaluations. Of one pilot-program graduate it was stated:

> She is an erratic worker. I would say that usually she meets our standards or is below our standards. Some days she is superior to our standards. She doesn't maintain a level of work performance. I would say generally she is an average nurse. I would say she meets our standards on the down-grade side. Some days she is a regular beehive of energy. She does her work beautifully. Everything she does is right. Other times, she just can't seem to get going. We have to remind her about something as little as putting up a crib-side. Other times her work performance is excellent. She works well when we are busy but she has a tendency to fall down when things are slow. (PP 55)

Another nurse who was judged to meet standards in general but "fall below in a few things, too" did not seem to show much independence in her work:

> She meets my standards in some things but I think she falls below in a few things, too. In the everyday work I would think that she falls below my standards in a few things. As far as her nursing is concerned, I would say that she tries to apply herself. I would say that she tries to do everything that is asked of her but she doesn't see things that many times should be done. There are times that she is not as neat as she could be in her work. I think that she knows her procedures. She has the theory behind them. (PP 56)

The next pilot-program graduate was judged to meet the head nurse's standards although she was not giving "complete nursing care" and lacked experience:

> She has improved. She meets with my approval but
> she could do better. She doesn't give complete
> nursing care. She is a little afraid of critical
> patients, but she is getting there. She is a
> little more sure of herself but mainly it is the
> lack of experience. She would rather do medications
> because she is not sure of handling the patients.
> (PP 56)

An evaluation of a nurse who "just meets" reflected the rater's opinion of the entire program:

> Just meets. Her experience has not been adequate,
> and you see, what she has learned in school she
> has not applied until she came to us. She has to
> be checked up on her work -- although she is improv-
> ing, she needs to be checked on. (What are the
> kinds of things she has to be checked on?) The
> orders that are written ... to see if she has carried
> out the orders. (Does she make mistakes on orders?)
> Well, she has improved but she did make mistakes.
> She would go off duty and forget to chart something.
> (Anything else?) No, that is all. (PP 56)

<u>Graduates of other programs who met head nurse standards</u>
<u>with some distinction</u>. Comments about graduates of other pro-
grams by head nurse raters often paralleled comments made about
graduates of pilot programs. One head nurse emphasized a
nurse's superior ability to work with co-workers. Interestingly
enough, she attributed this not to the nurse's training but to
the fact that her mother had been a nurse's aide:

> Superior in some specific areas, such as working
> with her co-workers. She seemed to understand the
> need that the aides had better than many nurses.
> She made them feel they belonged to the unit. Of
> course, I will say this much -- perhaps the reason
> she could understand this better than the other
> nurses was because her mother was an aide here once,
> and this may have played an important part.
> (Diploma 55)

Another diploma graduate was praised for her interest
in nursing, for reporting unusual occurrences, and for ability
to take over the ward:

> She does her work well. She shows interest. She
> reports anything unusual about the patient that
> should be reported to the doctor or head nurse.
> She gets along with the patients and the other
> members of the staff. She appears to be reliable.
> Her charting is fine. She did well on evening duty,
> which shows she is capable of responsibility for
> the ward. (Diploma 54)

A head nurse found that a 1956 diploma graduate had a
good approach to the patient and learned quickly. She also
made clear her view of the need for new graduates to learn
and for head nurses to teach:

> He carries out procedures very well; his approach
> to the patient is good. He is receptive to teach-
> ing and apparently learns quickly and thoroughly
> and he is dependable. You can't expect young
> nurses or young people to know something if they
> have never been exposed to it. I don't mind re-
> peating anything often enough for them to learn it
> thoroughly. (Diploma 56)

Another head nurse praised a diploma graduate for learning quickly and for asking questions:

> She adjusted to the hospital quickly and followed
> our procedures. If she doesn't know exactly how to
> do a procedure, she always comes and asks because
> she realizes the others are following what she does.
> She always seems to use good judgment in notifying
> the supervisor or doctor of a patient's condition.
> (Diploma 1955)

One head nurse praised the training a degree-program
graduate received and felt that as a new graduate she was up
to date on procedures. She felt that in some ways this nurse

was superior:

> I think there are some things that she excels in
> but in general I would say she meets. I think
> that she has had very good experience in her train-
> ing as to following procedures. Of course, she is
> a new graduate and a little bit more up to date on
> new procedure than maybe some of us are. One thing
> that I had noticed about Mrs. S is the way she
> handles the children. She does this very well.
> (Degree 56)

Another head nurse emphasized the ability of a recent

graduate to take charge of the floor shortly after she came to

the hospital:

> When she came, she adapted herself very well. It
> wasn't long before she was taking charge on my days
> off. Being from another hospital and not knowing
> the layout here, she did rather well, I thought.
> (Diploma 56)

Graduates of other programs who met head nurse standards

in spite of criticism. Several of the graduates of other pro-

grams who were judged by the head nurse to meet the standards

of good nursing care were seen to have difficulties which might

be labeled emotional or interpersonal. For example, one head

nurse found a recent graduate to do good nursing care but to

need calming down occasionally:

> She does good nursing care -- she carries out the
> procedures. She gets a little excited on occasion
> but she does calm down if you talk to her.
> (Diploma 56)

Another head nurse talked about the problems of all new

graduates in adjusting to a city hospital. She pointed out

that the "expertness of their nursing care is a little bit

hidden because of the graduates' feeling of insecurity."

>One of the things that affects a young graduate
>coming to our hospital is if her period of educa-
>tional experience has been in a private hospital
>school. The adjustment that these individuals have
>to make to a city institution can be a tremendous
>one. I think it takes a while for these new
>graduates to assimilate and become accustomed to
>city policies as to the general run of the private
>hospital. For a period of time, varying with the
>individual, the expertness of their nursing care
>is a little bit hidden because of the graduates'
>own feeling of insecurity. The care that Miss B
>gives is good but it is not what we would call total
>and complete care because for a while she is more
>or less submerged under the process of learning
>the various details that she needs to be concerned
>with. She has had a little bit of difficulty in
>learning our way of doing things. (Diploma 56)

One graduate who worked in the nursery was found to be

inconsiderate of mothers:

>Her knowledge is fine. She watches the babies well,
>but she is not very considerate sometimes with
>the mothers. She's really quite short with them at
>times. All in all, she isn't superior. (Diploma 55)

Several comments were made about graduates of other pro-

grams who had difficulty assuming supervisory responsibility.

For example, one head nurse stated that a diploma-program

graduate had difficulty fitting "into the role of team leader

because she is a recent graduate."

>She was not able to fit into the role of team
>leader easily because she is a recent graduate.
>(What graduate program?) Three-year program.
>There has been some reticence on her part to take
>hold and I notice that she had difficulty in
>taking hold of the reins. There is a lot of ten-
>sion on the floor and the parents are tense when
>their children are so sick. There are a lot of
>doctors milling around and there are a lot of
>things to carry out. There is a lot of tension,

and she felt it, just like any other nurse would
and she had some difficulties at first and she
didn't complete an assignment and she wasn't
giving able direction to the auxiliaries and I was
just about to have a conference with her when she
asked me what she was doing wrong, so at that very
time I told her and she was able to pick up the
reins at that point. I don't know where she got
them from, but she was able to take a tighter hold
and I have noticed a great improvement in her, although I do say that it's telling on her. I think
she feels a little tense now. She doesn't have
the same air about her as she did at first. I think
it's a shame. (What is?) That there is so much
responsibility as a team leader. (Diploma 56)

Another head nurse felt that a graduate nurse had been

pushed into doing charge duty when she was not ready for it:

I think she was pushed into doing charge duty when
she was not ready for it. I don't think she was
here three weeks before she did charge duty and I
don't feel she was given enough chance to become
oriented to the way we do our procedures. Just in
talking to her, she isn't sure of herself. The only
thing I observed and the only thing I heard commented on was the fact that sometimes on her orders
and the doctors' orders, she didn't always carry
through with them. (Diploma 56)

A graduate of a diploma program was criticized for being

unable to control a large patient load. Her head nurse stated:

Not superior in any way. Well, it is primarily
detail work. Also she is unable to control a lot
of patients. She is not to the extent we feel she
is falling down. She is there, but she doesn't
have complete control. She has never lost complete
control of it either but in a lot of ways she
doesn't handle the situation in the best possible
way. (Diploma 55)

Description of Nurses Failing
to Meet Standards

One head nurse who had considerable experience with pilot-program graduates stated that the nurse she rated as definitely failing to meet her standards was "one of the weaker students of the two-year program." She criticized her personal relations as well as her skills:

> She definitely fails to meet my standards of good nursing. She is one of the weaker students of the two-year program. She has trouble with personal relationships. She fills the physical needs of patients very well at times and then at other times not at all. Her skills are developed very poorly, such as therapy, special equipment, etc. They are difficult for her. Personal relations are her greatest weakness. (PP 56)

A head nurse who rated two pilot-program graduates as definitely failing felt that they needed to become more accustomed to hospital nursing:

> I can't say that she definitely fails but I don't think she meets the standards either. I think she will as she gets more accustomed to hospital nursing. But I don't think she is adequate. (PP 55)

> She is a little below average but I think it is a lack of experience. She's from the shorter program and I think her problem is that she hasn't had sufficient experience yet. (PP 55)

It is important to add that each of the two graduates had already had more than one year of experience. It is reasonable to suggest that these two did not learn quickly once they were placed on the job.

Another head nurse criticized a pilot-program graduate who had more than two years of graduate nurse experience for needing repeated exposures to procedures and for being late in reporting for duty.

> I feel that she was too immature to carry any type of responsibility. She could not carry out procedures without being repeated several times. It was very hard for her -- even though she lived within walking distance of the hospital -- to be prompt on duty. It was just a job and not something she was vitally interested in. (PP 54)

A particularly interesting statement by a head nurse who rated the three pilot-program graduates with whom she worked as failing to meet her standards used team leadership as the criterion for meeting standards:

> I hate to say it, but none of those three fall into it. I think Mrs. W is very capable, but she does not meet the standards of a team leader, as yet. I have very little doubt that she will be able to -- I am sure that once she is told and shown and given the opportunity to perform, she will do very well. She has adjusted very nicely. (PP 56)

Another head nurse specifically stated that a pilot-program graduate definitely failed to meet her standards but that this was due to her program. She also pointed out that this individual had "the initiative and ability to do better":

> She doesn't meet my standards but I don't think this is due to the individual herself. It has much to do with the way she has been trained. She needs a little supervision. She has the initiative and the ability to do better. (PP 56)

Some of the statements made about the graduates of other programs who failed to meet standards of the head nurses were similar. For example, one head nurse criticized a diploma-program graduate for having "no sense of time":

> She has no sense of responsibility for her own time. She was a part-time worker employed here from 9 to 5:30. This is the reason primarily that I had to have her removed from my floor. Some days she would come in 7 to 3:30. Maybe she would come in 8 to 4:30 without any advance notice -- whichever suited her convenience, those were the days she would come in. She had a very indifferent attitude. (Diploma 54)

Another head nurse stated about a graduate who failed to meet her standards:

> I don't think this girl is as good as she could be. She lacks the interest she should have. She doesn't check on things. I wouldn't class her above average -- if anything, below. (Diploma 54)

A head nurse commented about a diploma-program graduate she had worked with as a student:

> I sort of have to make excuses for S. She is trying very hard. She's a little below average. She forgets. She has a very poor memory -- doesn't organize her work as well as she could. Whether it was habit she formed in training, because I remember her as a student, she was that way ...
> But she has tried very hard and today she's my team leader and she is doing better work all the time. But she does forget lots of things and of course, we sort of joke about it, and that way I think I've gotten farther with her than if I criticized her severely. I've teased her about not charting things. I have to watch her quite closely to see that orders are carried out. (Diploma 55)

Summary

The ratings of the graduates of pilot and other programs warrant retaining the hypothesis that:

> ... given some work experience, the graduates of the pilot programs perform the functions of the staff nurse as well as graduates of other types of programs.

Although the ratings of pilot-program graduates who have been working three or more months as staff nurses indicated that they performed generally as well as graduates of other programs, the ratings and qualitative statements about the nurses indicated some differences between graduates of pilot programs and graduates of other nursing programs.

The ratings illustrated the competence of the graduates of pilot programs in that more than 80 per cent of the 85 pilot-program graduates were found by their head nurses to be as good as most or above most graduates of other programs with whom they worked. Of the 85 pilot-program graduates rated, 60 (71 per cent) met their head nurse's standards of good nursing, 13 (15 per cent) were rated definitely superior to the head nurse's standards. Comparison of the ratings of the pilot-program graduates with the ratings of 50 graduates of other programs revealed that the distributions were similar.

Significant differences were found between the two distributions on two behaviors pertaining to nursing skills. However, these differences disappeared for the pilot-program graduates who had had more than one year's experience. The one difference between the two groups that did not disappear with work experience was related to asking questions.

The qualitative statements by the head nurses indicated that the pilot-program graduates are interested in nursing, ask questions where they are not certain, and lack confidence when they first begin nursing. However, they were found to develop rapidly with experience. They are particularly strong in giving patient care and in interpersonal relationships.

The statements indicated that many of the raters were highly conscious of the pilot programs. In some cases they tended to rate the program and not the individual pilot-program graduate.

The qualities that head nurses find it most difficult to deal with are personality characteristics rather than qualities related to preparation.

CHAPTER XIII

THE GRADUATES EVALUATE THEIR PREPARATION

FOR NURSING

This chapter is concerned with the reactions of the graduates of the pilot and other programs to their preparation. The materials in this chapter come from the forty-five interviews with graduates of pilot programs and the eighteen interviews with graduates of other programs.

How the Graduates Feel about
Their Preparation

In general the graduates of the pilot programs were satisfied with their preparation. The majority of the pilot-program graduates responded without reservation that their preparation was adequate for the nursing jobs they have had (Table 48).

TABLE 48

REACTIONS OF 45 GRADUATES OF PILOT PROGRAMS AND
18 GRADUATES OF OTHER PROGRAMS TO THEIR
PREPARATION FOR NURSING

Feeling	Graduates of Pilot Programs		Graduates of Other Programs	
	N	%	N	%
Positive	26	58	11	61
Positive with reservations	15	33	6	33
Negative	1	2	1	6
Negative with reservations	3	7	0	0
Total	45	100	18	100

The graduates of the pilot programs were particularly positive about the approach to patient care they were taught. They emphasized the concept of "total care," which involved the emotional as well as the physical condition of the patient. Also they stressed the quality of their training in giving bedside care. For example, one pilot-program graduate said about her preparation:

> It was good. What was particularly good was the bedside care we were taught and the emphasis on the relationship with the patient. We dealt directly with the patient, giving treatments and medications as well as understanding him as a person. (PP 56)

Although the pilot-program graduates were generally satisfied with their preparation, and especially with their preparation for giving bedside care, many were extremely articulate concerning their limited practical experience, primarily the experience of assuming supervisory responsibility.[1] One pilot-program graduate put it this way:

> I came from a two-year program and starting at first on a new ward, I feel that I don't have enough experience in some ways. I feel that I have had good theoretical preparation; it was just the practical part that was limited in my training. That's why I actually start out new. I might know the theory but I can't put it into practice right away. (Does it bother you that you don't have this practical experience?) Well, in emergencies it might

---

[1]Since the interpretation of "practical experience" is perhaps the major underlying issue of the pilot-program experiment, the reader is cautioned not to draw conclusions from these statements alone but rather to see this very realistic problem in the context of the entire program before making judgments.

> but in routine things that might come up on the
> ward and I haven't done them before, I don't feel
> upset about it because if I have any questions
> there is always someone to answer them. It doesn't
> bother me to ask questions. (PP 56)

Another graduate who felt satisfied with her training

but felt that practical experience was a problem said:

> I'm awfully glad that I attended B. I finished my
> training in two years while other girls are still
> in school. I feel that we could have had a bit
> more practical experience but the program is work-
> ing itself out. At B they have some wonderful
> instructors and the program is working out. (PP 56)

Several graduates of the pilot programs emphasized the

lack of experience in assuming charge nurse responsibilities:

> We were prepared to be a bedside nurse, or a staff
> nurse. As far as my training is concerned all I am
> qualified to be is a staff nurse. We didn't have
> any responsibilities on the floor in training.
> According to the way we were trained we were sup-
> posed to only ask for bedside nursing, we were not
> supposed to be in charge, and we were never supposed
> to be a supervisor. Now this is fine in theory,
> but when you come out and get in a place like this
> there would be times when a nurse is sick or she
> has her days off and we just had to take over, and
> the first time I was scared. I didn't have any
> idea about how to give orders. I was used to tak-
> ing them. Here I am at the desk doing charts or
> something and I thought, "Who am I to tell them?
> They've been working longer than I and they know
> what to do." Just because I was a graduate didn't
> mean that I should be in charge, I felt, since I
> didn't have the background to be in charge. (PP 56)

Another graduate who pointed out the same problem con-

trasted the training of the diploma student with her own

program:

> In training they told us that even the three-year
> graduates are not prepared for charge nursing.

> However, they do have the experience, which we
> didn't. We didn't work the 3-11 or the 11-7 as
> students, so we had absolutely no idea of what was
> expected of us. I was awfully nervous to start
> with. I felt inadequate. As far as charge nurs-
> ing, our training wasn't adequate. I think that
> it should have been included. (PP 56)

One graduate who felt that her program had been good but
that there had not been enough practical experience in the hospital said that the instructors were improving in their selection of clinical experiences:

> Well, like I say I can't compare it but I felt that
> with what little time we had and since it was a
> fairly new program I felt they did a much better
> job in preparing us than they did the first class.
> I think they are still improving because I can tell
> when the student nurses come on the floor. The
> instructors are learning what to cut out and what
> to keep. Our experiences were all good but my chief
> complaint is that there wasn't enough of them.
> (PP 56)

By way of contrast, a hospital school graduate stated:

> I feel that they did a very good job. Before I
> graduated I got to charge, which was good.
> (Diploma 54)

Another graduate of a diploma program who felt that her
charge nurse experience was important stated that student
nurses had been given this experience because graduate nurses
were not available:

> I think I had a very good preparation because we
> had the experience of having responsibility on
> evening duty and during the day. During the night
> shift in several departments when I was in train-
> ing, they wouldn't have graduate nurses to cover so
> often a student nurse would take over the entire
> responsibility for all the patients on the floor.
> (What do you mean by the entire responsibility?)
> The treatments, medications, and everything.

(Did you have the responsibility of taking charge of the floor on days?) No, on days we just had the responsibility of taking care of patients assigned to you and also doing medications. (Diploma 56)

A graduate of a degree program emphasized that her program had not provided much hospital experience:

I think it was pretty good as far as book learning was concerned. It was very good. We didn't get too much experience. They expected that to follow when we were graduates. We didn't get the training on the floor as some of the schools do, since we were under a different concept. (Degree 56)

The "different concept" in this degree program seems similar to one of the educational concepts guiding the pilot programs -- that is, that extensive practice in giving nursing care follows rather than precedes graduation.

The nursing experience that a student in a diploma program has depends on the kind of patients in the hospital in which she trains. One nurse pointed out the difference between the private hospital in which she received her training and the public hospital in which she went to work:

I think that nursing requires experience, and I have learned more here in my three months than I did during my three years in my own training school. I learned good nursing care here, and, well, I've never seen such sick people. In Y, where I trained, we had sick people but nothing in comparison with the patients here. These patients really are a challenge to the nurse. (Diploma 56)

Not all graduates of diploma programs had responsibilities during their preparation. For example, one stated:

There are some things that could be improved. The girls should be given more training in responsibility. She shouldn't all of a sudden be a graduate nurse without having had responsibilities

at all. And there should be more practical experience. The teachers were good at the theory
but at the applying of the things it wasn't so
good. There were some procedures I didn't feel
at ease with because there just wasn't enough
practice, especially in obstetrics. (Diploma 56)

Not all diploma programs emphasize practice and learning
by practice. One graduate of a diploma program liked her program because it stressed the "principles of nursing":

I feel on the whole my preparation was adequate
because the principles of nursing were stressed
at the school where I trained rather than specific
instances so that I find it comparatively easy to
apply what I have learned in the past. (Diploma 55)

The majority of the graduates of pilot and other programs felt that certain aspects of their preparation were particularly good (Table 49).

TABLE 49

GRADUATES' RESPONSES TO: DO YOU FEEL THAT ANY
PARTS OF YOUR PREPARATION WERE PARTICULARLY GOOD
FOR THE KIND OF NURSING REQUIRED OF YOU IN THIS JOB?

Responses	Pilot Program N	%	Other Programs N	%
Yes	41	91	15	83
No	4	9	3	17
Total	45	100	18	100

The preponderance of responses of the pilot-program
graduates concerning the particularly good parts of their
preparation, as with the previous responses analyzed, dealt

with the quality of the patient care they were taught. One

pilot-program graduate stated:

> They developed an interest in the individual.
> We try to treat the patient as a whole person
> and see him not only as one that we are giving
> medication and baths to but as a total person.
> Our school of nursing is rather new and their
> conception of teaching is rather novel in that
> whenever we were reading or studying a type of
> disease, those are the kinds of patients we were
> assigned to. Our practice is correlated with our
> study and you get more out of it. (PP 56)

Another described the kind of clinical assignment used

to promote the learning of this type of patient care:

> We were assigned on the floor as first- and second-
> year students to a limited number of patients so
> that we had time to realize the full patient care,
> physical and mental. They gave us time to really
> understand our patients. We were able to correlate
> our own views with the doctor's diagnosis. (PP 55)

Several felt that their preparation in medications was

particularly good. One pilot-program graduate mentioned other

aspects of her program as well as medications:

> The instructors that we had made us be exact as
> far as measurement of medications and sterile tech-
> nique. Those things never leave my mind. We got
> a good background in why we do things. Some of
> the practical things, I didn't feel too secure in
> because we only did them once or twice. But,
> these things you can pick up easily if you have
> the theoretical background. (PP 56)

Other particularly good aspects of their preparation

were mentioned by the pilot-program graduates, such as: train-

ing in labor and delivery, pediatrics, the kind of supervision

they received, and the democratic atmosphere. However, none of these points was made more than once.

The graduates of other programs emphasized as particularly good their experience as charge nurses. A diploma graduate stated:

> When we were students even in our second year we had to take charge of the 3-11 and 11-7 shifts. It was difficult but that was the way we learned. (Diploma 54)

A diploma school graduate felt that her preparation as a team leader was particularly good:

> I did have preparation as a team leader in my school of nursing. So that at this hospital where they are using the team system, I believe it is of value to me now. (Diploma 55)

A graduate of a degree program referred to her course in ward management and team leadership as having been particularly helpful. Only one graduate of the other programs mentioned bedside nursing. She stated:

> I felt that the experience in bedside nursing and working with critical patients was good. (Diploma 56)

Other aspects of the preparation mentioned were: small classes, experience with oxygen and suction equipment, well-rounded training, and the variety of medical patients. None of these was mentioned more than once.

The majority of the graduates of the pilot programs felt that their preparation for nursing had particular weaknesses, while a minority of the graduates of the other programs felt that their preparation had weaknesses (Table 50).

TABLE 50

GRADUATES' RESPONSES TO: DO YOU FEEL THAT ANY PARTS
OF YOUR PREPARATION WERE NOT ADEQUATE FOR THE KIND OF
NURSING REQUIRED OF YOU IN THIS JOB?

Responses	Graduates of Pilot Programs		Graduates of Other Programs	
	N	%	N	%
Yes	28	62	3	17
No	17	38	15	83
Total	45	100	18	100

In specifying the weaknesses of their preparation, most
of the comments from the pilot-program graduates dealt with
practical experience. For example, one graduate stated:

> Well, in my case, I think the practical experience
> is about the only thing that holds me back a little
> bit. Treatments, medications, following doctors'
> orders, the doctor-nurse relationship -- we didn't
> have enough practice in these. (PP 56)

One pointed out that the size of the classes limited the
opportunity actually to do certain procedures:

> With the large classes there were things that each
> one of us did not get to do. For example, I didn't
> get to help with a colostomy until after I graduated.
> (PP 56)

Another graduate, who graduated in the first class and
felt that practical experience would have helped, questioned
the way she was treated:

> I think it would have helped if we had more prac-
> tical experience in the hospital than we did have
> when we were students. Then again it might have
> been a more narrow school (if this were done).
> When we were first graduated, we were just like

students, maybe it was because of the hospital
we worked in. I don't know. We were treated like
children, like we didn't know anything, and we did
know some things. (Did they let you assume charge
nurse responsibilities?) I got the 4-12 shift
and I got along pretty well. (How long after you
started working did you do this?) Right after we
graduated. I guess I had worked about a month.
(PP 54)

One graduate emphasized the lack of experience in assuming responsibility:

As time goes by, new things come out and improvements can be made. We weren't taught responsibility.
Of course each student is different and some are
able to shoulder responsibility better than others
but we never really had the chance to take charge
and things like that until after graduation and I
think that is a little hard. (Have you discussed
this situation with other graduates of your program?)
Yes, and we pretty much agree that there is really
nothing like the first time you take that responsibility. I think responsibility is a good thing to
make everyone shoulder. (PP 56)

One pilot-program graduate found that pharmacology was
weak:

Pharmacology was weak. (In what way?) You're not
familiar enough with drugs. But I find many nurses
with far more years of training who don't know as
much as we did. But we do understand antibiotics.
(PP 56)

Other weaknesses mentioned were: charts and slips, intravenous
feeding, pediatrics, treatments, too much supervision. Each
of these was mentioned only once.

The only parts of their preparation not considered
adequate by graduates of other programs were: the laboratory
work, lack of variety of diseases in the training hospital,
and the inadequacy of medical and tuberculosis training.

One of the most interesting comments was made by the degree-program graduate who had previously stated that her preparation was good "as far as book learning was concerned.... We didn't get too much experience. They expected that to follow when we were graduates." This nurse felt that there were no parts óf her preparation that were inadequate:

> I think they achieved just about what they went about to achieve. (Degree 56)

What the Graduates Would Tell Their Friends

The majority of the graduates of both the pilot and other programs stated that they would recommend their own programs to a friend interested in becoming a nurse (Table 51). The eight pilot-program graduates who did not specifically recommend their own programs did not state that they would not recommend their own programs or specifically recommend another type of program. Instead they suggested that selecting a school of nursing is an individual matter. The interested person should investigate all programs and make a choice based upon such factors as time and money. Eight of the 37 who did recommend their own program made the qualification that choice had to be based upon the individual's financial and home situation.

Twelve of the eighteen graduates of other programs recommended their own programs. Three suggested that it was a matter of individual choice. Three diploma-program graduates specifically recommended degree programs.

TABLE 51

RECOMMENDATION OF NURSING PROGRAMS TO AN INTERESTED
FRIEND BY GRADUATES OF PILOT AND OTHER PROGRAMS

Recommendation	Graduates of Pilot Programs		Graduates of Other Programs	
	N	%	N	%
My own program	37	82	12	67
Other than own program	8	18	6	33
Total	45	100	18	100

The nurses interviewed were asked to name three outstanding and three weak aspects that they would tell an interested
friend about their own programs (Table 52) On the average the
pilot-program graduates named slightly more outstanding and
weak aspects of their programs. The outstanding aspects mentioned by the pilot-program graduates were predominantly outside
of the specialized nursing preparation. Seventy-six (68 per cent)
of the 112 outstanding aspects concerned (a) attending college,
which included specific reference to taking other than nursing
courses, mixing with other students, and participating in extra-
curricular activities; (b) length of the program, which involved being able to complete training in two rather than three
years; (c) living arrangements, which involved being able to
live at home while becoming a nurse. Only five outstanding
comments from graduates of other programs fit into the categories above. Four of the five were mentioned by the three
degree-program graduates who commended the opportunity to be

TABLE 52

OUTSTANDING AND WEAK ASPECTS OF THE NURSING PROGRAMS THAT GRADUATES OF PILOT AND OTHER PROGRAMS WOULD MENTION TO AN INTERESTED FRIEND

Aspects of the Nursing Programs related to:	OUTSTANDING		WEAK	
	Number of times mentioned by: Graduates of Pilot Programs (N=45)	Number of times mentioned by: Graduates of Other Programs (N=18)	Number of times mentioned by: Graduates of Pilot Programs (N=45)	Number of times mentioned by: Graduates of Other Programs (N=18)
Attending college	38	4	8	
Length of program	21		1	1
Living arrangements	17	1	4	
Nursing preparation:				
teaching and supervision	13	10	1	6
total patient care	9			
bedside care	4			
in general	2	2	23	7
practical experience		12	11	4
specialized areas		5		
Not required to give service	5			
Cost	2	2	2	
Affiliation				
Learned to take responsibility	1		1	
First year -- too condensed			1	1
Third year -- nothing happened				
Study time			7	1
Newness of program			1	1
No chance to progress				
Total	112	36	60	20
Average number of aspects per interviewee	2.5	2.0	1.3	1.1

part of a college environment. The fifth comment was given by a diploma graduate who felt that the experience of living in a residence with other nursing students had been an outstanding aspect of her program.

Although the pilot-program graduates did commend their nursing preparation, their comments referred primarily to the kind of nursing they were taught, while the graduates of other programs tended to commend the practical experience in general and in specific areas of nursing.

Examination of the weaknesses mentioned revealed the most common category for both groups to be practical experience. Thirty-four (57 per cent) of the total number of comments from pilot-program graduates mentioned practical experience, including experience in assuming responsibility, as weaknesses of the program.

One pilot-program graduate felt that students observed but did not have the opportunity to practice treatments and procedures. Also, this graduate felt that students should be expected to work at the pace graduate nurses worked on the floor. She stated:

> Clinical experience -- they should give a little more time and teach the more complicated treatments and participate in them rather than just watching them done. They sort of protect their students. They only get two patients regardless of how busy the floor is ... they'll still have their two patients. I think that they should be more in the pace with the floor and give you three or four even though it is going to push them.... just so they'll get the feeling and won't panic when they get in the situation that there isn't anyone else to do it. (PP 56)

A pilot-program graduate who designated specific
clinical areas qualified her statement in an important way:

> I would mention that our pediatric training was
> not extensive enough. Most of us thought we
> didn't have enough, but I've worked it since and
> we got more than we thought. I would also like
> to have spent some time in surgery and learned
> the different types. (PP 56)

A pilot-program graduate who also felt that the
primary weakness of the pilot programs was in the lack of practical experience found that the lack of experience could be
made up with time:

> Lack of practical experience, but that can be
> quickly gained as you work. It doesn't take too
> much time if you have the basic training. (PP 56)

Several of the graduates felt that the program was too
condensed. One fixed this in the first year. Another felt
that the program could be revised by having a summer session:

> The amount of time is probably quite long enough
> in some fields but it isn't in this field. We
> had a summer vacation just like other college
> students and that made it even shorter. That was
> time wasted. More time could have been spent in
> nursing. (PP 56)

A pilot-program graduate who commented on the expense
also found the practical experience a weakness:

> Well, initially it's a lot more expensive. And,
> the way it is speeded up. I mean you don't get
> as much experience. Over all, I do think we get
> enough experience to function. (PP 56)

For some pilot-program students, the initial expense
was a very real problem. If they could not live at home, they

had the expense of room and board, which is not a problem in
hospital schools of nursing. If the person can afford the
initial expense for two years, it is possible to earn enough
as a nurse in the year of time saved to compensate for the
initial expense.

Although graduates of the pilot programs emphasized
the opportunity to attend classes as a positive aspect of
their training, this class work was mentioned as weak by eight
nurses. For example, one graduate stated:

> I think we could have had more instruction in
> anatomy and physiology, but as I understand it,
> they changed that. And we had to take many
> classes that were really irrelevant to nursing,
> and they have also changed that, and we could
> have had a better psychiatric or psychology
> class. Actually, when we were in the psychiatric
> area it was good but before that when we had the
> psychology class, it was a very poor class.
> (PP 56)

Although this nurse was dissatisfied with the course
offerings, she pointed out, as others who have already been
referred to have done, that changes have been made.

Graduates of the pilot programs also found weaknesses
that did not pertain to the class work or the practical experience. Seven made references to the experimental nature of
their programs. One pilot-program graduate referred to the
refusal of some people to accept the pilot programs:

> The reluctance of the nursing world as a whole
> to accept this new program is a little handicap
> but as time goes on it is going to be overcome.
> At the beginning they were a little skeptical to
> accept us. They doubted our ability to produce,

which is natural. It was new ... something
that they didn't know too much about. (PP 56)

Another person pointed out that the pilot-program

graduate had little chance to progress:

> There isn't much chance of progression from a
> two-year school. It's unlikely that you would
> ever become head nurse or anything like that.
> You don't have the educational background.
> (PP 55)

Some graduates of other programs mentioned weaknesses

in aspects of their clinical experience. One nurse felt there

was too little variety in the types of diseases they had had

experience with. Another pointed to the failure to give the

student responsibility:

> We could have been given more responsibility in
> the third year. (Diploma 54)

Another diploma-school graduate felt that there was

inadequate supervision in the hospital:

> Our academic program -- It was all right but I
> felt we could have had more things. On some
> services, we were just pushed into it without
> supervision. (Diploma 54)

Two other graduates of other programs mentioned inadequate

supervision.

A graduate of a newly established degree program found

the newness of the program provided some problems:

> Possibly the newness of the program is still
> a weakness. Not enough coordination between
> the head nurse and instructors concerning the
> students. (Degree 56)

The description of the strengths and weaknesses of their programs by the graduates of the pilot and other programs provides an important illustration of the effect of shifting the control of education from the hospital to the college campus. Having relinquished the hospital as the center of their training, the pilot-program graduates find that the biggest weakness in their preparation was the limited clinical experience. On the other hand, the outstanding aspects of the programs derived from the collegiate educational climate.

In eliminating some of the problems involved in hospital service, the pilot programs create new ones arising from the relationship between the independent school and the agency which supplies the experience. The problems created involve the optimal use of limited time in the hospital.

Summary

In general, the pilot-program graduates were satisfied with their preparation for nursing. The major portion of the positive comments concerning their preparation dealt with the quality of the instruction in total patient care. The weaknesses they reported were related primarily to the limited amount of practical experience in their program. The majority of the pilot-program graduates would recommend their own programs to an interested friend. The reasons they gave stressed the attributes of the college environment. In contrast, the reasons given by graduates of other programs for recommending their program dealt primarily with the variety of clinical experience and the experience of taking supervisory responsibility.

Some pilot-program graduates referred to changes that had already been made in their programs. The revisions pertained to aspects of the programs identified as weaknesses.

CHAPTER XIV

THE PILOT-PROGRAM GRADUATES AND THE PILOT PROGRAMS
ARE VIEWED BY DIRECTORS OF NURSING SERVICE

This chapter is concerned with the views of directors of nursing services concerning the pilot-program graduates and the pilot programs. The materials in this chapter come from twenty-five interviews with directors of nursing services in the hospitals visited. The interviews were unstructured and tended to elicit a particularly wide range of responses related to nursing services and nursing education as well as to the graduates and the programs.

The initial foci of most of the interviews were the problems of nursing service and the role of the staff nurse in the hospital. Once these aspects had been discussed, direct but unstandardized questions were asked about experiences with pilot-program graduates. Direct questions about the pilot programs were avoided until the director brought up the subject of preparation. This tactic was part of the attempt to stress experiences with the pilot-program graduates rather than opinions about the pilot programs as educational programs. As the quotations from the interviews indicate, the directors of nursing services were highly conscious of the pilot programs.

The Cooperative Research Project was not subject to laboratory controls. The description of factors that influence the interpretation of the present study pointed out some of the kinds of variables that were not controlled (Chapter VII). The existence of some of these variables is demonstrated in the quotations included in this chapter. They contain illustrations of the network of interrelationships between the attitudes and the perceptions of nursing service administrators.

The quotations are long. This length is justified because they provide a more complete picture of what happened in individual hospital situations than any of the previous materials. It was not the purpose of the interviews to discover the steps involved in integrating pilot-program graduates into the nursing profession. However, the quotations contain important implications for the relationship between the attitudes of nursing service administrators and the evaluation of the pilot-program graduates and the pilot programs.

Three judges -- a nurse practitioner, a nursing educator, and a psychologist -- were given the twenty-five transcribed interviews to read and rate. None of the three raters was connected with the Cooperative Research Project nor did he have a point of view concerning the pilot programs. The attitudes were rated on a five-point scale (Appendix K).

304

The Reliability of the Ratings

The ratings of the three judges were highly reliable.
The three judges were in complete agreement on sixteen of the
twenty-five ratings of attitudes toward the pilot-program
graduates and on fourteen of the twenty-five attitudes toward
pilot programs (Table 53).

TABLE 53

RATING AGREEMENTS AMONG THREE JUDGES ON ATTITUDES
TOWARD PILOT-PROGRAM GRADUATES AND PILOT PROGRAMS

Agreements	Pilot Program Graduates	Pilot Programs
Agreement among three	16	14
Agreement among two	9	9
No agreement	0	2
Total	25	25

Attitudes of Directors of Nursing Services

The majority (56 per cent) of the twenty-five nursing
service administrators interviewed held either "favorable" or
"mostly favorable" attitudes toward the pilot-program graduates, while nine (36 per cent) held "unfavorable" or "mostly
unfavorable" attitudes toward the graduates (Table 54). Twelve
(48 per cent) of the directors expressed "favorable" or "mostly
favorable" attitudes toward the pilot programs, while seven
(28 per cent) expressed "unfavorable" or "mostly unfavorable"

attitudes toward the pilot programs.

TABLE 54

ATTITUDES OF NURSING SERVICE DIRECTORS TOWARD
PILOT PROGRAM GRADUATES AND PILOT PROGRAMS[a]

Attitudes	Toward Pilot Program Graduates		Toward Pilot Programs	
	N	%	N	%
Favorable	12	48	9	36
Mostly favorable with some unfavorable	2	8	3	12
As many favorable as unfavorable	2	8	1	4
Mostly unfavorable with some favorable	7	28	3	12
Unfavorable	2	8	4	16
Not enough information to rate	0	0	3	12
Lack of agreement among judges	0	0	2	8
Total	25	100	25	100

[a]The classification of individuals into attitudinal categories
was based on the agreement among the judges. Since the
agreement among the judges was so close, classification was
simple.

The distributions of the attitudes toward the graduates
and the programs were dichotomous -- that is, the directors
seemed either to be for or against the graduates and the programs. This fact is illustrated by the relative absence of
ratings in the middle category, which helps account for the
high degree of reliability of the ratings. Since the favorable

or unfavorable character of each director's attitude was so
clear-cut, the rater's choice was limited to one of the two
favorable or unfavorable categories. It is the middle range
which provides the greatest difficulty in classification.

The attitudes of directors of nursing services toward
the pilot-program graduates and the pilot programs are positively correlated (Table 55).[1] Directors who described their
experiences with pilot-program graduates positively also expressed positive feelings about the programs. Directors who
described their experiences with pilot-program graduates nega-
tively also expressed negative feelings about the programs.
The existence of this relationship does not, however, imply
causation. Quotations given later in the chapter describe
several instances in which the negative attitude preceded experiences with the graduates. Such preliminary bias may or may
not have determined the director's perceptions of the graduates.
It must also be remembered that some of those who perceived
the performance of the graduates positively may have had preliminary bias -- either for or against the pilot programs.

---

[1]The probability that the relationship described in
Table 55 between attitudes toward the pilot-program graduates
and the pilot programs occurred by chance is less than one
in 10,000 as computed by Fisher's Exact Probability Test.
Description of the computational method can be found in Sidney
Siegel, Nonparametric Statistics for the Behavioral Sciences
(New York: McGraw-Hill Book Company, 1956), p. 96.

TABLE 55

RELATIONSHIP BETWEEN ATTITUDES OF NURSING SERVICE
DIRECTORS TOWARD PILOT-PROGRAM GRADUATES AND
TOWARD PILOT PROGRAMS

Attitude toward the Pilot-Program Graduates	Attitude toward the Programs		Totals
	Favorable or Mostly Favorable	As Many Favorable as Unfavorable, Mostly Unfavorable or Unfavorable	
Favorable or Mostly Favorable	11	0	11
As Many Favorable as Unfavorable, Mostly Unfavorable, or Unfavorable	1	8	9
Total	12	8	20

Five directors are not classified in Table 55. Three
of the five had not been classified on attitude toward the
pilot programs (Table 54). Of the three, two expressed favorable and one unfavorable attitudes toward the pilot-program
graduates. The remaining two were not classified because there
was no consensus among the raters as to their attitudes toward
the programs. Of the two, one expressed favorable and the other
unfavorable attitudes toward the graduates.

Of the eight directors who were generally unfavorable
to both the graduates and the programs, five were from one
pilot-program area. The sixth director interviewed from that
area was one of those unclassified because there was no

consensus among the raters concerning her attitudes toward the programs. However, her attitudes toward the graduates were generally unfavorable.

Analysis of Interviews of Directors of Nursing Services Holding Favorable or Predominantly Favorable Attitudes

Several of the directors of nursing services were extremely positive in their judgment of the quality of the pilot-program graduates. One found the two graduates employed by her hospital to be "excellent nurses," "enthusiastic about their work," and inferred that they must have had "exceptional clinical supervision." Other comments pertaining to the initial employment of the graduates are included in a quoted segment of the interview:

> (You have two graduates of the two-year programs. Did they receive any special orientation because of their different education?)
> No, we put them under what we consider strong supervision. They came to us at the suggestion of the secretary of the board examiners. She felt that the supervision here would be more adequate than anywhere else in this area. We placed them under strong supervision. They are excellent nurses. They do excellent bedside nursing. They get along well with the patients and with their associates. They were the kind of persons who show a constant interest in their work. There did not seem to be any lag in their enthusiasm. I felt at first that one of them was too closely tied to her home and that she was not as free to live her own life as she would have liked to but when we discussed that she said that she owed her parents some money and that her first job was to pay that debt and then she was going to go out and live on her own.

(Now you spoke of the strong supervision that they
had at the beginning. How long did it take before
they didn't need this kind of supervision? Were
they able to act as unit heads?)
Yes, they were and they did. They were placed in
charge of a unit or team in about three weeks.
(That soon?)
That is the usual procedure. We have fourteen
units or sections here and on each one we have a
head nurse and a supervisor and work is divided
into groups or units and that unit can be one or
more nurses for a team.
(So you found that they were the same as the graduates of the diploma programs?)
They certainly did not need extra help. What I found
about them was that they were more enthusiastic
about their work. That pleased me so. There was
a constant feeling of enthusiasm. That is generally
not true.
(I'd like to question their initial performance
here. Some people have said these girls have had
no nursing experience and only work under very close
supervision in their program. What happens when
they have to do a full day's work, which they have
never done in their training?)
They accept it without any apparent difficulty and
were able to organize it and carry it through.
They were the kind of persons who amaze me. They
are the kind who feel that if there was a need for
them they would work longer. That, of course, is
not our procedure but it was nice and it was impres-
sive. They must have had exceptional clinical
supervision or training. It must have been the best
kind of supervision. One had the feeling that they
would do only the best kind of work. They weren't
satisfied with less than a good job.
(When you speak of a staff nurse, do you consider
her primarily as a bedside nurse or also one who
manages?)
We try to emphasize the importance of bedside care
and that it is the nurse's responsibility to give
it and see that it is given. The nurse here has the
chance to give bedside care herself. We do not have
a school of nursing, you know.

Another enthusiastic director of nursing services

described similar experiences with graduates of a different

pilot program:

(I understand that you have two nurses who are
graduates of the two-year program and have just
hired two others.)
That's right and we'd be glad if we could get ten
or twelve more. We could use at least that many.
And, of course, in anticipation of our expansion,
we will be increasing our staff as rapidly as we
can.
(Have you been satisfied with their performance?)
We've been very happy with them. The outstanding
thing that we found about these girls is their
attitude. As they came to us, the first thing that
I noticed is that their approach was different from
the ordinary applicant. They would come to you
saying, "I'm Miss So-and-So," all prepared with
their credentials, which showed a very good training
from someplace. With all these credentials saying
they were two-year graduates, they'd say, "I'm a
two-year graduate. I am interested in anything you
have to offer me. And no matter what area you put
me in, I would rather not remain static. I would
like to move about because I have too many things
to learn to remain in one division."

Later in the interview this director of nursing services
pointed out that the pilot-program graduates needed some extra
support at the beginning but that they learned rapidly:

(Do you find that the graduates of the two-year
programs in the beginning had specific problems
concerning the service they could render because of
limitations in the two-year program?)
Well, I don't think you can pick this up and say
that this is a limitation of the program because we
don't know the program well enough. We don't know
the curriculum specifically ... but they were
floundering a little if you left them in the environment by themselves. I mean they needed support.
But, as I told you, their attitude makes giving
them support easy. They were willing to admit
their mistakes -- their deficiencies, and they were
easy to help. They learned rapidly. I think perhaps you find that the three-year graduate has a
little more solid basic foundation on which she
builds, but she is more reluctant to build and so
she doesn't develop. You see the eagerness in the
two-year girls.

(Is this extra supervision that they require something that deters them from doing a full day's job,
or are they able to carry a full day's job in the
first month?)
Oh yes, they can carry a full job very easily and
particularly if you give them a good strong head
nurse. If you get an insecure head nurse, which
happened in one instance, then the girl becomes a
little insecure ... and we misled you when we told
you we've only had two of them. We had a third
one we put into the wrong environment and it was a
very pressing environment, and she was frustrated
because she couldn't get the help she needed because of the busy floor.
(Would you describe what happened?)
She's now working in a doctor's office. She was
put on 3B, where Miss C is now. But Miss C has
had a year to adjust to our hospital and then she's
had a year's maturity beyond what Miss S had. It
is a very difficult floor. It moves very rapidly.
You consider perhaps sixteen major surgeries going
on in a day. The nursing care is pretty concentrated. It moves so rapidly that people tend to
think that they don't have the time to do what they
consider frills. They are supposed to produce when
they are put on that floor. However, I never heard
the statement, I never heard a head nurse say that
a girl wasn't producing because she was a two-year
graduate and didn't know how. I think that we have
had an amazing attitude toward this two-year
graduate. When I talk to other people who say they
have so much resistance to the two-year program I
felt ... occasionally you hear someone say, "Oh,
she's a two-year graduate," but this is the older
nurse, who doesn't understand the program. Normally,
in the working environment, I would say they have
done beautifully.

This director pointed out the importance of a "strong
head nurse" and the inability of one pilot-program graduate
to handle the assignment on a particularly difficult floor.
However, instead of describing the situations as reflecting
weaknesses in the graduates or the programs, she took the
responsibility herself for not providing the right kind of

supervision and assignment for the new pilot-program graduate. Her enthusiasm for the pilot-program graduates was not limited by recognition of their need for a "strong head nurse."

It is important to note that the three raters agreed in judging this director's attitudes as favorable to both the graduates and the programs. Even though she described the pilot-program graduates' need for initial support and the failure of one graduate to cope with the assignment on 3B, the raters did not find her at all critical of the graduates or the program.

Two hospitals that were used as the primary source of clinical experience for pilot-program students had nursing schools of their own that were terminating. This meant that the final graduating classes in the two terminating hospital programs were giving nursing service without pay in their third years at the same time that the first graduates of the pilot programs were being paid for working in the hospitals as staff nurses. Obviously these situations were ripe for conflict.

In the following lengthy quotation, the director of nursing services in one of the two hospitals describes some evidence of this conflict. The director mentions "rumblings." However, the problems encountered with students of their own programs and with some of their own staff did not prevent the hospital administration from cooperating with the new program. The cooperation on the part of the hospital administration was also evidenced in the establishment of a special orientation

program for the new graduates of the pilot programs (Chapter X).
Perhaps it was this cooperation that brought about the condition
that suggested the following question:

(My statistics indicate that a large proportion of
the graduates of D stayed to work here. Did the
graduates of your own program stay with you as
much as this group from the two-year program?)
My experience with the graduates of our own program was only for a couple of years. I've only
been here three and one-half years, and this experimental program began at about the time I came.
So there were two groups of three-year graduates.
The first group that graduated, the '54 girls,
stayed for quite a while. The '55 girls did not
stay with us. I heard from another director of
nursing that a lot of those girls are working at P.
The university is there and a lot were interested
in further education and the social life of the
school. They had their psychiatric affiliation
there in the summer quarter before they were
graduated. So they were very interested in P when
they graduated. The director of nurses also told
me that these girls wouldn't stay here because we
had changed our nursing program and they were a
little peeved about it. I don't know if that was
really right or not -- whether they would have
stayed or whether they wouldn't have. I do know
that we retained very few -- less than I observed
in prior years. So it may have been a factor. But
I think we have kept these people (the pilot-program
graduates) a little better than the other two groups
with which I have had experience. I don't know
whether they felt they wanted to stay and go through
the rotation (earlier the director described an
orientation and rotation plan for pilot-program
graduates). Some of them told me that they would
like to stay here until they could go through the
services and have had experience in a place that
understood them before they went out. That may
account for some of it. But we are happy to have
them stay because they are doing a good job.
(How does the fact that these girls are treated
differently affect their relationship with the
head nurses and supervisors?)
It's very difficult to assess. I think there is a
difference in what's occurring this year than that
which occurred with the '55 group. I think people
understand them better and are accepting them

better. We don't begin to hear the rumblings that
we heard in '55. The head nurses look for a worker
who can come in and do anything and everything
right from the start. Our orientation was planned
this way because of the feeling that we got both
from the worker and her supervisor. This year I
think there is much better acceptance. I don't
know if our orientation program is entirely responsible for the feeling or whether it is an acceptance
of the changes that occurred and going along with it
now. It was something new in '55.

The same director of nursing services had some ideas
about the amount of clinical experience that the pilot-program
students received. Her suggestion for "pretty concentrated experience" as a worker was not unlike the suggestions of several
students. However, it is important to note that at present she
finds the graduates acceptable. While she felt that some extra
experience would help in the transition from student nurse to
worker, basically she accepted the concept of the pilot programs
and found the graduates performed adequately. The director
could understand that experience outside the hospital, substituted for experience in the hospital, was valuable for the
student learning nursing. The acceptance of each experience as
a valid way of teaching nursing was an important indication of
her acceptance of the pilot programs.

(How do you feel about the clinical experience that
they get here as students?)
It apparently, from their performance, seems to be
fairly good. I do feel that maybe that's an area
that needs to be studied and I wouldn't think that
it could be dropped any. As I have seen them take
out a week or two at a time, I think many of us have
felt that they cannot afford to lose much. I think
Mrs. S (the director of the pilot program) has decreased the clinical experience just a little in the
second year over what the first year people have and

we all felt that they needed the time in the hospital, but they had good reasons and they substituted
the time with something that is valuable to the students. I have told her that I wondered what it
might mean to increase their course by including the
last quarter and the summer quarter left more or
less to the clinical situation where it would be
pretty concentrated experience and I would be interested in seeing what that would mean.
(Have you some idea of what the concentrated experience would mean?)
It should include more of the performance as a
worker. I would place more emphasis on the doing
-- the practicing of their skills. The performance
is on an individual basis and yet by and large
these people perform well.
(How well?)
They are able to assume responsibility. They can
do most of the treatment procedures and medication
procedures that our staff nurses can do. They are
probably weakest in more technical types of procedures because they have learned them or observed
them but they haven't had the experience of working
with them and consequently they need additional help.

An informed view of the purposes of the pilot programs

came from the director of nursing services of the other hospital

having a school of nursing that was terminating. This person's

understanding was probably influenced by her relationship with

the pilot-program students during the third year. As will be-

come clear in her statement, the hospital nursing service worked

closely with the pilot-program "student-graduates" during the

practicum period.

The director repeated what several of the already

quoted directors have stated about the rapidity with which the

pilot-program graduates developed on the job. Her statement

also included the following:

- There is something different about the graduates, and that is their desire to try new things.

- The teachers working in the program have changed their own attitudes toward learning and their methods of teaching.

- The pilot program was able to attract a wider range of students than the program that the hospital had run.

- There were advantages to teaching by correlating theory with practice.

- With two weeks of orientation after two years of training, the pilot-program graduates are "good team members."

- An informal evaluation of the pilot program by doctors from another community resulted in the recommendation that the junior college in their community establish a similar program.

(What has your feeling been about the kind of service that these girls give during the practicum year?)
They have had two years of training; the third year is really the practice of being a staff nurse.
They are not as ready as our girls who have graduated from a five-year program, but those girls were geared to giving service. These girls have been learning nursing techniques and so forth and are not able to take the load the first or second week. But after an orientation of two or three weeks, they are good team members. I might say that a little bit more orientation than the three-year graduate requires.
I would say that given some more orientation, within three, four, or five weeks the majority of them are learning to be team leaders.
(Not only do they give general bedside care but they are also able to function at the level of a team leader?)
That's right. I only know from the people who are supervising them, but just the other day we were pleased that one of our head nurses who was rather skeptical in her acceptance of this program and we felt that we had reached a goal when she said, "Yes, there is a difference. I can't put it into words but it's there." In talking to her for a while we finally got the idea that there is a difference in the performance of these girls. They want responsibility. They seek a challenge. They

don't take the attitude that they haven't had it yet.
There is also a difference in the approach of
teaching.
(This is somewhat shocking to me. In my experience
here I had come up with the impression that many of
the people who had taught in the program that you
had here before are also teaching in this program.
The students have the same hospital situation.
They have most of their clinical experience at
Huntington. Their teachers are the same. How then
would you account for the change in their conception
of nursing?)
That to me is the wonderful thing. It proves that
people can change, and teachers can change their
methods. The same people teaching nursing courses
have taken a different approach, a new approach.
(Do you mean that before they taught the courses
differently?)
Yes, before there was a different attitude. They
were afraid to let the student do this without their
supervision. Students hesitated to do things without being supervised. Now I say that they are
still being supervised, but somehow or other the
instructor is aware that this student must perform
in two years. There is a miraculous change. I
could name names. Teachers have changed their
attitudes toward learning. I don't know how to
explain it. There is a difference in philosophy.
(And these nurses who taught in the program that
you had here before, now approach the problem of
teaching nursing in a different way now that they
have been brought into this new program?)
I don't think that it was as integrated as this
program. I believe that the correlation of theory
and practice of nursing is accomplished better in
this new program.
(Yesterday when we talked about the five-year program you mentioned some of the problems of getting
twenty-five students to go into the five-year program.
Was it that you had a pretty selective approach to
recruitment in that program?)
I think that they were a very high-caliber group,
if I use that word correctly. They had two years
of junior college, so they were capable of junior
college work. I believe that one of the drawbacks
was the fact that we were selecting from a group of
girls that thought vocationally of nursing as a
career. Also from an income group that could afford
to go on for 30 unit credits, which cost about $20
a unit plus board and room.

(Then socially and economically the group attracted
might have represented a different group than those
going through now.)
This group to me represents a wider range in that
they can afford to come since they live at home with
their families. This way we are tapping new sources
plus an older age group. We have students with children, six, seven years old and even age fourteen.
The older woman is coming in and proving very good.
(You mentioned that the attitudes of these nurses
are outstanding. What about their skills, like the
skills involved in lifting and turning patients or
the giving of medications to a group of patients?
Do these girls have a level of skill that's comparable to that of the graduates of three-year
programs?)
I haven't seen it myself. So it's only hearsay.
But I would say that with this program it was
planned for a practicum, the faculty generaly knew
that the girls would have this practicum period in
which to develop their skills. Therefore I would
say the graduate who is beginning her practicum
does not have the skill in passing medications of
the five-year or three-year students. I consider
the five-year and the three-year graduates practically the same. But I should say that within two
or three weeks these skills become developed.
(It only takes two or three weeks for them to develop these skills?)
Yes, I think so. However, I can't prove it.
(What about the communication with doctors?
This seems to be a problem in some places.)
I think communications are good in this group.
One of the things our head nurses have said is
that their communications skills are developed and
I've not been aware of this difficulty. These students don't hesitate to ask questions. They'll go
right up to the doctor. That of course involves
individual differences. But I can't see where the
other girls have any advantages over the two-year
students as far as communication goes.
(What kinds of information do you have about the
doctors' attitudes toward the capabilities of these
nurses?)
Well, I believe that at one time they were concerned,
because they were not being asked to give lectures
as they did in the old days. Enough disturbance
and feeling in the group that they wanted to learn
about the program. They asked the director to
attend one of their staff meetings and gave her a
whole five minutes to talk about the program. She

> took ten and it was surprising how much she was able
> to get across during that time. From that point on
> our doctors came to realize and know what the pro-
> gram was about.... I think that we have a fine staff.
> (Do you hear any favorable comments from doctors
> about these nurses?)
> I might say there were two doctors who came here
> from B, where they were contemplating starting a
> program. They sent them down to Pasadena to see us.
> We hardly knew they were coming. Just meeting doc-
> tors at random in the hallway, those doctors went
> back convinced that our staff was for the program.

The next situation provides a dramatic illustration of
the demand for nurses in leadership positions. The director
of nursing services involved found her one pilot-program
employee to be "competent, technically good." However, the
graduate had "been a little slow in developing leadership."
An important aspect of this director's point of view is that
the graduate nurse needs more than experience but needs "to be
schooled" to assume a leadership role:

> She's competent, technically good, and fits into
> the hospital situation here. The one thing she's
> been a little slow in is developing leadership.
> (What do you mean by developing leadership?)
> Taking over as head nurse. After a nurse has been
> here about two months we feel that she should be
> able to take over for the head nurse. We rotate
> here and we wouldn't have enough for rotation if
> our staff nurses didn't take over.
> (You feel that this should happen after a nurse
> has been here for two months. She should be able
> to take over for the head nurse. Is experience all
> that the nurse needs to be ready for this?)
> No. We think she needs more than experience. She
> has to be schooled. The head nurse prepares her
> some but we have an in-service program. Let me get
> you the list of classes that all newly employed
> graduate nurses attend.

Following her description of the in-service program, the
director of nursing services was asked:

> (Would you tell me a little more about Miss B's
> difficulty in assuming head nurse responsibilities?)
> Well, we put her on as head nurse, substitute for
> the head nurse after she worked here for maybe six
> weeks. She handed us a formal complaint. She
> didn't want the responsibility. Actually there was
> another girl on nights with her who was very aggres-
> sive. We felt that she brought on the complaint.
> In general Miss B has been fine as an employee.
> Now she's taking over when the head nurse is off.
> (How do you feel about employing other graduates of
> two-year programs?)
> I'd hire them. Why not? They might require a
> little more attention, but if they all work out as
> well as Miss B, we don't have anything to worry about.
> (I have one general question concerning your experi-
> ence with Miss B. You have described her as com-
> petent and a good worker. The only trouble you've
> had involved her resistance to taking head nurse
> responsibilities. Now, isn't there a place in nurs-
> ing for a person who just wishes to remain as a
> staff nurse?)
> We push them fast. Whenever we find anyone who can
> do that extra work, we encourage their developing
> leadership. We are going to open a new Psychiatric
> Pavilion soon. Where are we going to get the per-
> sonnel for it? We'll need personnel to take respon-
> sible positions.

The directors of nursing services who were positive toward
the programs stressed both the quality of nurse-patient relationship and the initial lack of speed of the pilot-program graduates. One director who had worked with pilot-program graduates
over a period of three years, felt that it took the pilot-program
graduate six months to catch up in speed with graduates of
other programs. However, she found the quality of work was
"as good as any other graduate."

(You employ graduates of the two-year program here?)
Yes, we have ever since the first class graduated
from A. We have had six or eight over a period of
about three years. In general, I would say that when
they first come here they are a little bit slow in
their procedures and activities on the ward. I
think most of them have excellent nurse-patient relationships. I think this is outstanding among the
two-year program graduates. They are slow in techniques, however. After they have had, say, six
months experience, they pick up very rapidly. I
would say that after six months it is pretty hard
to tell the difference between a two-year graduate
and a three-year graduate.
(You say that it takes the graduates of the two-
year programs about six months to reach the level
of proficiency of other graduates. Do you mean any
graduates or graduates from your own school of
nursing?)
I am speaking literally. I would say a graduate
from any school -- three-, four-, or five-year --
I think almost everyone needs a certain amount of
experience -- six months to a year -- for any new
graduate to function well. However, it's not quite
the same for the graduate of the two-year program.
It takes the two-year graduate about six months to
catch up to the others in speed. I would say that
the quality of her work is just as good as any other
graduate. There may be a few procedures which she
didn't have in the shorter program for which she
might need a little extra coaching, but as far as
her efficiency goes and her accuracy, I would say
that they are up to par with any other graduate.

The actions of the director of a pilot program can influence the initial experiences of the graduates. One nursing
service director of a seventy-bed hospital learned about the
pilot program through an informal visit from the pilot-program
director who happened to be in the neighborhood. The visit laid
the groundwork for the future employment of pilot-program
graduates:

(What had you known about the two-year program?)
We have had an orientation with Miss L (the director
of the pilot program). She came up to the hospital

and talked with us.
(Specifically because you were getting Miss N?)
No, before. She came to give us an orientation so
that we were pretty well aware of the program and
what to expect with the nurse from that program.
(Were your expectations reasonable? Did you find
that your experience with this nurse bore out what
you had been told beforehand?)
Well, yes. We were very well pleased with the service that she has been able to render.

Later in the interview the director of nursing services
pointed out a problem involving the preparation of the pilot-
program graduates. In the words of the director, it was "no
surgery." Actually she referred to the absence of operating
room experience in the curriculum of the pilot programs. In
this particular area, which is sparsely populated and has small
hospitals, nurses are expected to assist in the operating room.
One pilot-program graduate was refused a job because she did not
have the operating room training.

Interestingly enough, the hospital which is used as the
primary center for the clinical experience of the pilot program
in the area described above offers a free six-week operating
room course for the pilot-program graduates. Many of the
graduates have taken it. The nurse referred to above went back
to take the course after she had been employed for six months.

The graduates of the pilot programs have been scrutinized
closely in the hospitals. The fact that their programs are
different leads to a special interest in the quality of their
work. Many directors of nursing services have closely examined
their behavior from the start, looking for faults. One director

described her experience with the one pilot-program graduate employed in her hospital as follows:

> (Have you found, in general, that her work has been satisfactory?)
> I've found that her work has been very satisfactory and I've been conscious of Miss D since she is the first one that we have had who came to use from this two-year program and I frankly have been looking for inefficiency or deficiency, you might say. Perhaps justifiably so. And she has worked out very well.

Analysis of Interviews with Directors of Nursing Services Holding Predominantly Unfavorable Attitudes

A major issue in the pilot-program experiment has been the effect of experience when nurses prepared in the pilot program did go to work. In the previous section several directors described how quickly the graduates learned. Others did not find this to be the case. For example, one director of nursing services described what happened when a pilot-program graduate rotated from obstetrics to a medical floor. As the director stated, "There was no transfer."

> (What about the girl's experience in obstetrics?)
> While she was in obstetrics, she did fairly well. It wasn't any worse than the head nurse expected it to be. The girl hadn't much practical experience. But she didn't improve as quickly as we thought. We give them six months in this rotation. At the end of the six months we thought you wouldn't be able to tell the difference between the three-year girl and this one. This hasn't happened. The one who was in obstetrics -- as I said -- she got by in obstetrics. From there I believe she went to medicine. She was right back at the beginning. She was no better off than if she hadn't had any obstetrics. There was no transfer.

The graduate referred to above was involved in an incident that centered about an error in medications.[1] The existence of initial bias toward the programs was illustrated by the sentence, "It wasn't any worse than the head nurse expected it to be."

Another director of nursing services felt that the weakness of the pilot-program graduate employed by her hospital rested in the limited clinical experience in training:

> (Would you describe your experience with the one pilot-program graduate who has worked here?)
> As I said, Miss B, from what I know of her, has been impressive to me. There have been reports that have come to me which made me doubt her understanding, shall I say, of professional ethics.
> Her reception of criticism, but I feel that the criticisms have been constructive. I think one is aware of this two-year program. I certainly am because I have been interested in nursing in the three-year program. She has a rather indifferent attitude. She is not secure in her preparation.
> (Is this a matter of her personally or is it her preparation?)
> You see, I feel that it could be either or both, but most important for me is the fact that there is not time for the student to become acquainted with nursing at the bedside. It is nothing that you just walk in and do for a day. It is something that becomes fun for you. You become part of it so that if the orientation isn't strong enough, then it shows on certain ones who haven't the security, or the feeling inside of them that they want to nurse.
> Does this make it clear what I feel?

---

[1]During this study the author was informed of three errors in giving medications. Two involved pilot-program graduates and one involved a graduate of another program.

The nurse referred to above, Miss B, was referred to earlier in the study by her head nurse (Chapter XII, p. 270 -- "She uses good judgment ..."). Obviously there was considerable difference of opinion concerning the quality of this nurse's performance. Even if the questions raised by the discrepancy between the opinions of the head nurse and the director of nursing services concerning the performance of this one pilot-program graduate were ignored, it is reasonable to question the director's extreme generalizations to the whole program after experience with one graduate.

Regardless of the questions involved in this director's statements, the focal point for most of the criticism of the pilot programs has been the kind and amount of clinical experience they provide.

The most illuminating statement of the experience-oriented position was made by a director of nursing services who felt that the new nurse should have had broad experience with all types of patients so that she could cope with any type of situation. This director saw similarities between the graduates of the two- and the four-year programs. Neither group has had the wide variety of clinical experiences that student nurses receive in diploma programs.

> (I don't know too much about the hospital, but it seems that you would have a great many critical patients and a great many emergencies?)
> Yes, this is the emergency hospital in the city and we have a great many hospitals on the outside where patients can go. The doctors send them there as soon as they are able to move. Our hospital is

really a very dynamic situation....
(You described this situation as stressful. How
do staff nurses find working in such a stressful
situation?)
Well, I think unless they have been through the
hospital they are many times at the beginning in
awe, but they do like the experience. They feel
that they get more experience here than anywhere.
They are grateful for being here, and usually
when they come, they say so. We have very few
people leave us for any other reason than some
personal or family situation.
(What characteristics or preparation should a
nurse have to work in your hospital situation?)
Well, I would say the nurse should be a professional
nurse and by that I mean she should have had all
the experiences; she should have worked with all
kinds of patients; her experience should be one
that has given her a confidence in herself and the
kind of background that will help her to cope with
any situation that she might meet here. I think
that anyone who came here poorly prepared would be
frustrated and find it extremely difficult.

Later in the interview this director of nursing services
gave her point of view concerning graduates of different types
of nursing programs:

(What about graduates of degree programs? Do you
find that some of them don't have confidence?)
There are individual differences, of course. We
don't say that all the graduates from a college
school can necessarily be competent. They may have
been excellent in care and the practice could have
been just so-so, and they might even find it difficult. We haven't had much experience along that
line but I think that there are areas where some of
our college people have had complications of theory
and the feeling that their experience is not
enough to make them confident.
(By college, you mean the four-year collegiate
programs?)
Yes.
(What about the graduates of diploma programs?)
Usually they have had enough practical experience
so that they adjust very, very well. In fact, I
would say the diploma people do better than the
degree program because of their experience with

> handling people -- you don't learn to handle
> people out of a book. You have to have that day-
> to-day contact with and that personal experience
> on the ward. The ward situation every day brings
> out the problem. These problems can only be
> learned in the ward situation.

The preparation of the pilot-program graduates is
obviously not compatible with this philosophy of nursing education. However, the criticism of the pilot programs by this
director went deeper into the structure of the educational
program. She made some statements before the formal interview
started. The interviewer, wishing to obtain her comments,
restated them, with the following results:

> (You expressed opinions before we started to tape
> the interview concerning the lack of experience of
> the two-year graduates. Let me interpret some of
> your remarks, and if you wish to qualify my inter-
> pretation or place an exclamation point on some of
> them feel free to do so. Now, you said that the
> experience which the diploma graduate has is far
> greater than that of the graduate of the two-year
> program. The graduate of the two-year program has
> had more theoretical background and less of this
> very crucial ward experience which is so important
> to work of this kind....)
> Not more of a theoretical background. They don't
> have as much. The two-year has more English and
> academic subjects and when you consider the two-
> year program with all that vacation time and so
> forth and you figure up the number of hours of
> instruction that are given that are not concerned
> with nursing and then you compare that. We are
> asking too much of this individual. She has to be
> a very remarkable person in order to face a situa-
> tion like this with emotional stability.

Another nursing service administrator from the same area
articulated her criticism of the amount of nursing experience
in the pilot programs:

(Now I think we could discuss the graduates of the
two-year program. Are there certain areas where
their performance falls short?)
I think it is hard to say specifically. We know
that the graduates of the first class were weak in
giving medications. It seems to us they did not
have nearly enough practice. They were slow, and
we think the reason for this is because they had
learned to take care of individual patients under
guidance and direction, but they did not have
enough responsibility for organizing and managing
a total assignment, where they had to figure out
for themselves how they are going to get the medications given, and get the treatments done, and the
patients cared for, patients off to surgery,
patients fixed and ready for diagnostic studies and
things of that sort. They couldn't organize for a
group of patients.

However, the criticism extended beyond this area into the under-

standing and care of individual patients:

I know where we had some instances where they did
not seem to know the clinical picture as well as
they ought to have. Now I'm thinking of specifically
coronary patients and diabetic patients where they
didn't seem to understand the care of these patients.
Their judgments in certain situations are not what
we have learned to expect from graduates of other
programs, and it again seems to us to be related to
the fact that they have not had a chance to have
enough exposure to the nursing situation for these
things to have come up often enough for these girls
to have it fixed. There are certain things that are
fundamental that they seem not to have known.

Later in the interview the director became even more ex-

plicit concerning the limitations in the educational method of

the pilot programs. She also clarified her earlier references

to coronary and diabetic patients:

I think it is fine for a student to learn patient
care by the case method in the beginning, so she
will learn to meet the patient's total needs; she
is responsible, totally responsible to meet these
needs. But I think it is wrong to teach her just

this. When she is going into an employment situation where this type of patient care does not exist, my feeling is that the graduates of that first class were not prepared to take care of the individual patients very knowingly, or as knowingly as graduates from other programs. Well, I do not see these girls day by day, patient by patient as much as the other staff nurses, the head nurses, supervisors, or assistant director. I am about five steps removed, so the big thing, the outstanding things I remember, and I am recalling now the day a doctor was very angry about something one of these girls had done in relation to a diabetic patient, and I think it was not the first time because he blew his stack and said, "Don't these girls know anything about diabetes?" And there was another occasion just before the girls graduated, but it could just as easily have happened afterwards, where they were having a little bit of afternoon and night experience, and there were three coronaries, all of whom had symptoms indicating that they should have had morphine. Now, the order was written for such symptoms. They did a beautiful job of noting the symptoms and charting the symptoms, and didn't realize the significance. Now any one of those patients could have had another coronary, and the doctor was extremely perturbed the next day to think that these patients had not had the morphine when obviously they needed it. It was on the chart. This is what I mean in saying they just don't know nursing yet. They haven't had enough exposure for opportunities to arise -- what I feel is opportunity, and frequently enough for them to begin to put two and two together and make judgments that have to be made now and not by consulting a book and not by consulting another nurse, do you think this and thus, although half the nurses do that when they get into a situation which is not familiar -- that's all right. But these are commonplace things; diabetes we have every day, and if they haven't learned this, then I think they haven't had exposure to clinical practice.
(And this you felt with the first class?)
Yes.
(They were exposed to nursing experiences when they worked for you here. Do you have any feeling about the length of time it took these girls to get enough experience so that they "caught up"?)
This I take from my head nurse group. It is a consensus of opinion. Now there were individual differences, but the consensus of opinion -- I think

there were eight girls in the first class -- was
that in approximately six months they felt reasonably secure with these girls. Some a little
sooner, some a little later, and one, much, much,
later, but in six months they felt reasonably secure.

The director's generalizations concerning her experiences
with the graduates of the pilot programs were based predominantly
upon her experiences with the first graduating class. Only one
graduate of the second class worked for this hospital upon
graduation. It is probable that only one person did apply because this hospital established a lower pay scale for the
pilot-program group until the individual person's performance
had been evaluated. The director spoke positively about the
performance of the one graduate of the second class:

(You mentioned the one girl who graduated in the
second class. About how long did it take her to
reach an acceptable stage of performance?)
She has only been here three months, and she has
shown herself to be a better nurse from the start.
I don't know what accounts for this -- I don't
know whether it is selection, whether it is
familiarity with the personnel where she feels
more comfortable the first week, although the
students knew our personnel, they knew the hospital set-up. It may be that she is a more mature
person, and I think maturity has something to do
with what you can do with anybody given a length
of time.

Nursing Service Directors' Conceptions of the Role
of the General Duty Nurse

Conceptions of the directors of nursing services of the
role of the general-duty nurse varied widely. The basic difference consisted in whether the newly graduated nurse was seen

as a nurse-manager or as a bedside nurse. One director who

conceived of the staff nurse as a manager related this role

somewhat to conditions that existed in her hospital:

> Because we have such a large number of attendants,
> and we are increasing our staff of practical
> nurses, the professional nurse, I feel, should be
> a manager, should be able to get along with people,
> learn how to organize her work in relation to the
> people she is responsible for supervising, so
> that the nurse is really in a responsible posi-
> tion in this hospital. In addition to knowing
> all the basic essentials of any nurse, she has
> much more of an opportunity to test her abilities
> to direct the work of others, and to evaluate the
> work of others.
> (Then from this description, you might say, the
> nurse has little time for direct bedside care?)
> She does not have as much time here as perhaps she
> does in the voluntary hospital -- of course, they
> are pretty pinched too, and they are increasing
> the number of subsidiary personnel too. The pic-
> ture is probably closely related except that our
> wards are large, open wards, and the smallest
> wards we have are twenty-eight beds, and we have
> only a couple of those; and they go all the way
> up to fifty-four beds in one large ward. And our
> problems are many in this hospital because our
> physical set-up is not good. This building was
> not meant for a general hospital and our nurses are
> working under a lot of handicaps. They have to
> walk far to get linen; the medicine cupboards are
> not located ideally at all. They have to walk
> through the entire ward in order to get to a
> medicine cupboard. We are handicapped while work-
> ing here, a lot of problems for the nurses to sur-
> mount that they had not been used to where they
> have had their education in their basic course.

This director seemed to accept the nurse's functioning in a

supervisory role as a result of changing conditions in nursing.

Others, while recognizing the changing conditions, expressed

the importance of getting the nurse back to the bedside. One

director felt that the nurse had to be "educated back to the patient":

> (There is considerable controversy in nursing as
> to what the role of the nurse is. In part this
> controversy stems from the traditional concept
> that the nurse belongs at the bedside. Does the
> nurse in your hospital spend much time at the
> bedside? Do you consider her a bedside nurse?)
> In general, I feel that here as well as many other
> places the nurse has gotten further from bedside
> nursing than we would like and it seems to be
> through no fault of hers or ours. It depends upon,
> I think, supply and demand for nurses. Our nurses,
> I feel, have been expected to do so many more
> things than bedside nursing. It seems at times
> almost impossible to get them back to the patient
> because they can't do everything at the same time.
> There are days when we are better staffed than
> others and the nurse is able to spend more time
> at the bedside. We are making an effort, of course,
> to extend that amount of time but we have as many
> problems as other hospitals. The nurse herself
> must be trained, educated back to the patient.

Most of the directors were in agreement that the general-
duty nurse had moved from the bedside. The essential difference
among the directors was whether or not steps should be taken
to bring her back to the patient.

Although there was considerable agreement that nurses
were expected to assume supervisory responsibilities, there was
considerable disagreement among the directors concerning the
preparation to assume such responsibilities. One director already quoted felt that the hospital's in-service program had
the responsibility for preparing nurses to assume supervisory
roles.

Another director, in discussing the ability of graduates
of other programs to take responsibility for an entire ward,

felt that these students had been given some experience as team leaders and had had responsibilities in running the ward on day duty. Although she felt that they had "a pretty good concept" of team method, she was not certain whether it had been part of the curriculum:

> (What about the graduates of other programs --
> what has your experience been with them as far as
> being able to handle the whole ward?)
> In general, nurses who have graduated at approxi-
> mately the same time, that means recently, have
> come from schools in this area, where the school
> of nursing education is giving them some experience
> as team leaders, and of course they have more ex-
> perience in the care of patients, they have respon-
> sibilities given to them for the ward, both on day
> duties in the absence of the head nurse, afternoon
> duty, and night duty, and they do function better
> from the standpoint of organizing their work, and
> seem to have better judgment of the total picture.
> Now we have had two exceptions to the general cali-
> ber of nurses we get from the schools of nursing.
> (Is team leadership part of the curriculum in
> diploma programs?)
> It is in some schools. They have done such a good
> job of selling this idea that when these girls come
> to me for interviews, they ask whether we use the
> team method, and they apparently have a pretty good
> concept of it. I have never asked them how much
> they go into it.
> (Do they have a series of lectures on it, or is it
> just experience that they're given on the job?)
> I don't know how they get it, but they do.

Another director, while using somewhat different termi-nology, felt that many schools of nursing were not preparing their students to manage other personnel. Also, she pointed out that individual nurses reacted differently to the respon-sibility of directing others:

(When you get a new graduate, do you expect her
to be qualified and experienced in management of
the sort required here?)
We hope that they would have it but I know from
past experience that there are many schools of
nursing that have not yet incorporated the principles of personnel management in their basic
course. They have not taught the nurses or perhaps impressed upon them the fact that in this
day and age, with so many subsidiary workers,
the professional nurse, even though she uses the
people to help her, is still responsible for the
work the subsidiary worker does. And I am finding and have found for quite a few years now that
the nurses just don't like to feel responsible for
what someone else does. They haven't alerted their
minds to thinking along these lines. Some nurses
take to it like a duck takes to water. They like
it; they like that sort of thing. A good many of
the nurses, I find, coming out of schools of
nursing would be better bedside nurses if they just
don't have these people (subsidiary workers)
around them. They are happy giving patient care
without being bothered with these people. If you
tell them "you are responsible for what the aide
does, or what the practical nurse does," they
just don't like it.

Regardless of the different opinions about what staff
nurses ought to be doing and are prepared to do, staff nurses,
including pilot-program graduates, are being asked to assume
supervisory responsibilities, and they are asked to assume
these responsibilities shortly after they graduate. Most of
the directors stated that it took at least a month before the
newly hired graduate was left alone on the floor. For example,
one director stated:

(What happens when the head nurse is off duty?)
Then the general staff nurse takes over. If we
have enough staff and she can get more help, then
we give the general staff nurse another nurse.
However, this does not happen too often and
usually the nurse ends up on the floor by herself
when the RN has her days off.

(This sort of situation would occur from the beginning of a nurse's experience on the ward?)
From the beginning the new staff nurse is never
left alone on the ward. We try to give her at
least one month before she is left alone on the
floor entirely. However, this does not always
happen but we try. She really hasn't had time to
know our procedures before then.
(That is, the new nurse spends one month on days
before she would be left alone on the ward?)
Yes.
(What about afternoons or evenings? According to
what you have said it would be at least two months
before she goes on either the afternoon or evening
shifts.)
Yes. We try to have them on several months before
they go on afternoons or nights. However, it might
be that they would only be here a month and they
would be asked to go on afternoons or nights.

However, in this hospital both a pilot-program graduate

and a diploma-program graduate described being required to re-

lieve the head nurse on her days off during the first week.

Summary

The majority of nursing service directors interviewed

were favorable toward the pilot-program graduates. More di-

rectors expressed favorable than unfavorable attitudes toward

the pilot programs. The attitudes of nursing service directors

toward the pilot-program graduates and the pilot programs were

closely related. Directors who expressed favorable attitudes

toward the graduates also expressed favorable attitudes toward

the pilot programs, and directors who expressed unfavorable

attitudes toward the graduates also expressed unfavorable atti-

tudes toward the programs.

The directors who were favorable in their attitudes toward the graduates and the programs mentioned such reasons as: the quality of bedside care given by the graduates, interest in learning, rapid rate of growth as nurses, attitudes toward nursing, and performance as team members. Some of those who were favorable stated that the pilot-program graduates need experience and supervision to develop into as competent practitioners as graduates of hospital programs. The estimates of the amount of practical experience required by the pilot-program graduate to develop into a fully competent practitioner varied from two weeks to six months.

The directors who were critical of the graduates of the pilot programs and of the programs stressed the lack of practical experience and the inability to handle a case load. One director criticized their lack of basic nursing knowledge.

There were several examples of initial bias against the graduates and the programs.

Not only did the directors differ in their attitudes toward the graduates and the programs, but they differed in their conception of the role of the general-duty nurse. In general, the directors agreed that the nurse had moved away from the bedside. While some directors accepted the departure of the nurse from the bedside and felt that the nurse should be prepared to manage others who give patient care, other directors suggested that efforts should be made to bring the nurse back to the patient.

There were indications that directors of nursing service were not informed as to what actually was done on the
floor in orienting and utilizing new personnel.

CHAPTER XV

CONCLUSIONS AND IMPLICATIONS

In the preceding chapters a report has been given of
the general plans and purposes of the experiment; the institutions that cooperated; the students; the faculty; the curriculum; and where and how the graduates perform. From the experiences during the slightly more than five years that the Cooperative Research Project in Junior and Community College Education
for Nursing has been in operation, certain conclusions can be
drawn with some degree of assurance. What implications these
conclusions have for junior-community college education, nursing education, and nursing service are also considered in this
chapter.

Conclusions

The conclusions are drawn from the evidence collected
over a five-year period, 1952-57. In the study of the graduates, two programs -- Virginia State College and Monmouth
Memorial Hospital -- were excluded because they had no graduates
before the end of the project. The study also excludes the
classes admitted in 1955 and 1956 to the other six programs
except in the analysis of the characteristics of the student
body. The importance of omitting the last two classes requires

338

some interpretation. The classes that were included come from that period characterized by the newness of the program itself -- newness for the college, for the faculty, for the hospitals, and for the students.

Although no systematic evidence has been collected to show how the programs have changed, there is considerable evidence to support the conclusion that the programs have improved each year. This conclusion is based on reports from the several faculties, the students, the graduates, and some hospital and nursing service administrators. It is supported also by the observations of the staff as they have visited the programs and consulted with the faculties.

Any evaluation study has some limitations. Some of the limitations of the present study lie in the factors cited and some in the method of evaluation used. The evaluation was made almost while the experiment was going on. The advisory committee has recommended that another evaluation be made five years after the end of the experimental period. Fortunately, funds have been set aside for such a study.

The conclusions which appear justified on the basis of the findings of the present study are:

1. Nurses able to carry on the functions commonly associated with the registered nurse can be prepared in the new type nursing program conducted by the junior-community college.

   a. They are able to pass licensing examinations successfully.

   b. With some experience, they are able to carry on the nursing functions as well as or better than the graduates of other types of nursing programs with the same purpose.

2. These programs attract students.

   a. The applications to the programs have consistently exceeded the number that could be admitted.

   b. Enrollments have increased and are increasing.

   c. Certain individuals who might otherwise not have been attracted to or able to attend another type of nursing school found these programs particularly desirable and accessible.

3. Nursing programs of this type can be set up as integral curricula in junior and community colleges.

   a. From an administrative point of view, it is possible to set up a nursing program as a department or division which can operate within the organizational framework of the college.

   b. From the point of view of the curricular organization, the general education requirement can be combined practically with the vocationally oriented nursing courses. The nursing courses can be set up within the framework of the total curriculum, using the same time and credit allowances as used in other courses.

   c. From the student's point of view, becoming a nurse in the community college setting is particularly gratifying. The inclusion of general education courses, taken with students of other programs, is desirable and helpful.

4. Junior-community colleges have found it possible to finance these programs within the financial structure of the institution.

   No particular study of costs has been made, but the administrators of several colleges have pointed out that while the nursing program is not the least expensive program, neither is it the most expensive. The cost of the nursing program is quite in keeping with the cost of other specialized programs. One president stated that the nursing program was less expensive, for example, than the specialized electronic technician program.

5. It is possible to utilize the facilities of hospitals and
other health agencies for the learning experiences desired
without payment of fees or through service by students.
What cost has been incurred by the agency in the use of
its facilities has been offset in part by services which
result as a by-product of the student's learning experiences.
The hospitals have recognized the need for the product of
these nursing programs and have accepted their social
obligation to provide their facilities without charge.
They also recognize the intangible but very real value
accrued from the added stimulation of the nursing staff.

6. Where nursing service understands and accepts the concept
of a graduate nurse as a beginning practitioner at the time
of graduation and not a finished product, the graduate of
the junior-community college nursing program is oriented
more realistically and absorbed more quickly into the
nursing service.

Implications

The conclusions reached in a study are based on the
data collected and evaluated. Equally important, though probably less specific, are the implications which these conclusions
have. What use is made of the study and its findings is perhaps more significant than the study itself. Obviously all
the possible implications cannot be seen at this time, and so
no attempt has been made at all-inclusiveness. However, some
of the implications of this study for nursing education
generally, for junior-community college education, for nursing
service, and for the nursing profession will be pointed out.

Nursing Education

Nursing education has been under scrutiny many times
in its history but never more so than in the last decade.
In spite of concern about where nursing programs should be
and what they should do, the Cooperative Research Project in
Junior and Community College Education for Nursing marked
the first systematic attempt to develop a new type program in
a new setting. It is true that a considerable number of junior
colleges have been involved in some way in nursing programs
for many years, but it is also true that the programs developed
in junior-community colleges in the project are completely new
and not a continuation or even a revision of those programs
previously carried on in this type of institution. Neither
are they shortened versions of the traditional three-year hospital program. It would be a great mistake if nursing educators and hospital administrators saw this new program only
as a shortened program and consequently believed that their
own nursing programs could easily be converted to two-year
programs. It is unfortunate that more emphasis has been given
to the shorter length of the program than to its changed
philosophy.

One of the strongest implications of these five years
of experimentation is the need for a clear statement of the
objectives of each type of nursing program. The statement of
objectives is dependent on a clear picture of the product to
be produced by the educational program and of the functions

this product should perform. We can no longer have programs
differing in length, content, and method and yet claiming to
be preparing professional practitioners of the same com-
petency. Until and unless the objectives of the several programs can be differentiated, there can be little argument for
the continuation of multiple programs. There can be little
justification for a program in nursing which requires four
years for its completion unless that program prepares a practitioner who is different in competence from the graduate of
the junior college program. There is little evidence to support the belief that in the majority, at least, of the present
four-year programs this is the case.

The question of what the four-year or baccalaureate
degree program should be is not easily answered. There are
suggestions made that the baccalaureate degree program has
wider cultural and general education advantages and that the
time spent is justifiable. Others suggest that the graduate
of the baccalaureate degree program becomes the nurse-manager
and therefore believe that the program should include courses
in management. To accept either of these conclusions is to
misunderstand the question or to underestimate its seriousness.
Still another proposal is made which is commonly referred to
as the "ladder concept." This plan would make it possible for
students to enter programs designed to permit the completion
of one year with employment possible thereafter as practical
nurses; the completion of two years permitting licensure as

344

a registered nurse; an additional two years providing for courses in management and teaching. There is in this plan considerable confusion about the objectives and methodology of technical and professional education. That there is a difference in nature, scope and purpose between these two types of education is well known. It is difficult to understand why nurse educators and others believe the two can appropriately be carried on within a single program. If curricula are built upon objectives and content and teaching methods are selected accordingly, then the ladder concept of curricular development is indefensible. The decision whether there is a place for the professional practitioner in nursing must be made, and programs set up to prepare those who wish to function at that level. The recent study by Lambertson[1] should be extremely useful in clarifying the role of the professional practitioner and in planning an educational program for that role.

Almost all criticisms of the pilot programs have been concerned with time. It has been said that the program is not long enough, that not enough time is spent in the clinical situation, and that nursing cannot be learned in so short a time. Much more rare, almost to the point of nonexistence,

[1]Eleanor C. Lambertson, "Professional Education for Leadership in the Practice of Nursing," Unpublished doctoral project, Teachers College, Columbia University, 1957.

have been comments about the quality of the content, the
instruction, and the learning experiences. It has been demonstrated in the pilot programs that less learning time is
needed when the learning experiences are carefully selected
and organized and when the teacher and student can concentrate
on teaching and learning. It therefore seems obvious that
the reliance on time spent units as the sole criterion for the
quality of a course or set of experiences is wholly unjus-
tifiable. Noteworthy progress away from such arbitrary time
limits has been made by the American Nurses' Association
Special Committee on State Boards of Nursing in their recommendations for standards.[2] It now remains for the state
boards of nursing to revise their standards accordingly.

However, great harm can be done to nursing programs
and to nursing if the notion gains currency that the simple
elimination of the third year is equivalent to what has been
done in the pilot programs. Because the junior college program has been attractive to students for a variety of reasons,
it cannot be assumed that hospital nursing programs can
attract students by the simple expedient of shortening the
program. The success of the junior college programs and that
of the one hospital included in the Cooperative Research
Project is by no means a directive for hospitals either to

---

[2] A.N.A. Special Committee on State Boards of Nursing,
"Progress Report of the Subcommittee on the Preparation of
Educational Standards to be Used as a Guide by State Boards,"
Mimeographed, May 1956.

shorten existing programs or to set up new two-year programs. When the nursing program at Monmouth Memorial Hospital is carefully analyzed, it will be seen to resemble the college programs very closely. Therefore, unless a hospital wishes to reorganize its nursing education program completely and, in essence, establish an independent school of nursing, it should not consider a two-year program at all.

Whether a hospital should carry on a nursing education program at all still remains to be answered. Can the hospital justify the expenditures necessary for a good nursing program? Is this a legitimate use for money the hospital receives? It was an assumption basic to this project that education for nursing is the legitimate obligation of educational institutions and experiences since have done nothing to lessen the acceptability of this assumption.

An important question arising from the pilot programs has been that of the interneship. Several junior-community colleges have indicated their intention of including a year's interneship so that the over-all time required would remain three years. This has been suggested for two basic reasons -- first, to meet the state board of nursing requirement of a three-year period, and, second, to avoid the criticism and opposition of nurses and nursing groups.

Hospital administrators have expressed considerable interest in the interneship. This is understandable since an interneship would assure them of the services of a given number

of nurses for a year, and then an easy replacement with succeed-
ing groups of internes. Findings of this study show that students in the practicum were functioning as graduate nurses, and
they were so considered in the evaluation. That the interneship is a period ripe for exploitation is all too evident.

Nurses who advocate an interneship may be doing so
because of the nature of their own educational program. When
time spent in the various services within a hospital is the
only matter of concern in setting up or in evaluating a nursing
program, it is scarcely surprising that the graduates of such
programs stress time. Unfortunately, nursing programs have
been more controlled by the time element than have any other
educational programs. Perhaps as nursing programs come increasingly under the direction of educational institutions,
the question of time will take its proper place.

The development of nursing courses within the curriculum according to broad groupings of subject matter has made
possible the inclusion of a great deal of material in a comparatively short time. Along with this, the planning of
learning experiences as laboratory periods has facilitated
learning. Since this idea was introduced into the pilot programs, many of the more traditional hospital programs have made
substantial changes in their courses. Fewer changes have been
made in the provision for learning experiences, since the student in the traditional program remains a worker. As long as
these two roles are not separated, few real improvements can

be made in the organization of learning experiences.

The concepts of beginning with the normal and progressing toward the deviations from normal; of beginning with the simple and moving into the complex, now seem to be accepted by many nursing educators. The implementation of these concepts, which is more difficult, is not found in many places outside the pilot programs. Although the development of a curriculum based on these concepts has by no means reached the desired point, enough success has been achieved to warrant encouraging others to adopt them and to develop them further.

New teaching methods and a refinement of older methods are needed if nursing programs are to train an increasing number of students with a limited number of qualified instructors. An increased ratio of students to teachers is inevitable in nursing programs as in other educational programs. In the nursing literature and in discussions by nursing educators, there is repeated reference to a desirable ratio of one instructor to six students. No basis for this ratio can be found in a search of the literature. No studies have been made to indicate what the optimal ratio might be. One of the research assistants in the Cooperative Research Project became intrigued with the acceptance of the one-to-six ratio among nursing educators. This is a ratio which would not be possible in colleges, and he attempted to find a basis for it in nursing. The only indication of the possible origin of this ratio was in the final report of the Grading Committee, which stated that among the conditions not to be tolerated was the "ratio of R.N.'s to Students less than 1 to 6."[3] This, of course, is far different from one instructor to six students.

Although much has been done in the pilot programs to increase the number of students taught by one instructor, much remains to be done. Carefully planned and controlled studies of student-teacher ratio are needed. They are considered desirable even though previous studies of class size have not been particularly helpful in determining the optimal class size. It is not enough to say that nursing is different and, therefore, makes its own rules, for in the course of five years of experimentation the great similarity between nursing education and other education has been shown again and again.

The nursing programs in the seven cooperating colleges have been financed in the same way as any other program they offer. This is true of both public and private institutions. The students have paid the same tuition as that charged for any student in the college. This fact is of more than passing interest to nursing educators and college administrators. The same statement could not be made of the nursing programs offered by senior colleges and universities. One is forced to ask why it has been possible for junior-community colleges to finance nursing programs, while senior colleges and universities

---

[3]Committee on the Grading of Nursing Schools, _Nursing Schools Today and Tomorrow_ (New York: The Committee, 1934), p. 202.

have failed to do so. Is it because of the philosophy of the community college? Do community colleges have a deeper and stronger concern for their communities and the needs of these communities? Is it because nursing educators have not seen it as desirable to have the nursing program independent of the hospital, and therefore have not advocated it? It seems increasingly difficult to explain why institutions of higher education, exclusive of a few community colleges, have not assumed the obligation of providing education for nursing. It is even more difficult to understand why publicly supported institutions, particularly the land-grant colleges, have not seen education for nursing as much their responsibility as education for teaching, social work, medicine, agriculture, pharmacy, and the like.

The problem of financing education for nursing has plagued the profession of nursing practically from its beginning. The kind of financing which has been the pattern has been the cause of many other problems nursing has had and continues to have. The curriculum, for example, has been developed in the way it has largely because of financial considerations. Until the financing of education for nursing is changed, nursing will continue to be beset by many difficulties. It is hoped that the pilot programs within the Cooperative Research Project have shown a better way of financing this education.

The students in the pilot programs were students throughout the entire period from admission to graduation. They were expected to meet the same standards and requirements and they enjoyed the same privileges and opportunities as other students within the college. At no time did they assume the role of worker as a part of the program. This does not mean that some students were not gainfully employed during the program, but such employment was determined by the student's financial needs. Students engaged in various kinds of part-time work. Some worked where they had been employed previously. Others worked in some capacity in hospitals but not as nurses, nor in student uniforms. Present practice in some schools of allowing students to work as nurses has legal implications rarely considered. This opportunity to be a student, a learner, has been attractive to students. It is the firm belief of those who have shared in their education that the opportunity to be a student has been largely responsible for the high motivation and for the speed with which the student learned.

It is becoming increasingly clear that educational programs offered to prospective nurses must be consistent with good educational practices and similar to other programs these young people may choose. No longer is it logical to expect nursing students to be content with different programs, different living conditions, different educational, social, and cultural opportunities from those offered to students preparing in other fields.

Perhaps one of the most important factors in the development of these new nursing programs has been the interest and cooperation of the junior-community college personnel, both at the local level and through the national organization. In each college the administration and faculty have given whole-hearted support to the new nursing program. Faculty members have given hours of their time to assist in the development of the curriculum. In all instances, too, the chief administrative officer of the college has taken an active part in the development of the program.

The American Association of Junior Colleges has taken an active interest in education for nursing for almost ten years. It has had a committee on nursing, a subcommittee of its curriculum committee. At each annual convention of the Association a part of the program has been devoted to nursing education. In both 1956 and 1957, the Association cooperated with the National League for Nursing and the Cooperative Research Project in sponsoring a two-day conference on education for nursing in junior-community colleges prior to the convention. A substantial proportion of the participants in these special conferences consisted of college administrators. The program sessions at the regular convention were similarly well attended. On the state level, also, committees have been functioning, special conferences held, and programs devoted to nursing education -- all under the auspices of junior college associations.

There can be little doubt that the active interest and participation of college administrators has been instrumental

in the development of nursing programs within the Cooperative
Research Project and outside the project. There has been no
corresponding interest or concerted action on the part of
senior colleges and universities with respect to the baccalaureate degree nursing programs. Have nursing educators seen
the necessity of interesting college administrators both indi-
vidually and collectively in nursing education? Has the
failure to interest them and gain their participation been a
real stumbling block to the development of nursing programs
according to college and university standards? The experiences
of the nursing programs in junior-community colleges may well
point the way toward faster integration of education for nursing into the educational institutions of the country.

The need for personnel prepared to teach nursing in
junior-community colleges is great. The programs now beginning
and those being planned are faced with the problem of securing
instructional personnel. Too few nurses are preparing to teach
in this type of nursing program. Few institutions offer programs for preparing instructors for junior-community college
nursing programs. Those now teaching in these programs have
indicated that broader preparation of instructors is necessary.
They feel that an understanding of areas other than their
specialties is essential. They also stress the instructor's
need for a broad general education as well as specialization
in a field of nursing. Teaching methods and curriculum development are also important, since these instructors have

obligations and opportunities in both of these areas that do not exist in traditional schools. The development of these new nursing programs is quite definitely related to the preparation of personnel equipped to carry on the program. This means both the quality of the preparation and the speed with which it is secured. The institutions offering preparation in teaching and administration have an obligation to prepare personnel for the new nursing programs.

Junior-Community Colleges

The nursing programs as developed within the Cooperative Research Project provide a unique illustration of the way in which the major purposes of the junior-community college can be fulfilled. The comparative ease with which they seem to have been developed should not lead other colleges to think that such programs may be introduced without effort.

Experiences in the development of the nursing programs indicate that a considerable period of planning must precede the actual beginning of the program. In no instance was a program begun without a year or more of planning. In some instances the planning took more than two years. The exploration of the feasibility of a program in any college of course takes place before staff is employed. It is highly desirable to have the chief administrator of the nursing program employed a year before students are admitted. If at all possible, other members of the teaching staff should be on the campus for a

period before the students begin. Thus any junior-community
college contemplating the offering of a nursing program must
count on an extended period of planning. Unlike some other
programs, the nursing program must be planned in its entirety
from the beginning, even though its implementation will be
gradual. Since licensing of the graduate is required before
employment, permission to operate a nursing program must be
secured from the appropriate body within the state so that the
possibility of licensure is assured.

The development of a nursing curriculum in the junior-
community college becomes the concern of the whole college.
When Orange County Community College made its decision to
undertake a nursing program, it decided on principles to guide
the faculty as it began its task of building the curriculum.
The principles they agreed upon were the following:

> The task must be approached with no pre-
> conceived prejudice;
>
> Specialized nursing courses must conform
> to the regular college pattern of hours
> and credit;
>
> Courses must be planned to provide
> effective learning experiences;
>
> The curriculum must include courses that
> prepare for life as well as work;
>
> Many people must contribute to the build-
> ing of the curriculum;

> The nursing curriculum must be kept
> flexible to permit change when the
> need for change is revealed.[4]

There is evidence that in those colleges where nursing

programs have been developed, they have influenced the entire

college curriculum. One dean has stated that if any college

wishes to have its curriculum reviewed and vitalized, it

should introduce a nursing program. One college reported that

the teaching methods used in nursing were being found suitable

for courses in similar programs. It also made plans to use

the same policies and procedures for its field practice in

retailing courses as those used for the laboratory practice

in hospitals and other agencies. In describing the effect of

introducing a nursing program in the college, the president

of the college said:

> ... Nursing has done a great deal for us....
> This has been one of the finest kinds of cur-
> riculum study that we could ever have tackled.
> It has involved our whole staff.... The results
> of this program are widespread throughout the
> entire college curriculum.[5]

That additional junior-community colleges should and

will establish nursing programs is evident. That to establish

---

[4]Walter E. Sindlinger, "Experimentation in Education
for Nursing at Orange County Community College," Unpublished
Doctoral Project, Teachers College, Columbia University, 1956,
pp. 89-91.

[5]Edwin H. Miner, "The Administrator Looks at Nursing,"
Nursing Education in Junior and Community Colleges (New York:
American Association of Junior Colleges, Cooperative Research
Project, National League for Nursing, 1956), p. 26.

the kind of nursing program discussed in this report takes
careful planning and considerable effort on the part of all
concerned is also evident. Not all junior-community colleges
can and should develop nursing programs. The use of the criteria described in Chapter III and the guiding principles developed by the joint committee of the American Association of
Junior Colleges and the National League for Nursing is strongly
recommended. The fact remains, however, that additional programs should develop. The Board of Directors of the American
Association of Junior Colleges, at its 1957 convention,
adopted a resolution favoring and encouraging the development
of nursing programs in junior colleges. The findings of the
Cooperative Research Project support and encourage the development of nursing programs similar to those in the eight cooperating institutions. The urge to establish nursing programs should not lead junior-community college administrators
to be satisfied with the traditional program or with the expedient arrangements which have been all too common in the
past. Even though these programs may be somewhat more difficult to develop than other programs the college offers, their
advantages are obvious to all those who have been involved.

The nursing programs as developed in the eight cooperating institutions have certain characteristics and assets that
might be used in other programs within the junior-community
college. The clarity of the vocational goal of the pilot programs is apparent. Chapter IX indicated that the graduates

of the pilot programs went to work after graduation, and they went to work in positions for which their programs had prepared them. This is not always true of other junior-community college vocational programs.

The organization of the curriculum in nursing is another area which other programs might find helpful. There is a broad grouping of subject matter into courses carrying a substantial number of credits, and these courses are definitely sequential in nature. Thus the fragmentation into 2- and 3-point courses is avoided, and the curriculum becomes more than a series of courses taken somewhat at random. The unity which is achieved in the nursing curriculum is possible only when all who teach the courses concerned participate in careful planning.

The relationships developed by the pilot programs have been advantageous to the colleges themselves and to nursing. It is hoped that they illustrate what can be accomplished for nursing within the junior-community college.

Nursing Service

The nursing services of all hospitals and other agencies employing nurses are dependent upon the educational programs in nursing for their supply of personnel. They are concerned not only with the number of nurses produced annually but also with the kind of preparation the nurses have received. At the same time, they need to adjust their programs within the nursing service according to changes in the ways and in the places nurses are prepared. Similarly, nursing curricula need to change when the needs of nursing services change. Thus there is reciprocal concern about what nurses are prepared to do and how well they are able to carry on nursing functions.

This project was not primarily concerned with nursing service, except as it was concerned with the preparation of personnel able to carry out the functions of the registered nurse. In the course of the project, as various hospitals were used to provide laboratory experiences for students and, more particularly, during the evaluation study of the graduates, many observations were made of nursing services. One of the most obvious observations was the vast amount of nursing care given by other than registered nurses. It was common to find nursing students carrying out functions comparable to those of practical nurses and aides, with registered nurses carrying on only managerial tasks. It is disturbing to find graduates of all kinds of nursing programs identifying the time they either were head nurses or relieved the head nurse as the time they assumed full nursing responsibility. It is apparently the common belief that direct care of patients lies outside the scope of the functions of the registered nurse. That the nursing service has promoted this idea, or at least condoned it, seems obvious. The purpose of the project was to prepare the bedside nurse, for it was felt that the need for this kind of nurse was great. The graduates expressed pleasure in giving direct care to patients and concern when they were not permitted to do so because auxiliary personnel were so assigned.

Nursing service must answer the question of who shall give direct nursing care to patients. If all nursing care is to be given by auxiliary nursing personnel, are they not in effect nurses? Is there not a place at the bedside for the highly skilled technician and for the professional nurse as well? A convincing argument for the nurse's doing nursing is made by Lambertson on the basis of several years of study and experience with the nursing team.[6] It is not enough to place the blame for the present situation on the so-called shortage of nurses. It is a problem much less easily solved than that. It requires a re-evaluation of what constitutes nursing care, and by whom it should be given. At the conclusion of this project, there is no change in the belief that there is a need for the registered nurse at the bedside. There is strengthened belief that the nurse must be permitted to do nursing and to do it well if she is to receive satisfaction from the job of nursing and to wish to continue in it. Those responsible for nursing service will have to find ways and means of organization that will permit nurses to nurse.

There has been a great deal of discussion in recent years about in-service education in hospital nursing service. Public health nursing agencies have long since assumed the

------

[6]Lambertson, op. cit.

continued education of their personnel as one of their responsibilities. Hospital nursing services have not felt this need
particularly because so many hospitals have schools of nursing
which prepare their own personnel. In fact, in the past, most
hospital schools have prepared nurses specifically for their
own institutions and not for nursing generally. It was common
practice for graduates to spend all, or almost all, of their
professional life employed by the hospital in which they were
trained. The reduction in the number of schools of nursing,
the increase in the number of hospitals, and the greater
mobility of nurses have changed this picture considerably.
Now less than one-fifth of all hospitals have schools of nursing, and personnel must be secured from other institutions.
Moreover, the medical treatment of patients has changed
drastically and continues to change at an unprecedented rate.
With these changes, nursing care must also change. A nurse
specifically prepared today may find herself ill equipped tomorrow. As the nursing service is organized increasingly as
specialized services, the difference between units within the
same institution is often as great as or greater than that between institutions. The nurse will need orientation to and
continued education in the service in which she is working.
Because of the great degree of specialization, nursing programs
must increasingly be concerned with basic nursing care, with
specialization coming after graduation as a result of in-service
or continuing training. The need for continuing education is

not a matter of choice, it is a matter of necessity.

There seems to have been a verbal or intellectual acceptance of in-service education or continuing education by nursing service administrators. It is unfortunate that there has not been accompanying understanding, for in too many institutions in-service education is only a word. Some institutions have a plan on paper, but it has not been implemented nor is there a real intention of doing so. In some institutions the concept of in-service education is a series of lectures. In others there is admittedly no plan at all. In all three types of situations, shortage of personnel and shortage of time are given as justification for doing so little in this area. The strongest implication of this study for the nursing service seems to be the need for a vigorous, dynamic, far-sighted and imaginative plan of in-service education.

The need for orientation of new personnel, or of personnel assigned to new departments, seems almost too obvious to cite as an implication of this project's findings, but it is an important one. The graduates reported again and again that no orientation, not even to the physical plant or unit to which they had been assigned, was given. They were expected to take full responsibility for the nursing care of patients on the first day of employment and to relieve the head nurse or even become head nurses within a few weeks after graduation. The documentation of the experiences of the graduate nurses included in this report can help nursing service administrators assess the problems of new personnel more realistically. Hospital and nursing service administrators, often because of the size of their jobs and sometimes because of their philosophy of nursing and administration, are removed from employee problems. Given information they can, even when they are unable to change practices, be more understanding of the problems of the new staff nurse.

Without doubt staff nurses will be placed on the job without receiving adequate orientation or supervision. They will be expected to assume responsibilities for which they are not prepared. These are "facts of life" in present nursing practice. Hospital practices rooted in nursing tradition and present conditions will not change quickly. This does not mean, however, that nursing service administrators have no responsibility or obligation to see that changes in practice do come about. As the changes do take place with time, new employees need not be punished for problems rooted in conditions they did not create. If it is not possible to give the nurse adequate job orientation or appropriate supervision, it is unfair at the same time to criticize her for having difficulties in becoming acclimated to the job. It should also be remembered that the initial floundering period is not the appropriate time for evaluating performance. It is a time for observation and supervision, but not a time to fashion judgments.

The occupational climate into which any new employee goes has implications for the kind of employee he or she will be. The occupational climate for people in nursing is inescapably influenced by the shortage of trained personnel. It is also influenced by variations in the functions and roles staff nurses assume from hospital to hospital and service to service. The nursing service must take major responsibility for the present occupational climate and for the changes that must come about if nursing care is to be of the quality and quantity desired. Under present conditions, programs of orientation and in-service education were found to be treated as expendable to immediate service demands.

The need to recognize that the role of any educational program is to prepare the beginning practitioner, and that expertness comes with experience, is another implication of the findings of this report. Where the nursing service had this philosophy, the new graduate was absorbed more easily and more quickly into the nursing service. Increasingly, nursing programs must content themselves with the preparation of those with the ability and skills to become nurses. One must be careful not to confuse what is intended in the educational program with the situation in which the typical student in nursing finds herself. Because the student is forced into the work situation, she has experiences which are not a part of the educational program. Signs point to an increase in the number of nurses who will be prepared in educational institutions.

Hence nursing services will need to make plans for the utiliza-
tion of larger numbers so prepared.

It is to be hoped that nursing educators and nursing
service administrators can accept the challenge offered. It
is not enough to prepare nurses as they were prepared twenty-
five or fifty years ago. Nor are nurses being unrealistically
prepared in the new programs. To simply prepare nurses to meet
today's exigencies would be shortsighted. Nursing service
will have to let, even require, nurses to do the kind of nursing now required by patients if their total needs are to be met.

The Nursing Profession

The responsibility of a profession for the service it
renders to society through its members is a well-accepted
principle. Thus a profession is responsible for the education
of its members. The nursing profession may well find implications for the practice of nursing from the results of the
Cooperative Research Project.

Perhaps the first and most obvious inference to be made
is the need for study of what the role and functions of the
nurse should be. The seeming reluctance of registered nurses
to give direct care to patients, and the preference for service
and institutional managerial functions, should cause concern
in the profession. To what extent will nurses take on functions the physician discards? To what extent will nurses be
drawn into management beyond that of the nursing of her patient?

Will nurses of the future nurse, or, as some studies indicate, merely see that nursing gets done -- by some other group? The nursing profession cannot afford simply to let changes come about or even be forced on it. It will have to look into the future and make plans to bring about the changes it considers best.

The statements of functions which have been developed by the various sections of the American Nurses Association are important statements. They should be more than words; they should be major agreements which govern the practice of nursing. At the beginning of the Cooperative Research Project the junior college presidents asked for just such statements so that their nursing programs could be planned to prepare nurses to perform those functions ascribed to the general staff nurse. At that time no such statements were available. It is questionable even now whether these agreements as to functions are well known to the practicing nurse or are in any way affecting what the nurse does or does not do.

One of the chief merits of the statements of functions is that in each category the nurses actually engaged in that branch of nursing were responsible for developing the statement. This is as it should be, for if the profession is to be self-controlled it must have the participation of the practitioner in decisions relating to the practice of nursing within the framework of the rightful province of other professions.

Nursing educators have probably not been as cognizant of these statements of functions as they should be. Curricular development in the schools of nursing is dependent on such decisions as the practitioner makes, for it is for the practice of nursing that the students are being prepared. Thus the statements of functions become, or should become, curricular guides.

The attraction of persons to a profession and the admission of those eligible is another responsibility of a profession. From the findings in this project, it seems obvious that changes in recruitment policies and procedures are in order. There has been an apparent reluctance, or at least too little emphasis, on the part of the profession to encourage either the development of nursing programs in colleges or the direction of attention toward such programs in recruitment activities. The evidence supporting collegiate programs seems clear. The slowness of the development of college-centered programs in nursing has not been equalled by any other profession.

The profession must recognize too the differences between professional and semiprofessional or technical functions and between professional and technical education. There are specific ways in which a professional person performs the functions ascribed to that profession. To be able to function in this way is one of the outcomes of professional education. It does not just happen; it requires a deliberately planned training. Nurses are frequently disturbed by any implication that all nursing functions are not professional in nature and that all nurses are not professional people. Simply to label a function professional or to name a person professional, either by law or custom, does not make them so. The recognition that there are differentiated functions within the occupation of nursing is a first step. It follows naturally that preparation for these different categories of functions must be differentiated. A natural consequence of these two is that in the practice of nursing, provision must be made for these nurses to work together. That there can be careers in either professional or semiprofessional nursing should be clear.

The nursing profession finds itself in a challenging position. What it does within the next few years may determine its entire future. Whether it will become a profession or whether it will abrogate its place and position to another group is within its power to determine. It is an exciting time to be in nursing. It is a discouraging time to be in nursing. Changes are needed so badly and they seem so obvious and so possible. Yet changes seem to be discouraged -- or at least not encouraged -- by so many in the field of nursing. The decision as to how the profession will move is in the hands of the nurses themselves.

APPENDIX

A. A PROPOSAL

B. ADVISORY COMMITTEE

C. STAFF

D. SURVEY FORMS FOR COLLEGES

E. SURVEY FORMS FOR HOSPITAL

F. STATEMENT OF AGREEMENT WITH
   COOPERATING COLLEGES

G. ORIGINAL EVALUATION FORM

H. REVISED FORM OF INTERVIEW GUIDE
   INCLUDING RATING FORM

I. STAFF NURSE FORM

J. LETTER FROM MONTAG

K. RELIABILITY OF JUDGES' RATINGS

APPENDIX A

RESEARCH AND EXPERIMENTATION IN JUNIOR COLLEGES
NURSING EDUCATION -- A PROPOSAL

The constantly increasing discrepancy between the need
for nursing services, and the supply of nurses makes it imperative that more students be enrolled in schools that prepare for
nursing. The burden which now falls so heavily upon hospital
schools of nursing must be shared, and perhaps eventually reduced. This can be accomplished by the establishment of new
programs in the new type of educational institution in which an
increasing proportion of the youth of America (over 500,000 per
year) are enrolling, namely, the junior or community college.

By the use of experimental methods, the Division of
Nursing Education, Teachers College, proposes to assist in
setting up this new type of educational program for nurses.
The nursing program will be made an integral part of the junior
or community college offering and will qualify selected students
for admission to licensure procedures for registered nursing.
Interest in such experimentation stems from a recognition of
the need for the development of a more economical and effective
system of education for nursing, as recommended by authorities
in the field.

370

Nature of the Proposal

It is proposed that a continuing organizational unit for planning and carrying on research in education for nursing in junior and community colleges be set up at Teachers College under the direction of the Division of Nursing Education. This appears to be an effective way to develop and to give direction to an organized program of research and experimentation in cooperation with selected junior and community colleges. Staff fully qualified for nursing education research will be assigned to the project for direction of the experimental program and for the conduct of the related research.

The Division of Nursing Education has already been approached by several junior and community colleges with a request for nursing education advice and continuing consultation service in curriculum development. Other suitable colleges are believed to be interested in such a cooperative undertaking. Teachers College has had considerable experience in cooperative educational projects in other fields. From this experience, a pattern of organization has been learned which channels a maximum percentage of funds into educational research rather than into the operation of the experimental school. It is anticipated that experimentation in junior colleges in nursing education would be developed along similar lines. The following steps would need to be taken:

1. Appoint research staff to develop the project and serve as consultants to the faculties of junior and/or community colleges cooperating in the experiment.

(Qualifications of staff: preparation in educational
research, well-grounded in curriculum development principles and in junior college education principles and
methods, experience in teaching and/or administration
in a collegiate school of nursing.)

2. Establish an advisory committee to review plans and
   purposes, to set criteria for appraisal of progress, and
   to evaluate the results. The advisory committee would
   include lay people representing the patient, the public,
   and the community; educators from the junior college
   field and members of the Association of Junior Colleges;
   nurse educators from national nursing organizations;
   nursing service administrators; and alumni of Teachers
   College.

3. Select from the several junior and community colleges
   that have already approached the Division of Nursing
   Education, or from others as need be, the number and
   variety of colleges needed to carry on the experimental
   program. This would require a survey of the facilities
   of the colleges and the resources available in each
   college community. The kinds of colleges that appear to
   present a satisfactory variation and that might be
   selected for the cooperative project are as follows:

   a. A large, publicly supported junior college conducting
      other technical or semi-professional programs.

   b. A smaller, privately supported junior college conduct-
      ing one or more technical or semi-professional programs.

   c. A community college with a wide variety of adult and
      other terminal education programs of a semi-professional
      nature.

   d. A junior college in a university which also conducts
      a school of professional nursing in a program leading
      to a bachelor of science degree.

   e. A college in a community where clinical practice can
      be arranged in a hospital where practical nurses are
      also trained and employed.

   The main criteria, however, would be that of eagerness
   on the part of junior college administration and faculty
   for the experiment, and their willingness and prepared-
   ness to share in the cooperative aspects of the research
   undertaking.

373

4. Plan for, organize, and conduct work conferences for selected instructional and administrative staff from these selected colleges, to interpret the purposes and plans for experimentation, and to groom them for full participation in this project. Draw up mutually satisfactory agreements regarding the tasks to be undertaken, and the responsibilities of each party, and the investment of time and funds by each party. (In general, full responsibility for the support and conduct of the educational program in nursing would rest with the junior college; responsibility for the research, with Teachers College.)

5. Work with the facilities of each of the schools from time to time, to participate in curriculum development, teaching, clinical field supervision as is necessary or desirable to develop the kind of instructional program desired, and to gather the data needed for research.

6. Arrange for further group conferences for representatives of each of the cooperating experimental schools and for the advisory committee on research, under the guidance of the Teachers College research staff, to review the total progress, to revise or further develop plans, and to evaluate results.

7. Summarize and evaluate progress and results, and report findings which have possibilities for improving education for nursing.

Possible Extension of the Project to Two-Year Hospital School Programs

As the problems and principles of planning and conducting the new type educational programs for nursing in junior and community colleges become clarified, their possible application to programs in hospital schools of nursing should be explored. It is quite probable that a hospital school willing and able to conduct a nursing program upon the same sound educational basis as developed in junior colleges could, with slight modification of program, qualify for a charter as an institution of higher education with power to grant an associate of applied science degree. Such a school would be virtually a Hospital Junior College of Nursing. This plan might assist many hospital schools in improving their educational programs.

APPENDIX B

COOPERATIVE PROJECT FOR JUNIOR COLLEGE EDUCATION
FOR NURSING -- ADVISORY COMMITTEE

Dr. E. Dwight Barnett -- Director, Institute of Administrative Medicine, School of Public Health, Columbia University

Dr. E. H. L. Corwin[a] -- Executive Secretary, New York Academy of Medicine

Dr. Ralph Fields -- Director, Division of Instruction, Teachers College, Columbia University

Miss Agnes Gelinas -- Chairman, Department of Nursing, Skidmore College, University Hospital, 303 East 20th Street, New York

Mrs. Lulu Wolf Hassenplug -- Dean, School of Nursing, University of California at Los Angeles, Los Angeles, California

Dr. Hugo Hullerman[b] -- Director, Children's Hospital Detroit, Michigan

Dr. William B. Langsdorf -- Principal, Pasadena City College, Pasadena, California

Mrs. Lucile Petry Leone -- Chief, Division of Nursing, United States Public Health Service, Washington 25, D.C.

Dr. Henry W. Littlefield -- Vice-President, University of Bridgeport, Bridgeport 5, Connecticut

Mrs. R. Louise McManus -- Director, Division of Nursing Education, Teachers College, Columbia University

Father Francis L. Meade -- President, Niagara University, Niagara Falls, New York

375

Mrs. Nelson Rockefeller -- Chairman, Board of Managers,
Bellevue Hospital Schools of Nursing,
New York

Miss Ruth Sleeper   -- Director, School of Nursing and Nursing Service, Massachusetts General
Hospital, Boston, Massachusetts

Dr. Albert W. Snoke   -- Superintendent, Grace-New Haven Community Hospital, New Haven, Connecticut

Dr. W. Fred Totten   -- The Mott Foundation, Flint, Michigan
(Formerly President Flint Junior College)

Mr. J. B. Young   -- President, Jones County Junior College, Ellisville, Mississippi

a. Died 1952

b. Appointed 1954

APPENDIX C

COOPERATIVE RESEARCH PROJECT IN JUNIOR AND
COMMUNITY COLLEGE EDUCATION FOR NURSING
STAFF

Director

     Mildred L. Montag   1952-1957

Research Assistants

     Walter E. Singlinger   1952-1953

     J. F. Marvin Buechel   1953-1955

     Alice R. Rines   1955-1957

     Lassar Gotkin   1956-1957

     Elizabeth Hagen (part time)   1954-1956

APPENDIX D

COOPERATIVE RESEARCH PROGRAM IN JUNIOR AND

COMMUNITY COLLEGE EDUCATION FOR NURSING

Division of Nursing Education
Teachers College, Columbia University
New York 27, New York

        The selection of the colleges that will participate in
the Cooperative Research Project in Junior and Community College Education for Nursing will be made from those colleges
indicating a desire and willingness to offer two-year programs
in nursing on an experimental basis. The attached questionnaire is intended to give us general information about the
college and community facilities. Field visits to certain
colleges will follow the questionnaire so that additional information may be secured.

        We will be able to select only a small number of col-
leges with which we will work intensively. It is our hope
that we may be able to organize a council of a larger number
of colleges so that we may also be able to work with a larger
number of institutions in the development of two-year programs
in nursing.

        We appreciate very much your interest in our project
and your desire to participate in it. Will you kindly fill
out the questionnaire as soon as possible and return it to:

                    Miss Mildred Montag
                    Assistant Professor of Nursing Education
                    Teachers College, Columbia University
                    New York 27, New York

COOPERATIVE RESEARCH PROGRAM IN JUNIOR AND

COMMUNITY COLLEGE EDUCATION FOR NURSING

Official Name of College:_____Telephone_____

Location:_____
      (street address)   (city)   (county)   (state)

Names of Administrative Officers

   President:_____Dean_____

   Registrar:_____Business Manager_____
                        or Finance Officer

Control or Affiliation:

   State__, City__, County__, Religious Denomination___,Private___,

   University Affiliation_____,Other_____

Classification of College: Accreditation of College:

   Coeducational____   State_____
   Men only   ____
   Women only ____   Regional_____
   Negro   ____   _____

Number of Faculty Members on the Staff:

   Full-time Faculty___, Part-time Faculty___, Equivalent Full-
   time Faculty ____

Instructional Facilities:

   Number of regular classrooms ___, Number of Science
   Laboratories_____

   Is there an auditorium or assembly hall large enough to
   accommodate the entire study body?_____
   What is the seating capacity?   _____

   What is the seating capacity of the library?_____

   Total volumes in library _____

   Is a librarian available full time? ____ _____

   List audio-visual equipment available:_____
   _____
   _____
   _____

   Is a budget provided for film rentals, etc.?_____

Tuition Costs and College Fees (Per Year):

Per Student Per Year	Tuition	College Fee	Library	Laboratory	Health	Student Activity	Other

Admissions Policies:

High School Diploma Required?__ High School Equivalency
    Total HS Units _____   Accepted? ____
    Scholastic Average _____ State Equivalency Test Accepted? ____
    Military G.E.D. Test Accepted? ____

State briefly other admissions requirements:_____
_____
_____
_____

What tests, if any, are used in connection with admissions?
_____
_____
_____

What is the minimum age at which students will be admitted? ____
What is the maximum age at which students will be admitted? ____
What is the average age of your freshmen? Men____, Women ____

Housing Facilities: (Check facilities used for housing students)
Dormitories___, Rented Rooms in Private Homes____, Student's
Own Home____, Houses Rented by College ____, Other_____
What are the costs to students for housing? High per year _____,
Low per year ____, Average per year ____

Total number of students who can be housed in facilities
provided by the college _____

Percentage of students who live in their own homes and who
commute daily to the college _____

Health Service:

Is physical examination required of all applicants?_____

Are individual cumulative records kept for all students? _____

Student illness is financed by:
    Health fee____, Group insurance____, Individual student____

Is a school infirmary provided for students? _____

Student Organization:

Is a student government organization function in your school? _____
Give details of the organization:_____

_____

_____

_____

Does the college have an organized social program? _____

Who is in charge of this program? _____

What recreational facilities and activities are available to students?_____

_____

_____

Guidance Program:

Is a counselor available to each student?_____

Does the college provide a testing program for all students? ____

Are psychological and psychiatric services available?_____

Explain briefly the counseling program:_____

_____

_____

_____

Curriculum and Enrollment:

Are there distinctive curricular features to which the college desires to direct attention?_____

_____

_____

What part do members of the faculty have in planning curriculum?
_____
_____

What procedures are employed to maintain uniformity of
instructional standards:

1. Within departments?_____

2. Between departments?_____

Is there a program for the follow-up of the college's
graduates? If so, please describe._____
_____
_____
_____
_____

Full-time and Part-time Enrollment by Programs (Two-year programs):

Program	Full-time Enrollment				Part-time Enrollment	
	Freshmen		Sophomores			
	Men	Women	Men	Women	Men	Women
Liberal Arts						
Business Management or Administration						
Secretarial						
Pre-engineering						
Med/Dental Technician						
Agriculture						
_____						
_____						
_____						
_____						
TOTALS						

What degrees or diplomas are authorized to be awarded by the college? _____

Clinical facilities in community

Hospitals (name)	Kind of Hospital	Control Official-Voluntary	Size	Approval
_____	_____	_____	_____	_____
_____	_____	_____	_____	_____
_____	_____	_____	_____	_____
_____	_____	_____	_____	_____
_____	_____	_____	_____	_____
_____	_____	_____	_____	_____

Nursing Staff

Hospital	No.Registered Nurses	No.Practical Nurses	No.Aides
_____	_____	_____	_____
_____	_____	_____ —	_____
_____	_____	_____	_____
_____	_____	_____	_____

Is nursing service administered by Registered Nurse? Yes__ No__

Public Health Nursing Agencies

Official
City___County___State___No. Public Health Nurses_____

Non-official (voluntary)
Visiting Nurse Service: Yes___No___ No.Public Health Nurses

School
No.School Nurses in community____Part-time___Full-time____

Nursery Schools -- Day Care Centers

Is there a nursery school? Yes___No___Size_____
Is nursery school staffed by prepared teachers? Yes___No___
Is there a day care center? Yes___No___Size_____
Is center staffed by prepared personnel? Yes____No_____

Convalescent Homes — Hospitals

Are there convalescent homes or hospitals? Yes___No___
Are they approved? Yes___No___ By whom_____

Is Nursing Service administered by Registered Nurse?
Yes_____No_____

Homes for the Aged

Are there homes for the aged? Yes____ No____

Control: Official ____
Non-official____

Present Relationships with Hospitals

Does college have any relationship with Hospital School of
Nursing? Yes____ No____

Offers individual courses ____   Which courses_____
Offers pre-clinical period____ _____
_____

Does college offer pre-nursing curriculum? Yes____No____

If experimental two-year program is undertaken, could
these relationships continue? Yes___ No___

Experimental Program

Is college desirous of establishing two-year program?
Yes_____ No_____ When _____

Will college assume full responsibility for program?
Yes____ No____

Have any explorations been made with hospital and other
agencies? Yes___ No___

Does their cooperation seem likely?   Yes_____ No____

If not chosen as pilot program would college be interested
in setting up two-year nursing program? Yes___No___When_____

Would college be interested in advisory service from
Cooperative Research Project Staff? Yes____ No____

Would organization of Council of Colleges offering two-year
nursing program be desirable? Yes_____ No_____

Would you join such a council? Yes____ No____

Please send a copy of your current college catalog.

APPENDIX E

COOPERATIVE RESEARCH PROJECT IN JUNIOR AND

COMMUNITY COLLEGE EDUCATION FOR NURSING

INSTITUTE OF RESEARCH AND SERVICE IN NURSING EDUCATION

Division of Nursing Education
Teachers College, Columbia University
New York 27, New York

The selection of the Hospital School of Nursing that
will participate in the Cooperative Research Project in
Junior and Community College Education for Nursing will be
made from those hospitals indicating a desire and willingness
to offer two-year programs in nursing on an experimental
basis. The attached questionnaire is intended to give us
general information about the hospital and community facilities. Field visits to certain hospitals will follow the
questionnaire so that additional information may be secured.

We hope to be able to select at least one hospital
school to participate in the project.

We appreciate very much your interest in our project
and your desire to participate in it. Will you kindly fill
out the questionnaire as soon as possible and return it to:

Miss Mildred Montag
Associate Professor of Nursing Education
Teachers College, Columbia University
New York 27, New York

385

COOPERATIVE RESEARCH PROJECT IN JUNIOR AND
COMMUNITY COLLEGE EDUCATION FOR NURSING

Official Name of Hospital_____Telephone_____

Location_____
(street address)   (city)   (county)   (state)

Control or Affiliation:

  State___City___County___Religious Denomination___Voluntary___

Administrative Officers:

  Director of Hospital_____

  Director of Nursing Service_____

  Director of School of Nursing_____

Hospital Information:

  Classification of Hospital: General____   Special____

  Size of Hospital: Number beds____Daily Average Patients_____

	Medical	Surgical	Obstet.	Pediat.	Comm.Dis.	Psychiat.	Other
Daily Average Patients							

Nursing Staff: Number

  Supervisors   _____

  Head Nurses   _____

  Registered Nurses (Staff)_____

  Practical Nurses   _____

  Aides (Nursing only)   _____

School of Nursing Information:

Who is responsible for setting the educational policies?

_____

Does the school have a separate budget?   Yes____   No____

Does the school have an advisory committee? Yes___ No___

    Advisory Committee -- Indicate members_____

_____

_____

Faculty: Number_____ Full time_____ Part time_____

Name	School of Nursing	Degree(s)	Position	Time Devoted to Teaching

    Will the hospital be willing and able to employ qualified instructional staff for the experimental program? Yes___No___

Instructional Facilities:

  Number of Classrooms_____   Laboratories_____

  Indicate kind_____, _____, _____

  Library_____ Number of volumes_____

    Librarian: Yes___ No___ Full-time Yes___ No___
                                       Part-time Yes___ No___

    Hours available to students_____

Facilities Available for Learning Experiences (outside hospital):

Public Health Nursing Agencies

  Official
    City_____ County____ State____No.Public Health Nurses___

  Non-official (voluntary)
    Visiting Nurse Service Yes___No___ No.Public Health Nurses_____

  School
    No.School Nurses in Community___ Part-time___ Full-time___

Nursery Schools -- Day Care Centers in Community

Is there a nursery school?   Yes____ No____   Size_____

Is nursery school staffed by
prepared teachers?   Yes____ No____

Is there a day care center?   Yes____ No____

Is center staffed by prepared
personnel?   Yes____ No____

Community Convalescent Homes

Are there convalescent homes? Yes____ No____

Are they approved?   Yes____ No____
                               By whom_____

Is Nursing Service administered
by Registered Nurse?   Yes____ No____

Homes for the Aged

Are there homes for the aged? Yes____ No____

   Control: Official_____ Non-official_____

Admissions Policies:

High School Course Required?   _____

   Total High School Units?   _____
   Scholastic Average?   _____

State briefly other admissions requirements:_____
_____

What tests, if any, are used in connection with admissions?

_____

_____

_____

What is the minimum age at which students will be admitted?_____
What is the maximum age at which students will be admitted?_____

Housing Facilities:

    Dormitories_____, Rented Rooms in Private Homes_____,
    Student's Home_____, Houses Rented by Hospital _____,
    Other_____

    Total number of students who can be housed in facilities
    provided by hospital? _____

Student Organization:

    Is a student government organization functioning in your
    school? _____   Give details of the organization:
    _____
    _____

    What recreational facilities and activities are available to
    students? _____
    _____
    _____

Tuition and Fees (per year):

Per student per year	Tuition	Board & Room	Laboratory	Health	Student Activity	Other

Present Relationships with Colleges:

    Does hospital have any relationship with a collegiate institu-
    tion? Yes_____ No_____
    If yes, name of college _____

    What is the nature of this relationship:
    _____
    _____

    Does the hospital wish to carry on an experimental program
    similar to those offered by the cooperating colleges?
    Yes_____ No_____

Is the hospital willing to set up an experimental program in which the nursing service rendered is a by-product of the educational experience? Yes_____ No_____

Is the hospital willing to set up a school independent of the nursing service? Yes_____ No_____

Name of person
filling out questionnaire_____

Title   _____

Date   _____

APPENDIX F

COOPERATIVE RESEARCH PROJECT IN JUNIOR AND

COMMUNITY COLLEGE EDUCATION FOR NURSING

INSTITUTE OF RESEARCH AND SERVICE IN NURSING EDUCATION

Division of Nursing Education
Teachers College, Columbia University
New York 27, New York

STATEMENT OF AGREEMENTS

(Cooperatively arrived at by Representatives of Six
Cooperating Colleges)

The Purpose of the Project

The Cooperative Research Project in Junior and Community
College Education for Nursing was established in 1952 by the
Division of Nursing, Teachers College, Columbia University.
The research project is under the general administrative direction of the Institute of Research and Service in Nursing Education at Teachers College and will extend over a period of five
years. Its purpose is to develop and test a new concept in
the preparation of young men and women for the functions which
are the province of the registered nurse.

The Assumptions of the Project

It is assumed that nurse preparation can be accomplished
more effectively and more expeditiously than is traditionally
being done.

It is also assumed that the college-controlled program
may attract more students into nursing.

Common Characteristics of the Programs

The program as proposed for the colleges cooperating in
the project would differ in several respects from the nursing
programs now in existence and among themselves. Some of these
common characteristics are:

391

The program is college-centered and college-controlled.
The faculty of the college is responsible for the
planning of all aspects of the program, including
clinical experience, and for all teaching within the
curriculum. It is an integral part of the total college
program and, in general, is organized and conducted along
the same lines as other similar programs in the college.

It is a two-year curriculum in nursing combining both
general and special education. General education will
usually account for about 1/3 of the total curriculum and
nursing about 2/3 of the curriculum. Students in nursing
will share the courses in general education with other
students.

The curriculum will offer fewer courses than the typical
three-year program but with broader grouping of subject
matter. Learning experience will be carefully organized
but with flexibility to provide meaningful learning without unnecessary repetition.

Facilities of the community, including hospitals, clinics,
visiting nurse association, convalescent homes and homes
for the aged and nursery schools, will be utilized to provide a variety of learning experiences under the direct
supervision of the college staff. No part of the program
will be hospital controlled.

The students will enjoy the same status as all other students in the college. They will be eligible for all
activities of the college and will be held to the same
standards of admission, graduation, etc., as all other
students. There may be certain additional admission requirements because of the nature of the nursing work.

The faculty for the specialized courses in nursing will be
selected as are other faculty members. They will enjoy the
same privileges and share the same responsibilities.

The program will be supported from the same sources and
in the same way as are other programs. The same tuition
fees, if any, will be paid by all students.

Students will live at home or make their own living
arrangements. No special housing for nursing students
will be provided.

Students who satisfactorily complete the program will
qualify for the Associate Degree or its equivalent.

Graduates of this program will be eligible for the licensing examination of the state in which the college is located.

General Plans for the Project

Each college participating in the project is responsible for planning and establishing its own experimental program in nursing. Since graduates of the program are expected to meet the requirements for degrees offered by the college and to be eligible for the state registered nurse licensing examination, the program offered by each college must have the approval of the college's governing board, the State Board of Nurse Examiners, and other agencies exercising control over the educational programs offered by the college.

An advisory committee to the project has been appointed to review plans and purposes, help establish criteria for the selection of the cooperating colleges, to give counsel as the project develops, and to review progress. The advisory committee includes representatives of the American Association of Junior Colleges, nursing education, allied professional groups, and the consumers of nursing.

Role of the Institute of Research and Service in Nursing Education, Teachers College

The Cooperative Research Project serves as a continuing organizational unit for planning and carrying on an organized program of research and experimentation with selected junior and community colleges.

The Cooperative Research Project provides a research staff which is responsible for the development of the project and for consultation service to the faculties of the cooperating colleges. The staff includes those whose major interests and preparation is the field of education for nursing and those familiar with administration of junior and community colleges.

The Cooperative Research Project selects the colleges that will participate from those colleges indicating a desire and willingness to develop and experiment with education for nursing and to share in the study of the problems related to this type of education. The colleges include both those privately and those publicly supported and are representative of various sections of the country.

The Project Staff plans and conducts work conferences for instructional and administrative staff from the cooperating colleges to interpret the purposes and plans for experimentation. The services of the Project Staff may be supplemented as needs arise to provide special services or consultation. It works with faculties at the cooperating schools from time to time on problems of curriculum development, clinical experience, and evaluation.

The Project Staff arranges for workshops and group conferences at Teachers College or elsewhere for the cooperating colleges for the exchange of information and ideas, to renew plans or to further develop plans for the research program.

The Project Staff gathers data necessary for research and reports findings which have possibilities for improving education for nursing. Periodic reports and a detailed summary of the research findings at the end of the five-year study will be issued by the Project Staff.

The Institute assumes responsibility for the salaries and expenses of the Project Staff including consultation service rendered to cooperating colleges, for expenses included in advisory committee meetings and special conferences called by the Institute in relation to research aspects requiring activities beyond the conduct of the ongoing program.

Role of the College Participating in the Cooperative Research Project

The College selects and appoints staff to carry on the experimental program and facilitate the developing of the curriculum as an integral part of the total program of the College and shares in the cooperative study of problems related to this type of education to the extent that it is found to be mutually desirable to do so.

The College assumes financial responsibility for the conduct of the program and participation of its staff in the research aspects as mutually agreed upon.

Criteria for the Selection of Cooperating Colleges[1]

In order to provide for the selection of those colleges best able to cooperate effectively in the Cooperative Research

---

[1]The responsibility of the State Board of Nurse Examiners to give approval to the establishment and conduct of a school preparing students for licensure is fully recognized. Where it is legally possible to do so most State Boards of Nurse Examiners are eager to see experimentation in education for nursing go forward under properly controlled conditions and with university supervision. It is the policy of the Cooperative Research

Project certain criteria were set up by the advisory committee.
These criteria include:

The willingness of the college to assume complete control
of the program in nursing.

The willingness and ability of the college to provide and
pay for the program.

The willingness of hospitals and other agencies to provide
clinical facilities for learning experiences with service
as a by-product only.

The availability within the community of adequate clinical
experiences in a variety of agencies. This is not only a
quantitative measure but also qualitative.

The acceptance of the program by the college faculty and
provision for students in nursing to become an integral
part of the college and eligible to participate in all
activities of the college.

Readiness in the community for this type of program.

The school, or division, or department of nursing should
be of adequate size. Success of the experimental program
will rest upon the cost as well as upon the quality of the
program.

Graduates of the program must be eligible for licensure
within the state in which the college is located.
Licensure laws and regulations differ with the various
states. A close working relationship with the State
Board of Nurse Examiners is essential.

The college should be prepared to carry through the research project to a logical conclusion.

Project Staff to invite the State Board of Nurse Examiners to
join them in any exploration with colleges looking toward the
development of such a program and to proceed in only those
states where State Board approval and cooperation in the experimental program is assured.

COOPERATIVE RESEARCH PROJECT IN JUNIOR AND

COMMUNITY COLLEGE EDUCATION FOR NURSING

EVALUATION FORM

Introduction

The effectiveness of any educational program can be evaluated only in terms of how well the graduates of that program perform in the job for which they have been trained. In order to obtain an indication of how effective the junior and community college programs are, we are asking you to rate the graduates of this program that you supervise.

We have identified 19 skills, abilities, or characteristics that are related to the effectiveness of a nurse. We do not assume that these 19 areas cover all of the skills or attributes of a good nurse. We have included these 19 areas because they represent behaviors that can be observed and rated and they represent some of the objectives that we are trying to achieve in our new program.

We are asking you to help us evaluate this program by giving us your opinion of how well the graduates compare with nurses who have graduated from other programs and who have had the same length of experience as a graduate nurse.

It is realized that it may not be possible to find graduates of other programs who have exactly the same length of experience as the graduate of the experimental program. Therefore, for the purposes of this evaluation you may allow a leeway of two months' experience. For example, suppose the graduate of the experimental program has had six months experience as a graduate nurse. For comparison you may use graduates of other programs who have had four to eight months' experience as a graduate nurse if you do not have any with exactly six months experience.

Instructions for Completing Evaluation Form

General

Think of all the times that you have observed the nurse whose name appears on this blank and graduates of other programs of approximately equal experience in situations where they have been giving general nursing care. For each of the skills, abilities, or characteristics listed on the form please check the answer that, in your judgment, best describes the graduate of the experimental program when she is compared with graduates of other programs who have had approximately the same length of experience.

If you have never observed the nurse carrying out the activity described, check "A" -- no opportunity to observe.

Specific Directions

A. Fill in the information asked for in items 2, 3, and 4.

B. Read the first item. Check the answer that, in your judgment, best describes the graduate of the experimental program when she is compared with graduates of other programs with approximately the same length of experience.

For example:
Check B, if you think that she falls somewhat below
graduates of other programs.
Check C, if you think that she is about the same as
graduates of other programs.
Check D, if you think that she is somewhat above graduates of other programs.

C. Rate items 2 through 19 in exactly the same way.

D. A space for comments has been left at the right of the answer choices. It would be helpful if you would give specific examples of behaviors that would help us to interpret the ratings that you assign.

E. In item 20 please give your over-all evaluation of this nurse as a practitioner of nursing. Indicate your evaluation of the over-all nursing ability of this nurse by assigning her a rank in the total group of graduate nurses with about the same length of experience whom you supervise.

Example: Suppose you are rating Jane Doe, a graduate of our experimental program. You have five graduate nurses, including Jane Doe, who have been working as graduate nurses about the same length of time. You think that Jane Doe is about the third best in the group in her over-all ability to give nursing care. Then you would indicate your judgment in this way. Rank of _3_ in a group of _5_ .

F.   In item 21 a space has been left for you to comment on any aspect of the graduate of the experimental program that has not been covered in previous items.

G.   Please fill in the information requested at the end of the form.

Thank you for helping us to evaluate our program.

Evaluation Form A

Background Information:

1. Name of Nurse_____

2. Length of time worked as a graduate nurse in your hospital
   (in months) _____ months.

3. Total length of time worked as a graduate nurse (including
   time worked in your hospital) _____ .

4. Please list below the number of graduates of each of the
   following types of educational programs that you now have
   on your staff and who have been working as graduate nurses
   for approximately the same length of time as the nurse
   named in item 1.
   A. Graduates of Baccalaureate programs _____

   B. Graduates of hospital diploma programs _____

   If you have no graduates of other programs with approximately
   the same length of experience, check here _____ .

Evaluation Form:

1. Carries out nursing techniques such as bathing, enemas,
   and medications including hypodermics.

                                                    COMMENT

___(a) No opportunity to observe.

___(b) Somewhat below graduates
       of other programs with
       equal work experience.

___(c) About the same as graduates
       of other programs with equal
       work experience.

___(d) Somewhat above graduates
       from other programs with
       equal work experience.

2. Shows skill in lifting and turning patients, getting patients up and making patients comfortable.

COMMENT

___(a) No opportunity to observe.

___(b) Somewhat below graduates of other programs with equal work experience.

___(c) About the same as graduates of other programs with equal work experience.

___(d) Somewhat above graduates from other programs with equal work experience.

3. Operates special equipment such as oxygen equipment, suction apparatus, irrigation equipment.

COMMENT

___(a) No opportunity to observe.

___(b) Somewhat below graduates of other programs with equal work experience.

___(c) About the same as graduates of other programs with equal work experience.

___(d) Somewhat above graduates from other programs with equal work experience.

4. Plans care of patient from the standpoint of the patient as an individual person, not as a series of jobs to be done.

___(a) No opportunity to observe.   COMMENT

___(b) Somewhat below graduates of other programs with equal work experience.

___(c) About the same as graduates of other programs with equal work experience.

___(d) Somewhat above graduates from other programs with equal work experience.

401

5. Reports observations of signs, symptoms, or changes in patient's condition to nurse in charge.

COMMENT

___(a) No opportunity to observe.

___(b) Somewhat below graduates of other programs with equal work experience.

___(c) About the same as graduates of other programs with equal work experience.

___(d) Somewhat above graduates from other programs with equal work experience.

6. Makes accurate notations on patient's record.

COMMENT

___(a) No opportunity to observe.

___(b) Somewhat below graduates of other programs with equal work experience.

___(c) About the same as graduates of other programs with equal work experience.

___(d) Somewhat above graduates from other programs with equal work experience.

7. Seeks opportunities to give direct care to patients.

COMMENT

___(a) No opportunity to observe.

___(b) Somewhat below graduates of other programs with equal work experience.

___(c) About the same as graduates of other programs with equal work experience.

___(d) Somewhat above graduates from other programs with equal work experience.

8. Uses opportunities to talk with patients but does not
irritate patient by talking too much.

COMMENT

___(a) No opportunity to observe.

___(b) Somewhat below graduates
of other programs with
equal work experience.

___(c) About the same as graduates
of other programs with
equal work experience.

___(d) Somewhat above graduates
from other programs with
equal work experience.

9. Explains procedures, diagnosis, or treatments in terms
that can be understood by the patient or by his family.

COMMENT

___(a) No opportunity to observe.

___(b) Somewhat below graduates
of other programs with
equal work experience.

___(c) About the same as graduates
of other programs with
equal work experience.

___(d) Somewhat above graduates
from other programs with
equal work experience.

10. Adjusts her approach both in general conversation and in
specialized explanation to the kind and type of patient.

COMMENT

___(a) No opportunity to observe.

___(b) Somewhat below graduates
of other programs with
equal work experience.

___(c) About the same as graduates
of other programs with equal
work experience.

___(d) Somewhat above graduates
from other programs with
equal work experience.

11. Puts patient's family and relatives at ease by being cour-
teous and keeping them informed about the patient.

COMMENT

___(a) No opportunity to observe.

___(b) Somewhat below graduates
of other programs with
equal work experience.

___(c) About the same as graduates
of other programs with
equal work experience.

___(d) Somewhat above graduates
from other programs with
equal work experience.

12. Requests supervision when she is not sure of procedure,
techniques, etc.

COMMENT

___(a) No opportunity to observe.

___(b) Somewhat below graduates
of other programs with
equal work experience.

___(c) About the same as graduates
of other programs with
equal work experience.

___(d) Somewhat above graduates
from other programs with
equal work experience.

13. Uses suggestions from other personnel to improve nursing
techniques and procedures.

COMMENT

___(a) No opportunity to observe.

___(b) Somewhat below graduates
of other programs with
equal work experience.

___(c) About the same as graduates
of other programs with
equal work experience.

___(d) Somewhat above graduates
from other programs with
equal work experience.

14. Uses opportunities to increase knowledge by asking questions, requesting explanations, and observing unusual or unfamiliar treatments, procedures, etc.

COMMENT

___(a) No opportunity to observe.

___(b) Somewhat below graduates of other programs with equal work experience.

___(c) About the same as graduates of other programs with equal work experience.

___(d) Somewhat above graduates from other programs with equal work experience.

15. Talks with doctors and social workers with ease.

COMMENT

___(a) No opportunity to observe.

___(b) Somewhat below graduates of other programs with equal work experience.

___(c) About the same as graduates of other programs with equal work experience.

___(d) Somewhat above graduates from other programs with equal work experience.

16. Shows same consideration and courtesy for all co-workers.

COMMENT

___(a) No opportunity to observe.

___(b) Somewhat below graduates of other programs with equal work experience.

___(c) About the same as graduates of other programs with equal work experience.

___(d) Somewhat above graduates from other programs with equal work experience.

17. Displays conduct appropriate to hospital situation; for example, uses well modulated tone of voice in speaking, enters room quietly, etc.

COMMENT

___(a) No opportunity to observe.

___(b) Somewhat below graduates of other programs with equal work experience.

___(c) About the same as graduates of other programs with equal work experience.

___(d) Somewhat above graduates from other programs with equal work experience.

18. Has a good personal appearance; for example, makeup that is appropriate, etc.

COMMENT

___(a) No opportunity to observe.

___(b) Somewhat below graduates of other programs with equal work experience.

___(c) About the same as graduates of other programs with equal work experience.

___(d) Somewhat above graduates from other programs with equal work experience.

19. Is sought by auxiliary workers when they need advice or instruction.

COMMENT

___(a) No opportunity to observe.

___(b) Somewhat below graduates of other programs with equal work experience.

___(c) About the same as graduates of other programs with equal work experience.

___(d) Somewhat above graduates from other programs with equal work experience.

20. Among all graduate nurses with about the same length of experience as graduate nurses whom you supervise, where would you rank this nurse according to her <u>over-all ability to give nursing care</u>? (See item E in directions for filling out this sheet.)

    Rank of _____ in a group of _____ .

21. General Comment (Describe here any of the strengths or weaknesses of the nurse whom you are rating, that would help us to evaluate the effectiveness of our experimental program).

Your Position_____

Length of time you have supervised this nurse _____

Size of your hospital _____

APPENDIX H

INTERVIEW GUIDE -- HEAD NURSE -- PART A

This study deals with staff nurse performance. Such a study must include the point of view of the head nurse as to what is required of the staff nurse in her own hospital situation and how well some staff nurses are meeting the requirements of the job.

1. To begin with, would you describe the process of assigning the staff nurse her patients on your floor?

    a. How many patients is she responsible for?

    b. Does she have auxiliary help to work with?

407

2. What ways do you have of seeing that these duties have been carried out? (Do you have the opportunity to observe her performance directly?)

3. Are there certain nursing skills and procedures that are particularly important for a nurse working on this floor?

4. When a new nurse is assigned to this floor, one who has just graduated from nursing school, do you have a special program or special arrangements to start her on the job?

Yes_____   No _____

Just what does this consist of?

Does it include any special supervision?   Yes_____   No_____

For how long?

5. What about a nurse who has already worked in a hospital as a graduate nurse ... does the orientation that you give her differ from that of the new graduate?   Yes_____   No_____

In what ways?

6. When is the new nurse usually given complete responsibility for her job as a staff nurse?

7. From your own experience and observation you have probably
   developed ways of judging what is and isn't good nursing.
   What do you consider the most important things a nurse
   should do and be to give good nursing care?

8. What things do you look for in a nurse's performance that
   enable you to make judgments about the kind of nurse she is?

PART B

Name _____   Service _____   Rated by _____

Now we are going to talk about nurses.   The first one is
_____.   She graduated from nursing

school _____   _____ .
        Month   Year

1. How long have you been working with this nurse?
   a. Less than one month   ____
   b. Less than three months   ____
   c. Less than six months   ____
   d. Less than one year   ____
   e. Between one and two years ___

2. What other sources of information other than your own direct
   observation have you to make judgments about this nurse?

3. On the basis of this information would you say in general
   that this nurse:
   a. is definitely superior to your standards of good nursing ___
   b. meets your standards of good nursing   ___
   c. definitely fails to meet your standards of good nursing   ___

4. Would you elaborate as to why you place her in this category?

412

5. Is she the kind of nurse you have to check upon to make sure she has carried out her assignments?   Yes___ No___

6. What parts of her nursing performance are particularly good?

7. What parts of her performance are particularly poor?

8. Now about those nursing skills and procedures that you mentioned as particularly important on this floor -- does this nurse know these skills and procedures?

How well does she carry them out?

9. How might her nursing performance be improved?

10. Have you any other comments about this nurse?

PART C

Introduction

You have discussed the nursing performance of two staff nurses. I am now going to ask you to rate these nurses on 23 nursing behaviors. These behaviors have been and are being used in other studies because they are the kinds of things that can be observed and noted.

Instructions

You are asked to evaluate each nurse by comparing her with graduate nurses of equal experience. As you make your comparisons keep in mind nurses whom you have supervised and who have approximately the same length of experience as this nurse.

Think of all the times you have observed this nurse and other nurses of equal experience in situations where they have been giving general nursing care. For each of the skills, abilities, or characteristics listed on the form please circle the answer that, in your judgment, best describes this nurse when she is compared with other graduate nurses who have had approximately the same length of experience.

Circling A means that you have not had the opportunity to observe this nurse carrying out the activity described.

Circling B means that this nurse performs somewhat below most graduate nurses of equal experience.

Circling C means that this nurse performs about the same as most graduate nurses of equal experience.

Circling D means that this nurse performs somewhat above most graduate nurses of equal experience.

Read the first item. Select the answer -- A, B, C, or D -- that in your judgment best describes this graduate nurse when she is compared with nurses with approximately the same length of experience.

RATING FORM

Name of Nurse_____

Description of Behavior

	Have not had opp. to observe	Below most	Same as	Somewhat above
1. Carries out nursing techniques such as bathing, enemas, and including hypodermics.	a	b	c	d
2. Shows skill in lifting and turning patients, getting patients up and making patients comfortable.	a	b	c	d
3. Operates special equipment such as oxygen equipment, suction apparatus, irrigation equipment.	a	b	c	d
4. Plans care of patient from the standpoint of the patient as an individual person, not as a series of jobs to be done.	a	b	c	d
5. Reports observations of signs, symptoms, or changes in patient's condition to nurse in charge.	a	b	c	d
6. Makes accurate notations on patient's record.	a	b	c	d
7. Seeks opportunities to give direct care to patients.	a	b	c	d
8. Uses opportunities to talk with patients but does not irritate patient by talking too much.	a	b	c	d
9. Explains procedures, diagnosis, or treatments in terms that can be understood by the patient or by his family.	a	b	c	d
10. Adjusts her approach in general conversation and in specialized application to the kind and type of patient.	a	b	c	d
11. Puts patient's family and relatives at ease by being courteous and keeping them informed about the patient.	a	b	c	d

415

RATING FORM (Continued)

Rating

Name of Nurse_____

12. Requests supervision when she is not sure of procedure, techniques, etc.　　a b c d

13. Uses suggestions from other personnel to improve nursing techniques and procedures.　　a b c d

14. Uses opportunities to increase knowledge by asking questions, requesting explanations, and observing unusual or unfamiliar treatments, procedures, etc.　　a b c d

15. Talks with doctors and social workers with ease.　　a b c d

16. Shows same consideration and courtesy for all co-workers.　　a b c d

17. Displays conduct appropriate to hospital situation; for example, uses well modulated tone of voice in speaking, enters room quietly, etc.　　a b c d

18. Has a good personal appearance; for example, makeup that is appropriate, etc.　　a b c d

19. Is sought by auxiliary workers when they need advice or instruction.　　a b c d

20. Organizes her own activities so that her patients receive their medications and treatments at correct intervals.　　a b c d

21. Organizes her own activities and the activities of auxiliary workers so that her patients receive the nursing care warranted by their condition.　　a b c d

22. Keeps patients' records, such as charts, cardex, diet lists, etc., so that they are organized and orderly.　　a b c d

23. Seeks opportunities to assist with the upkeep of the ward.　　a b c d

APPENDIX I

INTERVIEW GUIDE -- GENERAL DUTY NURSE

        With the shortage of nurses so acute, people concerned
with the health of our nation have become interested in nursing,
especially in the staff nurse. I would like to talk with you
about the job of the staff nurse in a hospital. First, I am
going to ask some questions about what it is like to start work
on a new job in a hospital.

1. When a nurse goes to work in a hospital, do you feel:

    that she is ready to take over the full responsibility of
    the job on the second or third day

                            or

    that she is ready to take over part of the job at first
    and gradually take over the full job?

    Is there some particular reason you feel this way?

2. What are the kinds of problems a nurse faces in her first
   days on a new job as a graduate nurse?

3. Some nurses mentioned the following types of problems that nurses encounter on a new job:

(a) not knowing where things are
(b) not knowing hospital procedures
(c) not having enough supervision
(d) too many patients

Would you put these four types of problems that the nurse faces on a new job in their order of importance?

a_____   b_____   c_____   d_____

4. Now I would like you to think back to when you started working at this hospital as a graduate nurse. Which of these four did you find most difficult?

a_____   b_____   c_____   d_____

Would you describe what it was like? (If none of these register as important, then just probe the initial experience on the job.)

5. When or how did you know that you had reached this "full responsibility"?

By the full responsibility of your job I mean having the same patient load as the other staff nurses and the same responsibility for the job here.

6. When you started working in the hospital, were you given any special introduction to the job?

Yes_____   No_____

What did this consist of?

a. Were you oriented as to the rules and regulations of the hospital?

In what ways?

By whom?

b. Were you oriented to the specific aspects of working on your ward?

          Yes_____   No_____

   In what ways?

c. Did you have any orientation to the special equipment?

          Yes_____   No_____

   How was this done?

d. Was there some one person you felt you could go to for help during this time?

7. Was this orientation adequate?   Yes_____   No_____

   How might it have been improved?

8. Was some special arrangement made for supervision during the first weeks on the job?

   By whom?

   For how long?

   Just what did it consist of?

9. How soon after you started to work at the hospital did you go on the 3 to 11 shift?

   What orientation did you receive before going to work on that shift?

Was some arrangement made for extra supervision when you first went on that shift?

10. How soon after you started to work at the hospital did you go on night duty?

What orientation were you given before going to work on that shift?

Was some arrangement made for extra supervision when you went to work on that shift?

11. I am going to ask you some questions about what is expected
    of you in your work.

    a. Approximately how many patients do you carry?

    b. How do you go about seeing they get the care they need?

    c. Do you have any auxiliary workers to help? How many?
       How do you work with them?

12. In a recent report on the functions of the general duty
nurse the following appeared. "When a head nurse is not
on duty, a staff nurse assumes head nurse duties and
continues with her own."

   a. Have you assumed head nurse duties?   Yes_____   No_____

   b. How often?

   c. Just what do these duties you assume consist of?

   d. How do you like assuming these duties and responsibilities?

13. Now that you have the practical experience of working as
a graduate nurse, how do you feel about your preparation
for the job(s) you have had in nursing?

a. Do you feel that any parts of your preparation were particularly good for the kind of nursing required of you in this job?

Yes_____   No_____

Which parts?

In what ways?

b. Do you feel that any parts of your preparation were not adequate for the kind of nursing required of you in this job?

Yes_____   No_____

Which parts?

In what ways?

How might they have been improved?

14. Do you have any suggestions as to how your entire training
    program might have been improved?
                                    Yes_____   No_____

    What are they?

15. Suppose a friend told you that she wanted to become a nurse but could not decide what school to select? What would you suggest?

Why?

16. Suppose this same friend asked you to tell her what you now consider to be the three outstanding features of your program? What three aspects of the program would you mention?

17. Suppose the same friend asked you to tell her what you consider to be the three weaknesses of your program. What three aspects of the program would you mention?

18. If you were choosing all over again, would you select nursing as a career?   Yes_____   No_____

For what reasons?
(Probe job satisfaction)

19. From what nursing school did you graduate?_____

20. When did you graduate?   _____
                             Class of

21. Since your graduation where have you been working?

a.   Position   Institution   From   To

1st_____   _____   _____ _____

2nd_____   _____   _____ _____

3rd_____   _____   _____ _____

_____   _____   _____ _____

_____   _____   _____ _____

b. What reasons did you have for changing jobs?

22. Have you attended school at all since graduation? Yes___No__

School   Type of Course Work   Goal

_____   _____   _____

_____   _____   _____

23. Are you a member of a nursing organization?
Which one?

24. Do you subscribe to any nursing journals?

APPENDIX J

Teachers College
Columbia University
New York 27, N.Y.

Institute of Research and Service
in Nursing Education

        The Cooperative Research Project in Junior and Community
College Education for Nursing has been experimenting for the
last five years with some new approaches to educating nurses.
A thorough evaluation of the graduates of the experimental programs is part of the experimentation. We have been collecting
data concerning the graduates for the past year. Head nurses
have been asked to compare the graduates with other graduate
nurses. While this has given us valuable information, we find
that it does not tell us enough about these nurses. Consequently we have decided we should broaden our approach to this
problem. A new study is underway.

        The interview has been selected as the most practical
approach for gathering the data. The interview has a major
advantage over other methods in giving a richness of response.
Graduates of two-year programs, three- and four-year programs,
head nurses and nursing directors will be interviewed. Each
interview will last about 40 minutes. We are again seeking the
cooperation of the hospitals employing graduates of the Junior
College programs associated with our project.

        It will be helpful if no one but the Director of Nursing
knows that this is connected with the Cooperative Research
Project. While the findings of the study will be published,
all hospitals and individuals will remain anonymous.

        Will you help us with this study? Mr. Gotkin who is
responsible for this study will call or write you shortly to
make arrangements for the interviews.

                        Sincerely yours,

                        Mildred Montag, Director
                        Cooperative Research Project
                        Junior and Community College
                        Education for Nursing

                        429

APPENDIX K

RATING PROCEDURES FOR THE ANALYSIS OF INTERVIEWS
WITH DIRECTORS OF NURSING SERVICES

The three judges rated the interviews according to the following
instructions:

Instructions to the Raters

From transcribed interviews you are being asked to rate directors
of nursing services on:

1. their attitudes toward graduates of pilot programs
2. their attitudes toward the pilot programs

In the interviews the graduates of the pilot programs are usually
not referred to as pilot-program graduates. Most commonly they
are described as graduates of two-year programs or the two-year
girls. Also, the pilot programs are labeled two-year programs
and sometimes experimental programs. In some instances the specific pilot programs are mentioned. The programs are: Orange
County Community College, Fairleigh Dickinson, Henry Ford Community College, Weber College, Pasadena City College, and
Virginia Intermont College. When individual nurses are referred
to, they are pilot-program graduates.

Read each transcribed interview. Then rate each interviewee
according to the descriptions below which most closely describe
her attitudes toward the graduates and the programs.

Attitudes toward the Graduates

Rating 1--Expresses favorable attitudes toward the pilot-program
          graduates
Rating 2--Expresses mostly favorable attitudes toward the pilot-
          program graduates with some unfavorable attitudes
Rating 3--Expresses as many favorable as unfavorable attitudes
          toward the pilot-program graduates
Rating 4--Expresses mostly unfavorable attitudes toward the
          pilot-program graduates with some favorable attitudes
Rating 5--Expresses unfavorable attitudes toward the pilot-
          program graduates
Rating 0--Not enough information to rate

Attitudes toward the Pilot Programs

Rating 1--Expresses favorable attitudes toward the pilot programs
Rating 2--Expresses mostly favorable attitudes toward the pilot
          programs with some unfavorable attitudes

430

Rating 3--Expresses as many favorable as unfavorable attitudes
        toward the pilot programs
Rating 4--Expresses mostly unfavorable attitudes toward the
        pilot programs with some favorable attitudes
Rating 5--Expresses unfavorable attitudes toward the pilot programs
Rating 0--Not enough information to rate

        The raters were given the following sheet on which to
record their judgments, by checking the rating next to appropriate interview number:

	Attitude toward Graduates						Attitude toward Programs					
No.	1	2	3	4	5	0	1	2	3	4	5	0
1												
2												
3												
4												
.												
.												
24												
25												

BIBLIOGRAPHY

A. Books

Brown, Esther Lucille. _Nursing for the Future_. New York:
    Russell Sage Foundation, 1948. 198 pp.

Buechel, J. F. Marvin. _Principles of Administration in Junior
    and Community College Education for Nursing_. New York:
    G. P. Putnam's Sons, 1956. 255 pp.

Burling, Temple, Lentz, Edith M., and Wilson, Robert N.
    The Give and Take in Hospitals. New York: G. P. Putnam's
    Sons, 1956. 333 pp.

Committee on the Function of Nursing. _A Program for the Nursing
    Profession_. New York: The Macmillan Company, 1948. 108 pp.

Corey, Stephen Maxwell. _Action Research to Improve School
    Practices_. New York: Bureau of Publications, Teachers
    College, Columbia University, 1953. 161 pp.

McManus, Louise R. _The Effect of Experience on Nursing Achieve-
    ment_. New York: Bureau of Publications, Teachers Col-
    lege, Columbia University, 1949. 64 pp.

Montag, Mildred L. _The Education of Nursing Technicians_.
    New York: G. P. Putnam's Sons, 1951. 146 pp.

National Manpower Council. _Womanpower_. New York: Columbia
    University Press, 1957. 371 pp.

Reissman, Leonard and Rohrer, John H. _Change and Dilemma in
    the Nursing Profession_. New York: G. P. Putnam's Sons,
    1957. 450 pp.

Roe, Anne. _Psychology of Occupations_. New York: John Wiley
    and Sons, 1955. 340 pp.

Sharp, George. _Curriculum Development as Re-education of the
    Teacher_. New York: Bureau of Publications, Teachers
    College, Columbia University, 1951. 339 pp.

Siegel, Sidney. _Nonparametric Statistics for the Behavioral
    Sciences_. New York: McGraw-Hill Book Company, 1956.
    312 pp.

432

Thorndike, Robert L. and Hagen, Elizabeth. Measurement and Evaluation in Psychology and Education. New York: John Wiley and Sons, 1955. 575 pp.

B. Periodical Articles

American Nurses' Association Special Committee of State Boards of Nursing. "Studying State Board Test Scores," The American Journal of Nursing, 55:1093, (September 1955).

Anderson, M. H., and McManus, R. L. "Interests of Nursing Candidates; the Patterns of Interests and Activities of 800 Pre-nursing Students," The American Journal of Nursing, 42:555, (May 1942).

Bailey, June Teig. "The Critical Incident Technique in Identifying Behavioral Criteria of Professional Nursing Effectiveness," Nursing Research, 5:52, (October 1956).

Basler, Roosevelt, "Consistent and Increasing Adaptability of the Junior College," Junior College Journal, 25:427-29, (April 1955).

Bogue, Jesse P. "Analysis of Junior College Growth," Junior College Journal, 28:357, (February 1958).

Henderson, Virginia. "Research in Nursing Practice-When," Nursing Research, 4:99, (February 1956).

Koos, Leonard V. "Preparation for Community-College Teaching," Journal of Higher Education, 21:309-17, (June 1950).

Leone, Lucile Petry. "How Many Will Choose Nursing," American Journal of Nursing, 55:1195 (October 1955).

_____. "People, Nurses, Students," American Journal of Nursing, 55:933 (August 1955).

Shields, Mary R. "A Project for Curriculum Improvement," Nursing Research, 1:4, (October 1952).

C. Publications of Learned Organizations

National Society for the Study of Education. MacLean, Malcolm S. and Dodson, Dan. "Educational Needs Emerging from the Changing Needs of Society," The Fifty-fifth Yearbook of the National Society for the Study of Education. Chicago: University of Chicago Press, 1956.

National Society of the Study of Education. The Public Junior
    College. Fifty-fifth Yearbook, Part I. Chicago:
    University of Chicago Press, 1956. 347 pp.

D. Reports

American Nurses' Association. Nurses Invest in Patient Care --
    A Preliminary Report of a Five-Year Program of Studies
    of Nursing Functions. New York: American Nurses' Asso-
    ciation, 1956. 62 pp.

_____. 1955-1956 Facts about Nursing. New York: The
    Association, 1957. 224 pp.

Committee on the Grading of Nursing Schools. Nursing Schools
    Today and Tomorrow. New York: The Committee, 1934.
    268 pp.

Cooperative Research Project in Junior and Community College
    Education for Nursing, Conference Report. Nursing
    Education in Junior and Community Colleges. 1956. 76 pp.

Michigan League for Nursing. Nurse Recruitment in Michigan.
    Lansing, Michigan: Michigan League for Nursing, 1956.
    17 pp.

National League for Nursing. Nurses for a Growing Nation.
    New York: National League for Nursing, 1957.

_____. Second National Conference on Junior-Community
    College Education for Nursing. New York: National
    League for Nursing, 1957.

President's Commission on Higher Education. Higher Education
    for American Democracy. New York: Harper and Bros., 1937.

Stewart, Donald D., and Needham, Christine E. The General
    Duty Nurse. Fayetteville, Arkansas: University of
    Arkansas, 1955. 101 pp.

E. Unpublished Materials

American Nurses' Association, Special Committee on State
    Boards of Nursing. "Progress Report of the Subcommittee
    on the Preparation of Educational Standards to be Used
    as a Guide by State Boards." Mimeographed, May 1956.

Institute of Research and Service in Nursing Education. "Cooperative Research Project in Junior and Community College Education for Nursing." Unpublished Document, November 6, 1953.

Izard, Carrol E., and Courtney, Douglas. "The Hospital Nurse in Greater Cleveland." Philadelphia: Research Associates, 1955.

Lambertson, Eleanor C. "Professional Education for Leadership in the Practice of Nursing." Unpublished Doctoral Dissertation, Teachers College, Columbia University, 1957.

National League for Nursing and American Association of Junior Colleges. "Guiding Principles for Junior Colleges Participating in Nursing Education." New York: The League, 1951. Mimeographed.

Sindlinger, Walter. "Experimentation in Education for Nursing at Orange County Community College." Unpublished Doctoral Dissertation, Teachers College, Columbia University, 1956.

Todd, Lindsey O. "Meeting the Needs of Junior College Students." Unpublished Doctoral Dissertation, George Peabody College for Teachers, Tennessee, 1943.

INDEX

Courtney, Douglas, 150

Curriculum

    annual workshops dealing with, 109-110

    characteristics of, 110-111

    development of, 81-83, 352

    discussion as teaching method in, 102, 107

    facilities and equipment for, 97-98

    laboratory period in, 99-101

    lack of clinical experience in, 325-327, 336

    length of program in, 87-91

    need for new teaching methods in, 98, 107-108, 112

    new, for nursing education, 70-71, 75, 80-81

    nursing courses in, 83-87

    observational experience in, 102-106

    plan, of Monmouth Hospital School of Nursing, 74

    plan, of Orange County Community College, 72

    plan, of Weber College, 73

    recruitment of students for, 340

    role of faculty in developing, 108-109

    selection of learning experiences in, 91-96

    use of resource persons in, 101-102

Dearborn Junior College (Henry Ford Community College), 35

Dee, Thomas D., Hospital, 77

Detroit Receiving Hospital, 77

Direct nursing care, 147

Faculty, of cooperating colleges

    annual workshops for, 109-110

    conditions of employment of, 64

    preparation of, 55-59, 66

    ratio of, to students, 61-63, 66

    responsibility of, for teaching nursing, 109, 111

    size of, 38, 59-64, 66-67

    stability and availability of, 64-66

Fairleigh Dickinson University, 35, 36-37, 38, 76, 79, 135, 430

    agencies cooperating with, 77

Fields, Dr. Ralph, 375

First Baptist Church Home for the Aged (Norfolk, Va.), 78

Ford Motor Company, 120

Functional nurse, 200, 202-204, 226, 227

    role of, 229-231

Fundamentals of nursing, 83-84

Gelinas, Agnes, 375

General duty nurse

    conception of, held by nursing service directors, 330-335, 336

    definition of, 133-134

    interview guide for, 416-428

    work of, 146-151

Global ratings, of pilot-program graduates by head nurses, 259-263, 281-282

Gotkin, Lassar, 377

Graduates of pilot program

aims for, 4

attitudes of nursing service directors toward, 304-308

bedside nurse as role of, 227-229

compared to other nurses, by head nurses, 248-259

definition of, 133-134

difficulties in evaluation of, 140-151

difficulties of, due to job demands, 191-196

difficulties of, in work situation, 185-191

dispersal of, 140, 156, 157, 182

favorable attitudes of nursing service directors
toward, 308-323

functional nurse as role of, 229-231

future employment of, 33

head nurse as role of, 235-239

lack of supervision of, 191-193

licensure of, 32-33, 43

median A.C.E. of, 160-162

nurse-manager as role of, 231-235

orientation of, 362

preparation for nursing of, 145-146, 288-293, 295, 300

rating of, by head nurses, 153, 157-158, 259-263, 281
413-416

ratings of, on nursing behaviors, 240-247, 254, 256,
281-282

Medications

    as staff nurse responsibility, 202-204

    and role of functional nurse, 229-231

Mental illness, nursing for, 85, 100-101

Metropolitan State Hospital (Pasadena, Calif.), 77

Michigan League for Nursing, 117

Middletown State Homeopathic Hospital, 77

Miner, Edwin H., 356

Monmouth County Organization for Public Health, 78

Monmouth County Welfare Home, 78

Monmouth Junior College, 46, 48

Monmouth Memorial Hospital, 45-46, 78, 81

    as cooperating institution in CRP, 47-50

Monmouth Memorial Hospital School of Nursing, 76, 78, 338, 346

    curriculum plan of, 74

Montag, Mildred, 1, 81, 144, 154, 155, 377, 378, 385, 429

National League for Nursing, 13, 14, 21-22, 90, 158, 357

Needham, Christine E., 137

Nightingale, Florence, 68

Norfolk Community Hospital, 78

Norfolk General Hospital, 78

Norms for evaluating nursing performance, lack of, 151-152

Nurse-manager, 200, 204-208, 226, 227, 231-235

    increase in need of, 331

Nurse Practice Act (Calif.), 1957 amendment, 89-90

Nurses

    bedside, 2-3, 200, 201-202, 226, 227-229, 237, 359-360

    charge, 233-234, 286-287

    competence of, at graduation, 184

    difficulties of, due to job demands, 191-196

    education for, 1, 4

    functional, 200, 202-204, 226, 227, 229-231

    number of, 13

    "professional", 14

    practical, 2, 14, 148-149

    rated "superior", 263-266

    recruitment of, 367

    shortage of, 1

    social need for, 12-14

    student, in hospital schools, 141-143

    study of role of, 365-368

    (See also General duty nurses, Head nurses and

    Staff nurses)

Nurses' aides, 2, 148, 150

Nursing

    course in fundamentals of, 83-84

    functions and types of, 3-4, 144, 367-368

    laboratory experience in, 94-96

    medical-surgical, 83, 85, 105-106

    for mental illness, 85, 100-101

    as profession, 365-368

Reissman, Leonard, 122, 148, 150

Research, in nursing education, 370-374

Residence pattern, of pilot-program students, 122-124, 130

Responsibility

    of staff nurse, assumption of, 183, 185, 198-201, 223

        difficulties in work situation relating to, 185-191, 222-223

    supervisory, lack of experience in, 284-285, 299

Rines, Alice R., 8, 377

Rockefeller, Mrs. Nelson, 376

Roe, Anne, 118

Rohrer, John H., 121-122, 148, 150

Rotation of service, as orientation, 219, 220

Rutherford (N.J.) Playground Physicians Office, 77

St. Barnabas Hospital, 77

St. Luke's Hospital (Calif.), 77

St. Luke's Hospital (N.J.), 77

St. Vincent's Foundling Hospital, 78

School for Cerebral Palsied Children (Pasadena, Calif.), 77

Sex, of pilot-program students, 116, 130

Sharp, George, 68-69

Shields, Mary R., 184

Shriners Hospital, 77

Siegel, Sidney, 306

Sindlinger, Walter E., 8, 356, 377

Sister Kenny Institute (Pasadena, Calif.), 77

Students, of pilot programs

    age of, 114-116, 130

    college status of, 113, 130

    intelligence level of, 124-126, 130-131

    marital status of, 116-118, 130

    recruitment of, 128-130, 131

    residence pattern of, 122-124, 130

    sex of, 116, 130

    socioeconomic background of, 118-122, 130

    as workers in the hospital, 347, 350-351

    (See also Graduates of pilot program)

Super, Donald E., 263

Supervision

    of general duty nurse, 149, 150

    lack of, in hospital, 299

    lack of, as problem, 191-193

    for pilot-program graduates, 309-311, 336

Supervisory duties, of graduates, 334-335

Team, nursing

    leader of, 145, 150, 200, 231, 232, 235

    staff nurses of, 146, 333-334

Terminal programs, of junior-community colleges, 19, 125

Thomas D. Dee Hospital, 77

Todd, Lindsey O., 128

Totten, Dr. W. Fred, 376

Tourtillot, Eleanor, 69, 95